Geologists' Association Guide No. 72

Lloyd's Register
Foundation

D1370807

Devonshire Marbles: their geology, history and uses

by
Gordon Walkden

Volume 1
Understanding the marbles

Guide Series Editor: Susan B. Marriott

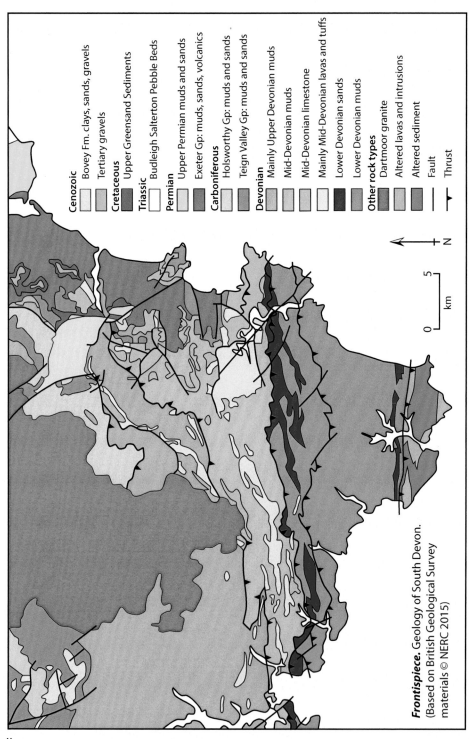

Legend:

Cenozoic
- Bovey Fm. clays, sands, gravels
- Tertiary gravels

Cretaceous
- Upper Greensand Sediments

Triassic
- Budleigh Salterton Pebble Beds

Permian
- Upper Permian muds and sands
- Exeter Gp: muds, sands, volcanics

Carboniferous
- Holsworthy Gp: muds and sands
- Teign Valley Gp: muds and sands

Devonian
- Mainly Upper Devonian muds
- Mid-Devonian muds
- Mid-Devonian limestone
- Mainly Mid-Devonian lavas and tuffs
- Lower Devonian sands
- Lower Devonian muds

Other rock types
- Dartmoor granite
- Altered lavas and intrusions
- Altered sediment

— Fault
⊢► Thrust

N

0   5
km

Frontispiece. Geology of South Devon.
(Based on British Geological Survey
materials © NERC 2015)

VOLUME 1. CONTENTS   Page

VOLUME 2. CONTENTS

LIST OF FIGURES   Page

PREFACE

Devonshire marbles got everywhere. They are in churches, cathedrals, great public buildings, institutions, museums and country houses, both in the UK and abroad. They are found as architectural decoration, ornamental objects and fine fossil specimens, yet we do not know them and their own stony silence has consigned them to anonymity. The Marble Works are gone, the quarries are overgrown, the working families have moved on and the labels and records are lost.

As the first comprehensive account of a once internationally renowned ornamental stone industry, this work should be of interest to geologists, historians, architects, conservationists, genealogists, planning authorities and antique experts. For the geologist there is the story of how the many different stone types were born in and around the ancient tropical reefs that once crossed a pre-Devon seascape and how they became colourful, richly textured, decorative marbles in the geological turmoil that followed. There is a guide to the best limestone/marble outcrops and guides to the marbles and the fossils that come from them. For the historian and industrial archaeologist we look at how the stones were discovered and by whom, how the coastline was regarded by different writers and was exploited, as well as at some of the inventions that aided industrialisation of quarrying processes. For the architects and conservationists there is a study of how marbles were used in buildings, the messages they conveyed, their architects, and a detailed account of 35 buildings out of more than 75 that are listed and known to contain Devonshire marble. Genealogists will be interested in the chapter on the marble dynasties; the families of marble masons, the Woodleys, the Grants, the Blacklers amongst others who built the industry and in some cases watched its decline. Planning authorities need to know the importance of some of the building interiors that are little known and precariously protected. Antiques experts will benefit from the descriptions of the spectacular Devonshire marble tables and how to recognise and distinguish them, as well as the many other types of ornamental object. These were once the most celebrated of British polished ornamental stones, able to hold their own in the aesthetic competition with the best of foreign marbles, yet our knowledge of them has withered.

They are Devonian rocks, both in geological age and geographical provenance, and their use for ornamental purposes goes back well over 200 years. Devon historian Richard Polwhele, in his *History of Devonshire* (1793–1806) wrote, *"This coast ... consisting chiefly of marble, exhibits a busy scene. Here boats are continually loading with stone, which is either used in building, or burnt into lime. The detached rocks, which are sawed into blocks, and which are so beautifully variegated, are from five to about ten tons."* This is one of the earliest eyewitness accounts of an activity that has physically shaped parts of south Devon and that has spread its durable prizes worldwide.

Taking stone from the ground remains one of our fundamental requirements. Quarrying and mining were once firmly in the West Country blood and the quests were for tin, granite, limestone, clay or even gold. As for marble, for those prepared to face the dangers and physical demands of quarrying, and beyond that perhaps able to develop the special skills of stone working, there was at least a living to be made and at best there was wealth and acclaim. For the most fortunate there was dynastic success, but for the least fortunate there was disaster and ruin. Most of the names that emerge are those of the crucial entrepreneurs who contributed to the development of the industry or to the art that stemmed from it and these people can now be acknowledged and celebrated.

In this study we can reclaim a little of the continuum that once existed between science and art, particularly in Polwhele's time, because natural materials such as rock are both scientifically recognisable and intrinsically attractive. Their natural beauty can be enhanced by what an artisan can do but it cannot be created. Seen from a geological perspective we can now more rigorously define why the marbles are the way they are, how we can recognise them and where they have been used.

The vases, tazzas, pen sets, boxes and specimen marble tables that once came out of the Devon marble workshops are seldom seen today and even in the best auction houses they have sometimes been overlooked, misidentified, or wrongly attributed. The great marble building interiors, silent in their borrowed splendour, project wealth, status and esteem that always outshone their Devonshire signature written in the stone. Geological awareness of the diversity of Devonshire marbles and of what has created the myriads of colours and textures seen in them allows us to redress some of that obscured identity. For the first time some of the world-class architectural interiors with Devonshire marble, and this work has revealed many, can be reconnected to the original quarries and sometimes even to the marble works from which they came. In some cases domestic products such as the magnificent inlaid specimen marble table tops can not only be attributed with confidence to a workshop but to a skilled artisan.

Today, Polwhele's 'coast of marble' is a treasured part of our national heritage, celebrated for its seascapes, landscapes, natural science, architecture and history. The treasured landscapes from which the stones came, once industrial wastelands, are now associated with a nationally important Geopark, a National Nature Reserve and a World Heritage coastline. We can be proud of Devonshire marbles and their legacy. They reflect a luxury industry belonging to a world that blossomed for a century before mostly disappearing with shifting fashion and the changed social and economic realities following the convulsions of WW1. The marbles were once respected by royalty, aristocracy, the indulgent, the pious and the simply curious. This book tries to bring back and understand some of the splendour and what lay behind it.

Gordon M. Walkden

ACKNOWLEDGEMENTS

Information, advice, access, reviewing, editing, arranging, alerting and standing-by; I have encountered a lot of generous and patient people, all interested, well-informed and motivated. I start with two.

Chatting with Trevor Ford one time about the Ashford Black marble industry of Derbyshire, I complained that there was nothing written about its rival Devonshire one. "Well why don't you write it yourself, then," came the unsympathetic reply. So a decade later here it is and without Trevor's challenge it might not have happened. My deepest thanks go to the key enabler throughout this project, my wife Mary, a trained geologist turned musician and protector of the private purse, now a marble expert. She has supported the work every step of the way and we have thoroughly enjoyed our countless visits to outcrops, buildings, experts and tea shops.

Of those experts, there is first Colin Scrutton, a remarkable geologist (and orchid expert), who has generously shared his unique knowledge and given regular encouragement. Then there are those at Torquay Museum, (herein appointed the official home of Devonshire marble), Clare Jones, Barry Chandler, Director Basil Greenwood and former Director Phil Collins. Colin Vosper, a senior museum trustee, has supported and contributed to the work tirelessly. Graham Lott and Brian Leveridge (formerly BGS) are geological experts who have enlightened me.

Others at museums, great buildings and useful places nationwide, who have been particularly helpful include Diana Clements, David Smith and the studio photographers (Natural History Museum, London), Dan Pemberton and Director Ken McNamara (Sedgwick Museum, Cambridge), Victoria Avery (Fitzwilliam Museum, Cambridge), Monica Price (Natural History Museum, Oxford), Florence Peltier (Musée du Marbre de Rance), Julien Parsons, Holly Morgenroth and Thomas Cadbury (RAM Museum, Exeter), Barbara Jones and Victoria Culkin (Lloyds Register, London), Eileen Kinghan (Lloyd's Register Foundation), Stuart Band (Chatsworth House, Derbyshire), Kate Crowe and Nina Milne (Foreign and Commonwealth Office, London), Warwick Rodwell, (Westminster Abbey), Ellie Jones and Dianne Walker (Exeter Cathedral), Sue Silkstone (St James's, Sussex Gardens), Paul Jones (All Saints, Babbacombe), Debbie Griffiths and Philip Sturman, (St John's, Torquay), Mark Searle, Edwina Corderoy and Rosie Dowell (St Mary Magdalene's, Torquay), Virginia Mullan (Christ Church, Cheltenham), Ian Day (Marble Church, Bodelwyddan), Dorothea Rowse, Sue Baker, Samantha Reeves and Judy McCowan (St Paul's Cathedral, Melbourne), Dee Prior (All Saints, Margaret Street, London), Andrew Allen (Exeter College, Oxford), Paul Brice and Colin Maxtead (Sidney Sussex College, Cambridge), Stephen Stokes (St John's College, Cambridge), Susan Morgan and James Slater (Grand Hotel, Birmingham), Sarah Dorgan (Westminster Cathedral), Ian Knight (Torquay Library), Charlie Bottrell (County Hall, Devon), Caroline Butcher (Great Ormond Street Hospital), Marilyn Hadfield (Rates Hall, Manchester), Geoff Taylor (Ely Cathedral), Thomas Clifford (Ugbrooke House), Royden Stock (St Pancras historian), Charles Crichton (HMS Drake, Plymouth), Ben Dormer (Stoneycombe Quarry), Ian Glendenning and Neil Gibbs (Linhay Quarry, Ashburton), Mary Skilton (St John's, Hooe Lake), Matthew Lloyd (on behalf of Palace Theatre, London), James Wilson (Diocese of Plymouth), James Graham-Stewart, Richard Gardner, Adrian Ager, Ivan Spurrier-Smith and Don Edwards (Antiques experts), Patricia Wilson (Devonshire Association), Barbara Silva (Geologists' Association).

Others to whom I am most grateful for their generous help and information are Nigel Overton (Plymouth City & Maritime Heritage), Andrew Saint (The Survey of London), Richard Parker (Devon historic buildings expert), Nick Garswood (Senior Engineer, Torbay Council), Roger Turner (Victorian Churches enthusiast), Robin Taylor and Stephen

Brindle (English Heritage), Robin Blithe-Lord (Plymouth expert), Mark Halliday (Master marble mason and proprietor, Grant's Marble), Ann Bligh (Ashburton expert), Liz Wells (Planning Office, Plymouth), Mark Rodgers (CEO Birmingham CC), Mark Hardy, (Millennium Gloucester Hotel), Jennifer Strawbridge (Keble College Chapel), Mark Hargreaves (St Peter's, Notting Hill), John Brownsell (All Saints, Notting Hill), Kay Norman and Stephen Platten (St Michael's, Cornhill), Paul Clark, (Brompton Oratory), Kayleigh Andrews, Chris Forrest and Katy Turner (Gibson Hall, London), Richard McCrow (Goldsmiths' Hall, London), Stuart Brady (Dobroyd Castle, Todmorden), Wes Paul (Todmorden Unitarian Church), Chris Lee (St Augustine's, South Kensington), Christopher Colven (St James's Church, Spanish Place), Penny Fussell (Drapers' Hall, London), Ann Smith (Sherbourne Castle), Geoffrey Tyack (author and historian), Malcolm Hole (University of Aberdeen), Martin Jenkins (Jenkins family historian), Tim Tatton Brown (formerly Salisbury Cathedral), Paul Ensom (Falmouth), Ron Austin (Swansea), Brian Jones (St Mary's, Greenham), Charles Bevan (Lupton House), Nicholas Pearkes (Broadhempston), Judith Lewis (St Andrews, Ashburton), Robert Ward (St Mary's, St Marychurch), Heather Crawford and the late Nick Crawford (Devonshire jewellery), Stephen Parry (BGS), Ted Nield (Geoscientist Magazine), Chris Rice (Birmingham City Museum and Art Gallery), Christopher Costelloe (The Victorian Society), Christopher Rowell (National Trust).

Most photographs and prints are my own, but for the impossible ones, acknowledged herein, I am grateful for the generous assistance of Nicole Baughan (copyright assistant at BGS), Agata Rutkowska (Picture Library, Royal Collection Trust), Paul Johnson (National Archives Image Library, Kew), Jan Wood, Stuart Tyler and Josephine Halloran (Devon Heritage Services), Julia Skinner (Photo Library, The Francis Frith Collection), Tom Smith and Rachel Rees (aerial pictures from English Riviera Tourism Company), Steve Johnson (for his specially flown aerial shots of Plymouth), Justin Hobson (Picture Library, Country Life), Ashley Chapman (Royal William Yard, Plymouth), Niki Harrat (Wolverhampton Art Gallery), Mark Norton (Historical photographs of Birmingham Central Library). Swete watercolours are from the Devon Record Office (Devon Heritage Services) and digital copies of Ordnance Survey maps were purchased with permissions from Old Maps. Special thanks are due to the Southwest Regional Coastal Monitoring Programme for the general availability of their high quality aerial pictures. The Natural History Museum, London, generously created research-quality images of the stones in their Woodley table.

Professor Malcolm Hart (Plymouth University) kindly reviewed the geological excursions, Professor Rob Butler (University of Aberdeen) cast an expert eye over my inexpert structural geology and Dr James Campbell, (Architecture & History of Art, Queens' College, Cambridge), kindly checked my buildings guides and architectural and historical tracts for gross inaccuracy. My eagle-eyed editor is Professor Susan Marriott. Her tactful persuasion, patient checking, imaginative design, careful corrections as well as some skilled maps and the geological frontispiece have improved the work immeasurably. It was a lengthy imposition. I am most grateful for the diligence and feedback of all four of these talented people but the remaining errors, deficiencies and excesses are entirely my own.

We are grateful to the Curry Fund and to Lloyd's Register Foundation for publication sponsorship. Lloyd's Register Foundation helps to protect life and property by supporting engineering-related education, public engagement and the application of research.

Gordon M. Walkden

1. THE MAKING OF MARBLE

1.1 The lost coral seas and the lost industry

Devonshire marble was once the the top British ornamental stone, used in cathedrals, churches, government buildings and mansions, with a flourishing sideline that produced ornaments, vases, jewellery and spectacular specimen marble tables. It came from the bed of a lost tropical sea, turned to stone beneath a lost range of highlands, was quarried from the eroded stumps by a lost industry and has been stripped of its identity by the passing of an age. Even the disused limestone quarries that pepper the fringes of Plymouth in west Devon and Torbay in the east (Fig. 1.1a-b) are not evidence of the extraction of ornamental stone. They reflect the more prosaic demands of a lime-starved agricultural hinterland and a building industry that once depended upon stone. Devonshire marbles were almost an incidental product of this quarrying activity but they can be rediscovered today dustily adorning some fine Victorian building interiors (Chapter 5) and occasionally formed as ornaments (Chapter 4) locked in museum galleries or antiques showrooms. Lost in plain sight today, these once eloquent witnesses of a burgeoning and prosperous industry are now anonymous relics of a forgotten chapter.

So where did all the marbles come from? The intensive quarrying was restricted to the eastern and western extremities of south Devon because that is where most of the limestone lies (Fig. 1.2). Quarries survived and grew large only where stone availability, markets and transport came together and where output could fulfil the high-volume needs of construction projects and lime burning. The geology of south Devon is a complex palimpsest (Chapters 7–9) and the scattered limestone distribution results from a rich and turbulent geological history. The coral seas once stretched all the way between Plymouth and Torquay, reaching inland past Stoneycombe, Ogwell, Ipplepen, Ashburton and Chudleigh (Fig. 1.2), all once great marble localities. The lime sediments of these coral seas are what started the marble story, soon becoming rocks that were first deeply buried and then lofted to form eroding highlands.

At the modern western end of the coast around Plymouth many old quarries now provide convenient hiding places for unsightly industries (Fig. 1.1a) whilst at the less-industrialised eastern end around Torbay, trees, shrubs and grass are slowly healing the quarried coastal scars (Fig. 1.1b). The waves that churn beneath these have long since turned quarry rubble, once tipped carelessly into the sea, into striking beach pebbles. We have only to pick up a few of these to recognise, still sparkling, the remains of Devon's ancient warm, shallow coral seas (Fig. 1.1c). Corals, shells, sponges and even rare primitive ammonites can be found profiled across worn stones (Fig. 1.1d), whilst the abundance of colours and textures reveals something of the profound geological changes that affected them and of the potential 'marble' they must have come from.

The textural richness and tonal diversity seen in the pebbles (Fig. 1.1c-d), give us only a rough idea of the beauty and variation of Devon marbles that proved good enough to leave some other worldwide marbles looking downright inferior. The drawback of this superiority was that the combinations of characters that defined the best Devonshire marbles were usually unique to a particular locality, perhaps even a single quarry. They are accidents of local reef growth, geological structure, ancient fluid movement and modern exposure, so that the best stones come from a few restricted sites. In the more permanently viable marble centres elsewhere in the world, such as parts of northern or central Italy, where there is still commercial quarrying, marble belts stretch across large tracts of countryside, attracting more durable investment in equipment and infrastructure. Devon stones were commonly quarried from wherever the whims of geological evolution had left behind a single opportunity to win a beautiful stone and when it was gone, it was irreplaceable.

1

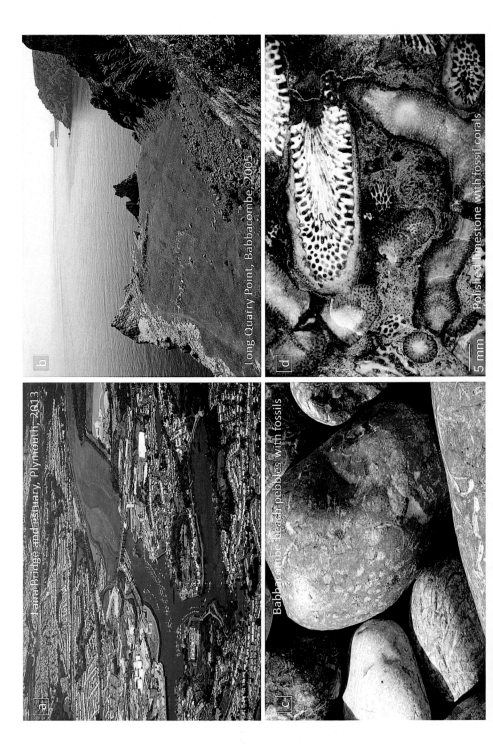

a. Laira Bridge and estuary, Plymouth, 2013

b. Long Quarry Point, Babbacombe, 2005

c. Babbacombe beach pebbles with fossils

d. Polished limestone with fossil corals

5 mm

Figure 1.1. (facing page) Quarries, reefs and corals. a: The Plym estuary and Laira Bridge, east of Plymouth, looking north. Much of the ground south of the bridge consists of reclaimed limestone quarries. The original landscape consisted of rolling wooded hills separated by drowned river valleys. Many of the quarry floors and quaysides are now occupied by large commercial premises or housing estates. A few quarry faces are still detectable (*Photo courtesy of Steve Johnson, Cyberheritage*). b: Long Quarry Point east of Torquay, looking south towards Berry Head. This quarry cuts into an ancient Devonian reef (described in Chapter 9 Itinerary S2). The ground is too sterile and exposed to have recovered substantially since quarrying finished a century ago. c: Wave-washed limestone pebbles up to 150 mm show fossil coral, shell and stony sponge embedded in coloured stone. d: Fossil branching corals, *Thamnopora* (top, with overgrowth) and *Parastriatopora* (bottom). These are 'finger corals', some broken before preservation, in a coloured and altered limestone matrix.

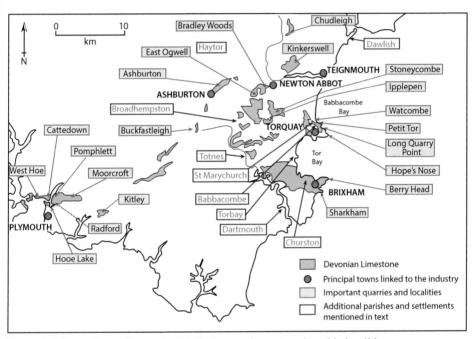

Figure 1.2. South Devon limestone distribution, settlements and marble localities.

1.2 Some technicalities: 'marble' and 'Devonian'

When Richard Polwhele wrote of a "*coast of marble*" (1793–1806) he was using a lay term that applied to any lime-rich rock regardless of its ornamental properties. In stricter geological terms, a marble is a limestone that has been distorted, compacted and recrystallised by heat and pressure; a process known technically as metamorphism. This usually obscures original fossil and sedimentary features, resulting in a dense, streaked, crystalline rock, normally still made of the mineral calcite and capable of taking a high-quality polish. Compared to granite, which contains the harder minerals quartz and feldspar, true marble is relatively quick and easy to prepare either by hand or machine.

When it comes to the Devon 'marbles', though, there is little evidence of any extreme metamorphism. They still display their fossils and sedimentary characteristics (Chapter 7), so that strictly speaking they are not marble at all—they are just ordinary limestones. Their 'polishability' is attributable to burial by several km (Chapter 8) and to prolonged

3

and repeated soaking in hot mineral-rich groundwaters. This introduced extra calcite and some dolomite into veins and cavities and added mineral stains in a rich variety of reds, pinks, browns, yellows and even greens. Some of this alteration and mineralisation is directly linked to the arrival, then deep underground, of the nearby Dartmoor granite and its impact on the local groundwater, to be explored later. In fact the landscape of the time just above the granite probably included some fairly active volcanoes, now long since removed by erosion.

The term 'Devonian' is usually taken to mean things pertaining to Devonshire, but it is actually also a technical geological term. The Devonian Period (of geological time) and resultant Devonian System (of rocks, created during that period of time) were first scientifically defined in Devon and despite now being recognised worldwide, and with some far more complete successions elsewhere, the name has to remain. It all stems from the rules by which scientific terminology is allowed to develop yet remain meaningful and verifiable, and the 'Devonian' precedent was set by some of the most influential pre-Darwinian figures in the history of geological science. In the early 1800s naturalists were increasingly recognising the fossil contents of rocks, amongst whom was the amateur palaeontologist Rev. Richard Hennah whose simple publication *"Observations respecting the limestone of Plymouth"* (1817) and subsequent papers (to 1830) attracted serious professional interest. Four of the greatest names homed in, Henry De la Beche (1839) with his *"Report on the Geology of Cornwall, Devon and West Somerset"* and then Rev. Prof. Adam Sedgwick and Sir Roderick Impey Murchison (1839) with a classification of the deposits. They then joined forces in 1840 with fossil coral expert William Lonsdale to include consideration of *"the age of the limestones of South Devonshire"*. We now know that the Devonian Period lasted from around 420 million to 359 million years ago (Fig. 1.3). The sediments that were deposited in Devon's warm coral seas and eventually became Devonshire marbles were deposited around the middle and end of that period of time, but their full conversion to coloured and textured 'marble' took anything up to a further 100 million years (Chapter 8). The eventual 'toughening' of the limestones in the direction of marble involved some crustal convulsions that buried them, faulted and folded them and then lofted them into a landscape. This was not the landscape that we see now, for it is long lost, buried once again and long ago, by desert deposits of Permian and Triassic age (Fig. 1.3).

1.3 Devon marble in context

Devon marble was very much a latecomer in the grand history of European ornamental stone. Used in high status buildings, sculpture and ornaments, marble has been big business since the dawn of civilisation. Much well-known evidence survives of the extensive ornamental uses of Mediterranean marbles by the Greeks and Romans for cladding buildings, embellishing interior walls and floors, creating impressive colonnades and carving striking ornaments and sculpture. The seductive use of plain, coloured and textured natural stone in buildings projects wealth and creates impact.

This was a commonplace conceit in the classical world and it re-emerged in medieval Europe and Asia when the technologies of cutting and polishing were rediscovered and taken forward. Great temples, mosques and cathedrals around the 'old' world, and later the new, were embellished and glorified with polished marble, one of the highest tokens of worth that we can bestow on a building. Many of the techniques for cutting and polishing were reintroduced to Britain by itinerant stonemasons who built the great Norman and Gothic cathedrals and churches after the start of the second millennium. With these amazing craftsmen came some of the prized marbles from Europe, such as pure white *Carrara* marble from Italy and black *Tournai* marble from Belgium. Given the problems of transporting stone in the middle ages, it was not long before local British stones such

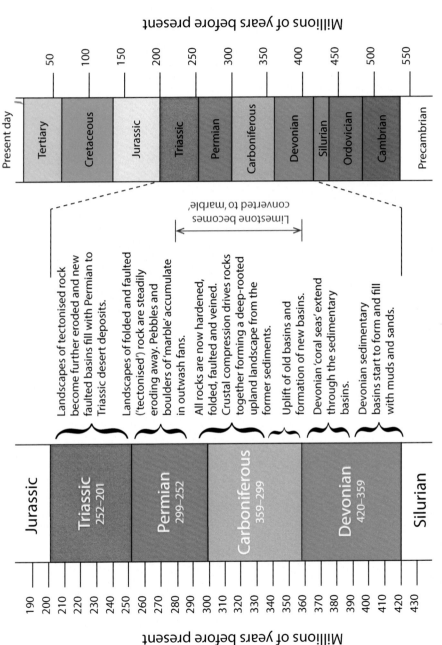

Figure 1.3. The Devonian period in its place amongst the other geological periods and a summary of the epic geological events that surround the generation of Devonshire marble. All numbers count as millions of years before the present.

Millions of years before present

50	Present day
100	Tertiary
150	Cretaceous
200	Jurassic
250	Triassic
300	Permian
350	Carboniferous
400	Devonian
450	Silurian
500	Ordovician
550	Cambrian
	Precambrian

Limestone becomes converted to 'marble'

Jurassic

Triassic 252–201
Landscapes of tectonised rock become further eroded and new faulted basins fill with Permian to Triassic desert deposits.

Permian 299–252
Landscapes of folded and faulted ('tectonised') rock are steadily eroding away. Pebbles and boulders of 'marble' accumulate in outwash fans.

Carboniferous 359–299
All rocks are now hardened, folded, faulted and veined. Crustal compression drives rocks together forming a deep-rooted upland landscape from the former sediments.

Uplift of old basins and formation of new basins.

Devonian 'coral seas' extend through the sedimentary basins.

Devonian 420–359
Devonian sedimentary basins start to form and fill with muds and sands.

Silurian

Millions of years before present

190
200
210
220
230
240
250
260
270
280
290
300
310
320
330
340
350
360
370
380
390
400
410
420
430

5

as polished Portland, Purbeck and Carboniferous were in widespread use along with the imported marbles in high status buildings. Later, towards the end of the second millennium, especially in an increasingly wealthy Imperial Britain, red and pink marbles, some of which were very similar to Devon marbles, flooded in from France and Belgium. Often these were fashioned into much more prosaic items such as bedside tables, washstands and fire surrounds.

Perceiving that 'foreign' marbles had fast gained the upper hand around the start of the 19th century, the *Society for the Encouragement of Arts, Manufactures and Commerce* (now the *Royal Society of Arts*) offered challenges to the public in 1802 and 1804 in an attempt to redress the balance. The first was an offer of their Gold Medal and a premium of 100 guineas "*to the person who shall discover within Great Britain or Ireland a quarry of white marble fit for the purposes of statuary, and equal in all respects to those kinds now imported from Italy*" (Society of Arts, 1802). The second was a call to quarry proprietors for polished blocks of available British marbles, to be placed on show to the public, in the Great Room of the Society at the Adelphi, central London. "*By such arrangements,*" they proclaimed, "*it is expected that the interests of the proprietors of the quarries will be promoted and the use of British marble much extended*" (Society of Arts, 1804). Their calls lasted for 20 years or more, and the first was never answered, even to this day. There is no white marble in the UK or Ireland that can rival that of Carrara. Their second call was met by the progressive accumulation, in their ones and twos, of stone types from all over the country, but one submission in 1809, eventually comprising 60 specimens of polished stone from one small quarry in Devon blew the rest away. It was so convincingly special that they at once awarded it their Gold Medal, despite that fact that a medal had never been offered for that particular challenge in the first place. The Quarry was at Petit Tor, in Babbacombe.

1.4 The foundations of the Devon marble industry

Marble was neither the first nor the most long-lasting extractive activity in the rock economy of south Devon. Stone has been taken from the ground for as long as there have been humans to excavate it. At some stage or another, stone has provided us with the durable raw materials for everyday objects ranging from weapons to tools, figurines and jewellery, and from drainage systems to roads, buildings and major civil engineering projects. The production of lime for spreading on acidic soils, or for making mortar to hold buildings together, may go back as far as it has been possible to construct and fuel the kilns that enabled the prior burning of limestone. Stone is the most durable of all unprocessed natural resources and quarries have been staples of local economies from the earliest times. South West Britain has always been particularly rich in mined and quarried natural resources and there were major extractive industries based upon metals, clay, granite and limestone well before the growth in ornamental stone production. The extensive granite quarries on Dartmoor and further south-west in Cornwall were the basis of a notable parallel stone industry that had its own manufacturing centres and uses, particularly for masonry and paving. The Rev. Thomas Moore in his *History of Devonshire*, (1829) notes that "*the principal exports of Plymouth are copper ore, silver, tin and lead antimony from Cornwall, manganese, marble, slates, granite, limestone, pilchards etc.*". Getting stuff out of the ground, or the sea for that matter, was in the blood of the people of Devon and Cornwall.

The early history of Devonshire marble is closely intertwined with stone extraction in general and bits of information come from several historical and 'popular' information sources. A serious obstacle to the growth of a regional-scale stone industry prior to the 20th century, ornamental or otherwise, was transport, so that the distribution and extent of extractive activity closely reflected the ease of movement of its products. In the early

1800s shifting heavy and bulk goods by road was problematic as there was not yet the universal use of tarmac surfacing which would only come with the exploitation of mineral oil a century later. Canals and then railways became the most effective means of transport for bulk goods after the industrial revolution, but most of the south Devon hinterland, enjoyed neither. The "*old Devonshire lanes*" in the St Marychurch area were "*hilly and circuitous*", according to JY White in his *History of Torquay* (1878). The great network of turnpikes, the main roads of the day, did not extend everywhere. Even these were normally only finished with a spread of field stones or quarry rubble, road engineering techniques and the labour market not matching the way the Romans did things two millennia earlier.

The Plym was an important waterway for granite export on the west side of Devon but there was little limestone inland beyond the Plymouth estuary. In east Devon the famous Haytor granite tramway, used from 1820 to move granite down from Dartmoor to the Stover canal and thence to the coast at Teignmouth, was a beacon of enterprise and in-genuity but it represented a local solution to a high-volume transport problem that would have been uneconomic for the scattered Devon marble outcrops. The answer had to be to concentrate quarrying effort on sites where limestone could be extracted either from sea cliffs or beside navigable rivers. In these places overburden was minimal, gradients were maximal and ships with wind in their sails could do the rest.

Somewhat anecdotal early records of quarrying around Torquay focus on two Devon rectors, Robert Ball, of St Marychurch and William Lane of Aveton Gifford, who were deprived of their livings during the upheavals of the English civil wars in the 1640s and were obliged to work in local quarries, the first at Petit Tor and the second at Hope's Nose (Pateman, 1980; Shaw, 1966). Here is the message that labouring in quarries was a com-monplace and low-status activity and also that as far back as the mid-17th century some of the known coastal quarries were already active, with stone going directly into ships, but there is no indication of ornamental stone production. J Y White (1878, p. 101) notes legal documents revealing the letting of quarries at Meadfoot and Anstey's Cove in 1652 and 1665. These are also coastal sites, located on the rocky headlands near to 'Fleete' before it became Tor Key and then Torquay.

Lime production was the main driver for these early coastal endeavours, perhaps along with some extraction of building stone. Somewhat later Moore (1829) noted that so ex-tensive was the use of lime as "*manure*" in Devonshire that "*prodigious quantities were raised from the limestone and marble rocks in various parts of the county*". He described how there was "*scarcely an inlet or creek either on the northern or southern coast of the county... not supplied with a limekiln*" and notes that the "*immense quarries at Oreston near Plymouth and the adjacent parts supply the kilns on the whole range of the Tamar, Tavy and St Germains rivers as well as some other districts*". Moore described how "*the beautiful cliffs at Berry Head in Torbay and at Babbicombe furnish*" (limestone to kilns) *on the Teign the Exe and the adjoining coast*", but he lamented the "*ruthless hand of commerce*" that was leading to the piecemeal demolition of the "*grand and magnificent ornaments of the coast*". Here was the start of the landscape modification further explored in Chapter 6. Inland, Moore says that "*nearly the whole of the south western portion of Devon abounds with lime works*". "*Those of Chudleigh especially and its vicinity are numerous and the rocks here have long been celebrated not only for their beauty but the excellence of the lime which they supply which is remarkable for its extreme whiteness.*" That whiteness is a real surprise, for the marbles are black. Their colour comes from par-ticulate carbon, which actually burns and aids the lime production process.

Two important inland routes for stone to the sea became those from Chudleigh above the Teign and out to sea via Teignmouth (Fig. 1.2), and from Broadhempston across to Totnes and down along the Dart to Dartmouth and the sea (Fig. 1.2). For example, noting quarrying next to the river Dart, Moore records the manual production of "*ready broken*" *stones for forming roads in the neighbourhood of London*". He says that "*this latter article is obtained on the banks of the river and the getting it from the quarries and breaking it affords employment to a great number of persons*".

1.5 Some early glints of marble

Thomas Moore's (1829) accounts go a little further, though, raising the status of Chudleigh and the Teign connection. At the turn of the 18th to the 19th century the Chudleigh quarries were evidently more than just sources for ordinary utility stone, for he notes that stone "*obtained from the Chudleigh and Harcombe rocks is manufactured into beautiful chimney-pieces, and sent from the port of Teignmouth*". Indeed, Chudleigh could be the earliest ornamental marble locality of importance. An anonymous writer (Anon, 1817) claimed that "*the quarries in the great and lofty rock of Chudleigh are the oldest in Devon*" and the marble "*blackish intersected by veins of white spar (and) has often red and yellow threads and is maculated with white shells*".

Equally, the Broadhempston/Dart connection also has an important place in the early story of decorative marble because in the late 1700s Broadhempston was not only a known source in itself of finished marble, it became an important dispersal point for skilled stonemason families. The earliest businesses were based upon memorial stones supplied to local churches, but from the incidental record of a Newfoundland researcher (Pocius, 1981) we discover that locally manufactured grave markers in the 1790s were exported from Broadhempston as far as Newfoundland, the other side of the North Atlantic. Their creator was Daniel Woodley, who, along with the families Grant, Blackler, Coleman, Pearce and Jenkins subsequently moved to St Marychurch and beyond in what seems to have been a marble 'goldrush' in the early 1800s. At least three of these families developed a direct connection to the remarkably diverse and iconic Petit Tor Quarry at Babbacombe, St Marychurch. The Broadhempston link is explored in Chapter 3.

In the early days of the marble industry, cutting and polishing were undertaken in the immediate vicinity of extraction; manual effort and horse power being the early enablers. John Swete in his *Picturesque Sketches of Devon* (1793) describes how, on one of his walks, he encountered in Petit Tor Cove, Babbacombe, "*several persons at work sawing slabs of various sizes from blocks of marble*" that had been detached from the cliff and rolled to the beach. Swete goes on to note that a Mr Fulton of London who, recognising the potential of *Petitor* marble for the market in London, had been at "*considerable expense in erecting a large building which contains a machine for the sawing of the blocks of marble; this his own invention and by the means of a single horse turning a wheel will so expedite the business as to saw as much stone in a day as a labourer hath been accustomed to do in fifteen*". Swete actually sketched the headland in his 1793 journal, with stone extraction taking place in the bay (Fig. 1.4b), but not Petit Tor Quarry itself. His "*Mr Fulton*" turns out to have been the notable American engineer, artist and inventor Robert Fulton, who had stayed in Torquay for a short period in the early 1790s (Dickinson, 1913, Ch. 3). Evidently Fulton made a model of his invention which he submitted to the *Society for the Encouragement of Arts, Commerce and Manufactures*, for in 1794 he received in recognition

Figure 1.4. (facing page) Some of the earliest views of marble localities and their modern equivalents. a: Oddicombe Beach, Babbacombe, in 2010. Red sandstone cliffs centre and Petit Tor Down right. b: The above view dated 1793; watercolour by Rev. John Swete (Swete, 1789–1800). A boat is being loaded with stone in mid-view (*Photo courtesy of Devon Record Office and Devon Heritage Services*). c: "*Marble Quarries at Petit-Tor near Torquay*" Lithograph by Villeneuve, *c*. 1828. Printed in Paris. Note cottage, lighthouse and rock pinnacle, all now gone as seen in 1.4d.d: Modern view (2012) of Petit Tor Beach, taken *c*. 100 m east of c. Limestone pebbles on the beach are white and the headland immediately beyond is where the lighthouse in 1.4c was located.

Oddicombe Beach, 1793

Oddicombe Beach, 2010

Petit Tor Beach, 2012

Petit Tor Beach, 1828

b

a

d

c

9

their Silver Medal (Society of Arts, 1794). Fulton went on to excavate canals, experiment with submarines and explosives, and successfully to pioneer steam-powered ships.

1.6 The fame of Petit Tor spreads

Petit Tor Quarry soon became just about the most celebrated ornamental stone quarry in Britain. From a retrospective article in the *Western Daily Mercury*, April 9th 1886, we learn that when Robert Fulton moved on to pastures new, his tenure at Petit Tor was adopted by another entrepreneur by the name of Hubbard. He established workshops, building them on the beach. Unsurprisingly some of these were soon destroyed in a heavy easterly gale in the first decades of the 19th century. The article claims that some of Hubbard's buildings were still to be seen at the time of writing in 1886, and a superb 1828 lithograph of the *"Marble Quarries at Petit-Tor"* (Fig. 1.4c) shows two, but they are long gone today (Fig. 1.4d). The fact that this marble quarry so soon became a tourist attraction is a confirmation of its importance. There is more to this Mr Hubbard. He was evidently John Hubbard, a local furniture-maker with a fine summer residence on Babbacombe Cliff (Anon, 1817), and he turns out to be the 'Mr John P Hubbard' of Picket St, Temple Bar, London who submitted the Gold Medal-winning collection of 50 (later 60) *Petitor* marbles to the *Society for the Encouragement of Arts, Manufactures and Commerce* in London in response to their call for British marbles. In his supporting written address to the Society on March 1st 1809 (Society of Arts, 1809) John Hubbard talks of "*the numberless obstacles*" he had encountered during a period of two years, as well as "*heavy expenses, and local prejudices*", probably a reference to his losses in storms and a bit of resentment from others with second homes in the cliffs (listed in Anon, 1817). The detail that Hubbard provides on the quarry itself is remarkable, picked up in Chapter 3, but in a clear reference to Robert Fulton's failed enterprise, Hubbard notes that "*the quarry was first opened about sixteen years ago* (i.e. in 1793), *and was afterward neglected; but that it has been now worked by him for two years*" (i.e. since 1807). Sadly, Hubbard's tenure at Petit Tor did not last long after that. Despite his uplifting prizewinning success in 1809, his luck ran out, and the business was soon failing.

This part of the story of Devon marbles is that of two crucial pioneering entrepreneurs, both in receipt of prestigious medals for their vision, determination and investment, but both of whom seem to have lost heavily in the process. At least Robert Fulton, who was only 29 in 1794 when he experimented with sawing marble at Petit Tor, went on to a productive career, despite an early death aged only 50 in 1815. As for John Hubbard, likely to have been no younger than Fulton, perhaps his summer residence became his place of retirement, but according to later accounts he may not have been quite the same man again following his disillusionment at Petit Tor, and the marble quarrying business thereby entered another lull.

1.7 The rise of Plymouth

We owe something to William Gilpin (1798) for his 'observations' concerning the marbles quarried at Plymouth Dock on the west side of the city. He noted "*several of the blocks polished; and thought them more beautiful than any foreign marble. The ground is dark*

Figure 1.5. (facing page) The earliest illustration of limestone quarrying in Devon. The print is inscribed as a "*View of the Marine Barracks, Stonehouse*" and dated March 16, 1786. The foreground shows quarrying of paving slabs at West Hoe Quarry. Main picture: The print is from an original painting by W Hay, engraved by BT Pouncy (*Image courtesy of Royal Collection Trust,* © *Her Majesty Queen Elizabeth II 2015*). Insets: Enlargements showing activities, stock and tools (*High definition extracts, courtesy Plymouth Library Services*).

West Hoe Quarry. 1786

brown, the veining red and blue. The colours are soft in themselves, and intermix agreeably". Although it is not clear where this was, there is a remarkably early 1786 pictorial record of hand quarrying (perhaps the earliest) beside Mill Bay on the west side of the city (Fig. 1.5). The print marked the completion of the Royal Marine Barracks in 1785, so that the extraction of paving slabs at West Hoe Quarry in the foreground was incidental to the subject, but the 'marble' pavements of Plymouth were subsequently endorsed by amateur palaeontologist Richard Hennah (1817). After a shower of rain there were, *"veins of different colours, and beautifully shaded: not unfrequently, too, full of animal remains of various kinds".* This tradition of Plymouth as the *"Marble-Streeted Town"* (e.g. Fig. 1.6) is followed in Chapter 10 (DMB SW/PL2a) for it was later picked up by Thomas Hardy in his poem of that name in about 1914. By Hardy's time most of West Hoe Quarry was a housing estate, but its former lime kilns are recorded a century before in a further historical print (Fig. 1.6) made at the time the active quarry was still in the hands of the developer, Thomas Gill.

On the other side of town the impetus for the development of an ornamental stone industry was somewhat different. It came with the building of the Plymouth breakwater, a linear artificial island in Plymouth Sound that still shelters the anchorage and harbours. This enormous structure, nearly a mile (1.5 km) long, was started in 1812 and finished about 35 years later, consuming around 4 million tons of stone, and doing much to forward techniques in quarrying, engineering and shipping on a national scale (Chapter 6). The project made particular demands on quarries on the less-developed east side of Plymouth, particularly on the east side of the estuary at Cattewater where there was a specially purchased 25-acre site at Oreston near Plymstock that would become 'Breakwater Quarry'. The accelerated quarrying activity serendipitously exposed new sources of stone that could be lent to ornamental purposes, and Cattedown, Radford, Pomphlett and Hooe Lake, all known Devon marble localities and accessible by sea, owe much of their early development, directly or indirectly, to this project.

The Breakwater Project enhanced the early reputation of west Devonshire marbles principally through promotion by one man, Superintendent Engineer William Stuart. Stuart took the time out to manufacture two items made from Breakwater Quarry limestone and he displayed these at the Great Exhibition of 1851. One was a two-pedestal table of polished Breakwater marble, and another a marble model of the Breakwater itself, which was good enough to receive an honourable mention along with the Prize Medals (Royal Commission, 1852). These were not the only Devonshire marble exhibits at this crucial and formative exhibition and more are noted in Chapter 2. In his professional capacity Stuart did much to develop methods of quarrying and transport of materials (Chapter 3), for example, publishing details of his gunpowder blasting techniques (Stuart, 1838). Lengthy fuses and electronic firing were many decades away but he had an intriguing method of remote blasting achieved by firing a lit fuse down a shot hole in order to ignite the basal charge.

Robert Fulton also had a penchant for explosives, and it was he that hopped over to France for a short while in the late 1700s when the Napoleonic threat to Britain and all its coastal enterprises seemed precariously unresolved. In 1797, just 3 years after his innovative skills had been recognised in London, Fulton left for France to experiment with explosive weapons on behalf of Bonaparte himself (Chapter 3). If he had ever previously used gunpowder at Petit Tor we know nothing of it, but it might well have become part of his undoing there. William Renwick, in his *Marble and Marble Working* (1909) loftily observed a century later that in Devon marble quarries *"blasting is often resorted to with the result that the force of the explosives used has a tendency to shatter the stone, causing vents to be developed when it is sawn into slabs".* He complained that *"this gives to Devonshire marbles a reputation for unsoundness which is largely undeserved".* Of course

Figure 1.6. West Hoe Quarry *c.* 1825 *"Mount Edgcumbe from the Hoe"* looking over West Hoe Quarry and south-west out to sea. The island is Drake's Island. The foreground shows several lime kilns and one in use. Lithograph by JD Harding. The backdrop to this print is the post-war re-use of original West Hoe paving slabs at the Civic Square, Guildhall, Plymouth.

the best way to release workable ornamental marble blocks was not by the use of explosives and it was common knowledge amongst marble workers. The Devon quarries were a different matter, though, producing stone for mixed uses, so that there was a necessary balance to be achieved between volume of production and quality of stone.

1.8 Towards National status

With increased mechanisation, especially with the application of steam power in the mid to late 1800s, quarrying, finishing and movement of goods became faster, cheaper and more efficient. Large centralised marble works became established away from the points of quarrying in Plymouth (Goad's Steam Marble Works) and Torquay (Jenkins and Blackler). Innovations for cutting large slabs from faces by the use of cables, for sawing single blocks into multiple slabs and for polishing large surfaces all came with steam power, but the means of cutting took a lot longer to move away from the technique of feeding 'sharp' sand on to wires or steel saw blades. The diamond-impregnated cutting edge was a revolution of the early 20th century.

Aided by mechanisation, Devonshire marbles rose to national status through the 19th century alongside an increasing appetite for luxury stone ornaments and architectural tokens of wealth and esteem. Like the extractive industries before it, ornamental stone became a significant source of local wealth and employment in its own right. Both before and after the establishment of the centralised stone works, there were numerous small local businesses that provided work and employment for quarriers and specialist marble masons, initially as itinerant workers, and then in recognisable communities. There were

13

also many who were employed directly or indirectly as carriers and mariners, moving raw materials to workshops and factories and taking completed products to market both by land and sea.

A tantalising glimpse of the importance of the smaller and non-architectural ornamental 'chattels' produced in Devon marble comes from the privately published inventory of a distant stately mansion, Hendersyde Park, near Kelso in Roxburghshire, Scotland. Published in 2 editions, 1835 and 1859, the Hendersyde Park *Catalogue of pictures, statues, busts, antique columns, bronzes, fragments of antique buildings, tables of Florentine and roman mosaic, scagliola and inlaid wood; Indian, Neapolitan and other china* (Hendersyde, 1859) lists the particulars of thousands of precious objects owned by a Newcastle and Bohemia coal baron. These include more than 20 artefacts in Devon Marble such as specimen marble tables, vases, desk and display items, and a further 60 or more pieces of polished specimen Devon marbles. Nine of the itemised artefacts were by "*Mr Woodley*" of "*Marychurch*", including a large round specimen marble table occupying the middle of the grand entrance hall. We know what this table may have been like from another large Woodley table to be described in Chapter 4. There was also a "*bagnarola*" in Devonshire marble in the Large Drawing Room. This, if we take it literally, was a bathtub!

At the peak of production in the mid to late 1800s, south Devon was by no means the only centre for 'marble' extraction and manufacturing in Britain. As the Hendersyde Park inventory so eloquently reveals, there were stones from many parts of the British Isles that had come into ornamental use where colour, texture, hardness and available size encouraged extraction and polishing. Examples were in Dorset, (*Purbeck* marble), North East England (*Frosterley* marble), Cumberland (Crinoid Limestone), Western Ireland (*Connemara* marble) and western Scotland (*Iona* marble). John Watson (1916) and Monica Price (2007) cite examples, but the most prominent of the mid-19th century centres outside Devon was Derbyshire. The Derbyshire industry was based upon a dark organic-rich limestone termed *Ashford Black* marble, quarried near Bakewell. Superficially the products of the Devon and Derbyshire industries can be similar. The inlaid marble ornaments and tables of both industries attracted patronage from royalty and aristocracy in both the UK and Europe but, in terms of range of products, the Devon industry had the edge. The intrinsically beautiful, patterned and coloured marbles of Devon were more cheerful than the black marble of Derbyshire, and the polished-stone architectural products from Devonshire such as fireplaces, pillars and pilasters were more diverse and popular than their Derbyshire equivalents. Devon marble architectural products such as pillars, staircases, fire surrounds and floors are found in churches, cathedrals, museums and corporate and public buildings throughout the UK and they reached colonial countries worldwide. Devonshire marble was well able to hold its own in the aesthetic competition against some world-famous foreign rivals.

1.9 Then decline

We could blame the death of a Royal patron of ornamental stone, Queen Victoria, and we could blame the social and economic upheavals following the first World War, but the statistics show that Devonshire marble was already in decline before the end of the 19th century (Chapter 5). In 1909 marble expert William Renwick complained (1909, p. 104) that the cost of rail freight for marble in block from Devon and Derbyshire to London was so prohibitive that it was cheaper to import marbles from France and Belgium. The demise of Devonshire came through the triple blow of changed fashion, new priorities and pressing competition. It dwindled rather than suddenly collapsing. The interwar years saw sporadic resurgence and there was a brief resurrection following WWII as well, but south Devon stopped pumping out grandeur on the industrial scale around the turn of the 19th century.

Many of the smaller specialist marble quarries are now either overgrown or have long since been subsumed into larger general purpose excavations. Some are housing estates and several are modern industrial sites. The lasting mark of the wider quarrying industry survives, but only with the large echoing quarries that started the Chapter. Many are highly visible, but inaccessible except to the most determined either because of erosive degeneration or through encroachment of industrial development and they are dangerous anyway. Good stone samples are better obtained where old quarry float (rejected rubble) is reaching the beaches.

Not all else is lost, though, for the beaches provide another way of sampling Devonshire marbles, provided we do not need to know exactly where the samples are from. In the long linear seep of red sandstone cliffs that forms the full length of Babbacombe Bay, north of Torquay, there are abundant pebbles and boulders of eroded Devonian limestone contained in deposits of Permian age, perhaps 275 million years old and a good 100 million years younger than the original Devonian deposits (Fig. 1.3). The Devonian sea floors had long since been turned to rock, swallowed down into the crust and then regurgitated again as hills or mountains. These were whittled down by erosion as they rose and the limestone pebbles and boulders are part of the debris that came out of this first and lost Devonian landscape, entrained in storm-generated torrents, rushed through rocky wadi channels, and expelled into wide outwash plains. The reworked limestone debris has all the fossils, colours and textures of the marbles (Chapters 10, 12 and 13) and it became the basis for the parallel industry to the ornamental marble interiors, the manufacture of elaborate Devonshire marble tables, ornaments and utility items (Chapter 5). These pebbles and boulders provided much of the essential jewel-like feedstock used by the highly skilled marble masons and 'madrepore workers' (Chapter 4).

Of the dozens of original quarries, there are just three still working: Moorcroft (Plymouth), Stoneycombe (Newton Abbot) and Ashburton. Rock is no longer freed by gunpowder or laboriously levered out, and nor is it patiently cut by wire or machine. It is blasted out by the thousands of tons, using modern explosives and shot-firing techniques, carted by giant trucks, and then crushed to create road stone and aggregates for the construction industry. It is still used for building and agricultural purposes but in very different ways. Devon marble working is gone today, although there are a few modern firms still willing to try it on a very small scale. Even the original factory buildings are lost. Apart from one sadly undervalued small remnant in St Marychurch (Chapter 11, Group 8), north of Torquay, the sites have all been redeveloped.

The lasting legacies are the beautiful but anonymous marble interiors of churches (e.g. Fig. 1.7) and public buildings worldwide, and the exotic range of rare embellishments (e.g. Fig. 1.8) and ornamental items made from the great variety of stones (e.g. Fig 4.1). These are analysed, resurrected and visited in the ensuing Chapters, as are the materials they are made from and the people who made them. Many of the spectacular interiors remain in good shape whilst the surviving smaller ornamental items are now valuable antiques that can pop up unrecognised in a car boot sale or become catalogued with some fanfare when recognised by a major auction room.

St John's Church, Torquay

Grey Lummaton

Red Ogwell

Ashburton

Fossil Petitor

Fitzwilliam Museum, Cambridge

Red Ogwell

Peterhead granite

Red Ogwell

Green Genoa

Red Ogwell

Yellow Siena

Red Ogwell

Yellow Siena

Figure 1.7. (facing page) Two great Devonshire marble interiors: Fitzwilliam Museum, Cambridge and St John's Church, Torquay. a: The stylish and spacious Baroque stair hall at the Fitzwilliam Museum, Cambridge. *Red Ogwell* marble is used in panels and balustrades alongside the most famous of the Italian marbles, *Green Genoa* and *Yellow Siena* (identified as shown). b: The bright interior of St John's Church, Torquay. One of the chancel shafts with drums of varied Devonshire marbles (identified as shown). There is more Devonshire in the nave shafts and in the colonnettes beside the windows. The marbles in this building are exclusively Devonshire.

Figure 1.8. Balusters of *Petitor* varieties support the chancel screen/communion rail in Christ Church, Cheltenham (DMB SW/GL/1) (fuller view inset). The plinth is also a Devonshire marble, probably *Ashburton*, whilst the panels inside the white *Tuscan* newels are *Ipplepen* (left) and *Ogwell* (right). An unhappy accident has befallen the balusters at some time in the past, for one has come out, only to be inserted the wrong way up!

2. RECOGNISING AND DIFFERENTIATING: THE DIVERSITY OF DEVONSHIRE MARBLE

2.1 Rediscovering Devonshire marbles

The quest to rediscover Devonshire marbles, to recognise their types, to distinguish them from one another and similar non-Devonshire stones and to pinpoint their sources on a map starts here. There are no Devonshire marble building interiors with neatly labelled stones; there are no handbooks with carefully photographed examples of the 20 or so distinct types and there are few quarries left where we can collect and compare examples. The evidence has to be pieced together from old stone collections, contemporary records, industrial waste tips and the few remaining accessible exposures of Devonshire marbles.

Fortunately, there are surviving collections of reference samples prepared by the marble companies themselves, now in museum and building stone collections around the country. Much is owed to the manufacturers who created the samples for their showrooms (mainly Andrew Blackler & Sons of Babbacombe and H J Jenkins & Son of Torquay) and to those who placed the specimen samples into safekeeping. There are three main UK collections of worldwide marbles and other building stones, one in Cambridge, another in Oxford and the third, and most accessible, held between London and Keyworth near Nottingham. The Cambridge collection is the John Watson Building Stone Collection, named after the man who first conserved and catalogued it (Watson, 1916; Andrew, 1994). This includes 25 samples of typical Devon marble and is the most useful source of information. At Oxford is the Corsi collection, assembled by an Italian enthusiast and later donated to the University (Price, 2007). There are few unequivocal Devon marbles in this collection but it is a wonderful resource for worldwide marbles, especially Italian. The London/Keyworth collection, which includes the British Building Stones Collection, lists 169 specimens of Devon marble, of which about 100 are viewable online (GeoScenic). Torquay Museum also holds a small collection of named marble showroom samples and there are more at University College London (UCL).

Few samples are very big, which makes it hard for them to be representative, and in some cases there is just a variety name attached. Luckily, most Devon marbles, unlike a good few of their European counterparts, take their name from the locality from which they come. Thus *Clouded Yellow Petitor*, *Red Ogwell* and *Plymouth Black*, are unequivocally linked to a specific area, but just where were the quarries? Petit Tor, near Torquay, has three, all with very different characteristics. Ogwell was once surrounded by a dozen or so working quarries, each of which might have been the locality, and Plymouth covers a large area. More helpfully, *Silverleigh*, *Ipplepen* and *Happaway* have romantic names that can eventually be linked to a specific village or quarry, but quite unhelpful are the more pretentiously named varieties such as '*Spangled Devon Spar*' and '*Coombe Rosa*' which both come from somewhere in the Plymouth area. From these collections it has proven possible, first, to recognise some main types, then to build a picture of their provenance and of some of the important buildings and artefacts where they are used, and finally, to put together an identification guide for the 20 or so most distinguishable of these as the main Devonshire marble types (Chapter 10).

Many of these stones are used in buildings alongside other British stones, most of them easily distinguishable, but problematically, there are two groups of European stones, one from Belgium and one from France, that are similar and easily confused with the Devonshire ones. This chapter therefore also looks at some of the stones that were used both in conjunction with and in competition with Devonshire marbles.

2.2 The range of the Devonshire marbles

The three most widely used Devonshire marbles are *Grey (Clouded) Petitor* (Fig. 10.1a) from Petit Tor Down, Babbacombe, Devon, *Red Ogwell* (Fig. 10.4a) from Ransley Quarry, East Ogwell, Devon and *Ashburton* marble (Figs 10.6a-b), from Linhay Quarry, Ashburton, west of Newton Abbott. Localities are shown on Figure 2.1. These three stones are brought together in several buildings, most notably in architect Thomas Collcutt's 1901 Lloyd's Register building on Fenchurch Street, London (Fig. 5.5). This building is listed and visited in the Buildings Guide (Chapter 11, Group 1, DMB L/C/3). Thomas Collcutt had taken his first job with the renowned Gothic Revival architect Thomas Edmund Street so it is no surprise to learn that two of Street's own buildings also display great examples of these three marbles, St John's Church, Torquay (Chapter 11, Group 8, DMB SW/TQ/4) and St James's Church, Sussex Gardens, Kensington (Chapter 11, Group 3, DMB L/W/4). Another spectacular building with variants of all three is the Officers' Mess at HMS Drake, the Royal Naval base at Plymouth (Fig. 2.3, also Chapter 5, Fig. 5.3).

This stone trinity makes a spectacular combination. *Grey Petitor* is a reef rock, made of stony sponge fossils held together by a form of calcite deposited direct from seawater (Figs 2.2C; 2.3C). The sedimentary history of Devonshire marbles is explored in detail in Chapter 7. The depositional characteristics give the marble its dominant grey colour, commonly verging on pink when there is a lot of original lime mud present. At its grey and blotchy textural extreme it resembles one of the classical white to grey Italian stones from Tuscany that can achieve similar textural effects through being fractured and folded

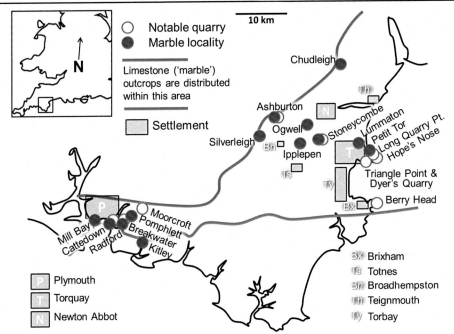

Figure 2.1. Settlements, major quarries and marble localities in south Devon.

Figure 2.2. (following page) Marbles in use: Lloyd's Register, Fenchurch Street, central London. The marbles are identified as follows: A: Emphases - *Ashburton*. B: Shafts - *Red Ogwell*. C: Flush panels - *Grey (Grey Clouded) Petitor*.

19

HMS Drake, Plymouth

Figure 2.3. (previous page) Marbles in use: Officers' Mess, HMS Drake, Plymouth. The marbles are identified as follows: A: Pedestal - *Ashburton* marble. B: Shaft - *Red Ogwell*. C: Shaft - *Grey (Grey Clouded) Petitor*. D: Base and plinth - *Grey Fossil Petitor*. E: Base - veined *Ashburton*.

and this similarity may have encouraged its popularity. *Grey Petitor* is one of several grey, pink and red marbles that came from the most famous of the Devonshire marble quarries at Petit Tor Down; the quarry first exploited by Robert Fulton in the early 19th century (Chapter 1) and which later became the iconic source of many of the varied marbles used in John Woodley specimen marble tables (Chapter 4).

Red Ogwell (Fig. 2.3B) is a pink to red rock commonly containing fossil coral, though the colour comes from the sediment rather than the fossils and is attributable to mineral alteration. *Ogwell* is studied in Chapter 7 and it is spectacularly displayed in the Fitzwilliam Museum, Cambridge (Chapter 11, Group 6, DMB E/CB/3) where it is analysed in some detail. Many of the fossils contained in *Red Ogwell* are shown in the fossils guide (Chapter 12). *Red Ogwell* is very similar to some of the French and Belgian Devonian marbles and points of distinction are discussed below.

Of these first three Devonshire marbles, *Ashburton* (Figs 2.2A; 2.3A) is most obviously a bedded sediment. It usually shows masses of round stony sponges and coral fossils in a dark grey limestone matrix (Chapter 7). It is a spectacular stone, often used for emphasis in skirtings, arches, door cases, or pedestals (architectural uses are discussed in Chapter 5). *Ashburton* is the only marble that is technically still in production, now mainly serving the aggregates industry. The marble can still be purchased.

Another common east Devon marble is *Ipplepen*, of which *Red Ipplepen* and *Grey Ipplepen* are named varieties. It is the stone in the celebrated marble pillars in the Gibson Hall, London (Chapter 11, Group 1, DMB L/C/2, Fig 11.2) and it was also used by architect John Gibson (after whom the hall was named) in the northernmost Devonshire marble interior so far discovered, at Todmorden in West Yorkshire (Chapter 11, Group 11, DMB NY/OL/1-2). The example shown here is the fascinating Baroque Christopher Wren Church, St Michael's, Cornhill (Fig. 2.4) which is not otherwise studied in this book. It would be exciting to think that this church, built 1670–77, got its Devonshire marble through Wren himself, but unfortunately not. By the 1850s the church had become swept up into the contemporary interior-remodelling fever (Chapter 5), but the authorities brought in no less an architect than George Gilbert Scott (GGS), soon to be knighted, who was an inveterate embellisher with British marble. His work is noted in Chapter 5 and there are visits to GGS buildings in Chapter 11 (Volume 2).

The *Ipplepen* in St Michael's, Cornhill is modest by Gibson Hall standards, but it dominates the pillars and panels in this Victorian Baroque chancel (Fig. 2.4b). The central three-arched reredos in English alabaster is supported by six *Ipplepen* shafts and alabaster frames the panels of marble on either side of the chancel where *Ipplepen* alternates with a dusky green *Verde Genova* from Italy. *Ipplepen* marble varies between grey, brown and red and became highly fractured at a late stage in its geological development so that its appearance is blocky with extensive veins of red sediment and pink calcite that obscure the original sedimentary texture (discussed in Chapter 8). All these 'flaws' subsequently became annealed into a robust and variegated rock and the complex veined and brecciated texture hides its reef-like origins with typical fossils, here including pockets of small brachiopod shells (Fig. 2.4d and Chapter 7). The associated alabaster work has abundant floral carving and was once a lot brighter, finished with gold leaf. Several of the marble

Figure 2.4. (facing page) Marbles in use: St Michael's Church, Cornhill, London. a: Church exterior in Portland Stone. b: The chancel and reredos. c: A panel in *Red Ipplepen* set in a frame of English alabaster. The marble shows a veined and fractured texture. d: Base of one of the reredos shafts in *Red Ipplepen*. The grey areas are 'nests' of small brachiopod shells. e: Veined and fractured textures in a *Red Ipplepen* shaft.

St Michael's Church, Cornhill

23

panels, now plain, once displayed biblical inscriptions, forgotten until the stones were surveyed for this book.

Of the Plymouth marbles, the most widely used is *Radford*, of which a red to grey variety embellishes the interior of the Foreign and Commonwealth Office in Whitehall (DMB L/W/5). Owing to access difficulties, this building is not offered in the guides so these marbles are illustrated here for the record (Fig. 2.5a, b). More *Radford* is seen in Brompton Oratory, Cromwell Road, West London which is described in Chapter 11, Group 2 (L/W/1). *Radford* is characterised by abundant stony sponges that show growth stages, a bit like tree rings, and it has large red sediment- and pink calcite-filled veins.

Of the rarer marbles, a good example is *Silverleigh*, from Buckfastleigh, near Ashburton (Fig. 2.5c, d). This stone has been identified through its complex white veining and dark grey fossil content that has similarities with *Ashburton*. Only two reference samples are known. The spectacular example used here (Fig. 2.5d) is at All Saints Church, Notting Hill, London (DMB L/W/8) where the veins are arranged in typical 'en echelon' sets that reflect the opening and filling of whole families of veins resulting from substantial shear forces during late formative stages deep underground (Chapter 8).

Silverleigh is by no means the only complex sheared stone in the Devonshire palette. There are several similar dark grey and black sheared stones, mainly from the Plymouth area, but these are not yet distinguishable with confidence when trying to draw together reference samples, buildings and outcrop. Three of these are shown in Figures 2.6a and b from the Duke of Cornwall Hotel in Plymouth, a remarkable survivor of the WWII blitz that destroyed much of the surrounding area, city centre and commercial docks around Mill Bay. The base is a black-veined marble, possibly *Pomflett Black*, the dado above that is likely to be *Flashed Mill Quay* from nearby Mill Bay, also seen in Brompton Oratory (see above), and the shaft base may be *Plymouth Lavender*. These stones are all likely to have been supplied from the nearby Steam Marble Works of John Goad, the former showroom of which was a marble treat in itself (Chapter 3) but did not survive WWII.

In no doubt, however, is the final generic example of Devonshire marble illustrated here, the elusive and mysterious *Green Kitley* (Fig. 2.6c, d). This is used in the spectacular arch at the east entrance to the Natural History Museum in London (Chapter 11, Group 2, DMB L/W/2; see also Chapter 5), formerly the Geological Museum. The capping entablature of this arch (Fig. 2.6d) has fine *Kitley*, capped by sparkling *Ashburton* and resting on a stair cope of rare *Green Purbeck* marble from Dorset.

2.3 What makes a good marble?

Looking at these finished products, it is easy to see why the stones have become renowned marbles, but there is more to success than just appearance. Some important prerequisites must be met before a good-looking rock can become a commercial marble. The first essential is strength and a good marble must lack flaws such as holes and fractures and it must be evenly hard and dense. Without these it will not be workable, capable of surviving quarrying, cutting and polishing whilst remaining in one piece. Even Richard Polwhele (1797) observed of Devonshire marble at the end of the 18th century that, "*The detached rocks, which are sawed into blocks, ...are frequently found shaken, and are therefore cast headlong for lime, to the great loss of the proprietor*".

Figure 2.5. (facing page) Marbles in use: Foreign and Commonwealth Office, Whitehall, London (DMB L/W/5) and All Saints Church, Notting Hill, London (DMB L/W/8). a: The first floor of the Stair Hall, Foreign and Commonwealth Office. b: Detail of one of the *Radford Red* shafts in the Stair Hall, Foreign and Commonwealth Office. c: Nave shafts in Devonshire marbles at All Saints Church. d: Close up of veined textures in *Silverleigh* marble from Buckfastleigh, Devon.

All Saints Church, Notting Hill

Foreign Office, London

a

b

c

d

25

Figure 2.6. (facing page) Marbles in use: Duke of Cornwall Hotel, Plymouth and the Natural History Museum, South Kensington, London. a: The dining room, Duke of Cornwall Hotel. b: Uncertain varieties of Plymouth marble in the Duke of Cornwall Hotel include *Pomphlett Black* (plinth), *Radford* (veined central dado) and *Plymouth Lavender* (light veined shaft base). c: Devonshire varieties and *Green Connemara* in the entrance archway, Natural History Museum, Exhibition Road entrance. d: *Green Kitley* marble (two varieties, centre), *Ashburton* (top) and *Green Purbeck* (bottom) in the archway entablature, Natural History Museum.

The second essential is texture, mostly an aesthetic call centring on what looks good, but it is determined both by the original contents of the sediment before it became rock and its subsequent history after it became one. Polwhele's (1797) phrase was *"beautifully variegated"*. Original textures are provided by fossils and other contents (explored in Chapter 7), whilst later textures are created by folding, shearing, vein filling and recrystallisation (Chapter 8). Devon marble specimens selected for ornamental tables by John Woodley were sometimes deliberately segregated into those with typical fossil types, mainly the corals and stony sponges, and those with spectacular rock textures that originated from depositional features and later fracturing and veining (Chapter 4).

Possibly the most immediate feature of a marble, though, is its third essential, colour. To Rev. Thomas Moore, in his *History of Devonshire* (1829) colour was all important. He says, *"the colour of the Plymouth limestone varies considerably, although the prevailing one is a light blue or gray, changing at times into a much darker shade or becoming nearly black"*. He adds, *"these tints again are frequently intermixed and marbled with an indefinite variety of red and other colours"*. Since most rocks are grey, anything that is black, red, yellow or somewhere in between these can make a nice marble provided it has robustness and texture.

2.4 The Devonshire competitors

It is unusual for Devonshire marbles to be used in buildings on their own. Marbles are normally selected for colour and texture, their decorative rather than geographical attributes referred to above, and it is normal to find a range of marbles drawn from a wide geographical area that can extend to Western and Southern Europe or beyond. Even Lloyd's Register, introduced as perhaps the finest Devonshire marble interior that we have, confines use of Devonshire marbles to the stair hall, displaying 'international' marbles in the old Library and the General Committee Room upstairs (Chapter 11, Group 1). The main stairways in George Gilbert Scott's (1861–75) Foreign Office building on Whitehall, London, where we have already met *Radford Red*, made a great virtue of British stones, for obvious reasons, which then included some notable Irish ones. George Edmund Street, also noted above, and William Butterfield, were other regular users of Devonshire and other British stones, but not always exclusively so.

William Butterfield's assiduous use of durable structural and surface materials, selected primarily for their colour and texture, is explored in Chapter 5 and the style came to be known as 'structural polychromy'. Polished ornamental stone served well as a durable and colourful material and not only that, Butterfield preferred to use local stones where he

Figure 2.7. (following page) Some non-Devonshire ornamental stones, All Saints Church, Margaret Street, London. a: The decorated chancel and chancel arch, All Saints. b: Nave shafts and basal toruses in *Peterhead granite*. Plinth in uncertain black marble. c: Chancel shaft in red *Lizard Serpentine*. d: Floor in coloured ceramic tiles and *Derbyshire fossil*. The elongated fossils are pieces of the stems and 'arms' of sea lilies or crinoids, a form of echinoderm related to starfish. e: The chancel screen in carved alabaster. Shafts are *Red Languedoc* and grey *Bardiglio*. Copes are *Derbyshire fossil*. Base course is in red Belgian. f: Pulpit with elaborate *pietra dura* inlays; colonnettes in *Connemara* and *Languedoc*; basal shafts in *Peterhead granite*; plinth and copes in *Derbyshire fossil*.

27

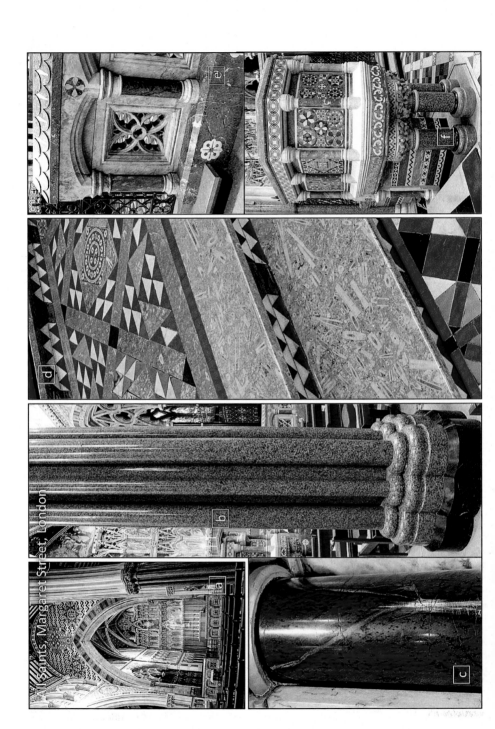

All Saints, Margaret Street, London

All Saints, Margaret Street, London

a

b

100 mm

c

100 mm

d

Figure 2.8. (previous page) Further non-Devonshire stones at All Saints, London. a: The red *Belgian* marble plinth beneath the chancel screen. b: *Connemara* marble shaft in the pulpit. c: *Red Languedoc* marble in the pulpit. d: Reproduction of a William Doyce Pre-Raphaelite fresco in the reredos with a paint and gold-leaf-ornamented alabaster shaft.

could, so that provenance did come into his consideration. His All Saints Church at Babbacombe is the perfect Devonshire Marble church, both outside and in, and it is celebrated in several parts of this book; visited in Chapter 11 (Group 8, DMB SW/TQ/1). Nevertheless, All Saints, Babbacombe has an even more revered namesake in West London, All Saints Church, Margaret Street, which is regarded as probably his finest building. There were not many durable materials in the London area apart from brick for Butterfield to draw upon, so that he went considerably further afield for his colour-enriching ornamental stones, bringing in types from Northern England, Ireland and Scotland as well as Europe. It is likely that there is not a scrap of Devonshire at All Saints, Margaret Street, but the building gives us a grandstand overview of some of the important competing ornamental stones (Figs 2.7; 2.8).

All Saints is a physical manifestation of the spiritual passion of a complex man. Butterfield's internal use of pattern and colour rivals Byzantine and even Islamic embellishment (e.g. Fig. 2.7a), and for all its modest size the church, built between 1849 and 1859, became one of the most expensive of its time. The nave is held aloft by some slender but complex nine-element compound columns in *Pink Peterhead Granite* (Fig. 2.7b), single shafts nearly 3-m tall, whilst the open and attached arcades in the chancel are supported by sumptuous red *Lizard Serpentine* from Cornwall (Fig. 2.7c). Flooring ('pavement') throughout contains Butterfield's usual mix of coloured or patterned encaustic tiles set with marble, in this case grey crinoidal stones from Derbyshire. In the chancel steps and pavement (Fig. 2.7d) the coarse variety is the generic *Derbyshire fossil*, probably from Wirksworth, of which there is more in the baptistery pavement, pulpit coping and chancel screen coping (Figs 2.7e, f). The chancel side-arches, tracery and chancel screen are carved English alabaster whilst the small colonnettes in the screen, pulpit and font include light- and dark-green *Connemara* (Fig. 2.8b), red *Languedoc* (Fig. 2.8c) and grey Italian Tuscan *Bardiglio*. Taller alabaster colonnettes in the east wall above the altar are given longitudinal and transverse chevron designs in black paint and gold leaf (Fig. 2.8d).

2.5 Some rival reds

The stone at the base of the chancel screen (Fig. 2.8a), as well as that in the baptistery arch pilasters (flat attached columns) looks a lot like *Red Ogwell*, but surprisingly, given Butterfield's use of Devonshire marbles elsewhere and his use of Cornish serpentine here, these are not *Ogwell*, but a very similar red Belgian stone. This raises the whole spectre of how we distinguish between the Red Devonshire stones and the swathes of other ornamental reds that came here from Europe, and the best recourse is to introduce a few. Four such European reds are shown in Fig. 2.9. These were photographed in very different lighting conditions in building interiors, but their key differences still come through. The two most similar to *Red Ogwell* (compare Figs 2.3b and 2.9) are the Red *Belgian Rance* (Fig. 2.9a) and the *Red Languedoc* (Fig. 2.9d). Both started life as very similar muddy mounds of sediment on a Devonian seabed and contain the characteristic former cavities, now filled with white and grey calcite crystals. The Belgian stone is more purple and brown than *Ogwell*

Figure 2.9. (facing page) Four difficult non-Devonshire 'reds'. a: *Belgian Rance* marble, nave shaft, 'Marble Church', Bodelwyddan, North Wales. b: Irish *Red Cork* marble, Gurkha Stairs, Foreign and Commonwealth Office, Whitehall, London. c: French *Red Griotte* marble, chancel vaulting shaft, 'Marble Church', Bodelwyddan. d: French *Red Languedoc* marble, chancel arcade, 'Marble Church', Bodelwyddan.

whilst the *Languedoc* is a brighter red. *Red Ogwell* usually contains more abundant flat, platey fossil corals. Veining in Belgian and French stones is generally dominantly white, whilst in *Red Ogwell* the veins can be red or brown as well.

The two remaining stones in Fig. 2.9 have a different character in common that marks them out. They both contain lumps, better known to geologists as nodules. *Red Cork* has cream-coloured nodules (Fig. 2.9b) whilst *Red Griotte* has red ones, set in a brown matrix, that sometimes contain little coiled ammonoid (goniatite) fossils with white interiors. All four of the foreign stones have variants, however, that converge more closely upon *Red Ogwell*. Stick to the rules above, though, and they generally work.

The review of All Saints, Margaret Street, provided the opportunity to illustrate and distinguish ornamental stones that are commonly seen alongside Devonian marbles and included some stones that are not true marbles, granite and serpentine. Chapter 10 (marbles guide) covers the British ornamental stones noted, as well as a few of the foreign ones. All these stones and more are encountered and described in the Buildings Guide (Chapter 11).

2.6 Commercial reality versus sheer extravagance

Choice of stone for a building interior was necessarily a complex issue and for those at the paying end of an architectural specification it cannot have been just about colour and texture. Ornamental stone, as opposed to ordinary building stone, carried an added premium to cover the care needed in quarrying, working, transport and emplacement, and the cost of using it had to be balanced somewhere against the big question 'why'? Marble looks great, but it also puts out messages, and behind many of the finest building interiors there was an influential owner, benefactor or committee, occasionally all three, with strong opinions, mixed motivations and a sense of mission and posterity. All Saints, Margaret Street, was no exception.

Back at the marble works, it was a lot less complicated, but there were two further requirements on top of strength, colour and texture for a marble to become commercially successful, and these were volume and marketability. There needed to be lots of it and it had to be competitively priced after production costs, transport, any levies and, of course, profit had been taken into account. Quarrying itself was sometimes an added complication where quarried stone had to be laid aside whilst batches of matching types of the right sizes were assembled. This volume-versus-value balance could condemn a nice marble to obscurity or, alternatively, it could launch it into a sought-after and even semi-precious category. The price that the market would bear was crucial. The particular problem for the Devonshire industry was that great stones were not always on great transport routes. A key to the early success of *Petitor* marbles was that they came from sea cliffs and could be loaded straight into boats (Chapter 1), thence to the stonemason (Mr Beale) at Exeter (Swete, 1793), or direct to London (Chapter 1). That was not the case for *Red Ogwell* or *Red Ipplepen* that were located in remote countryside. Even after the advent of the railways, which turned out to be a significant means of distribution of the marbles both east and north, these two sites were isolated. William Renwick's (1909) complaints (Chapter 1) about the cost of rail freight of marble from Devon to London, in comparison with shipped varieties from the continent, brings us face to face with the reality of the competitive pressures provided by the very similar French and Belgian marbles that we have just examined, that made increasing inroads into the British market in the mid 1800s. Perhaps this is exactly why Butterfield chose *Belgian* over *Ogwell* at All Saints. What he wanted was the colour and texture and given that there was no local option and both sources were approximately equally distant from his project, provenance got relegated.

Nonetheless, where cost does emerge, the Devonshire option seems incredibly cheap even by today's standards. It is St Peter's Church in Notting Hill that gives us a figure. The chancel was added in 1879 and supplied with four great *Red Ogwell* shafts nearly 4-m tall, each made in three sections (Fig. 2.10a, b). According to local records (St Peter's, 1997, primary reference not found) these cost a mere £48.00 each. Inflated to 2014 prices that is still only about £4800, and even if the price was £48 for each drum in the four shafts (12 pieces altogether) the whole collection would have cost no more than £576 in Victorian pounds and £58,000 today. Whatever the truth about the costs of the *Red Ogwell* shafts, when it came to building the substantial altar steps at St Peter's Church it was not *Ogwell* that was turned to, but Belgian marble, identical to that below the chancel screen at All Saints. This Belgian stone was abundantly available at the time for surfacing boudoir tables and washstands and it looks as though for standard architectural blockwork applications in London it had the edge, but for special orders such as large cylindrical drums, perhaps just at that time, costs tipped in favour of *Red Ogwell*.

Does that work elsewhere? There are some spectacular collections of red marble pillars in some central London buildings but the choice of stone seems to defy any obvious explanation. Certainly there was nothing wrong with Belgian marbles, for the eight *Belgian Rance* pillars and 16 pilasters specified prior to 1871 by Robert Hesketh for the Stair Hall at Goldsmiths' Hall, central London (Chapter 11, Group 1, DMB L/C/1) are not only enormous (*c.* 4-m tall) but the shafts are all in one piece. The pillars each weigh up to four tonnes. At about the same time, architect Herbert Williams was installing 58 equally monolithic, but smaller, pillars and pilasters at the nearby Drapers' Livery Hall (DMB L/C/4), for which he sidestepped *Red Ogwell* and went for the geographically nearby but equally remote *Red Ipplepen*. A decade later, in the early 1880s, architect John Gibson capped that with his 32 pilasters, 32 half columns and 18 freestanding columns in monolithic *Red Ipplepen* at the Gibson Hall (Chapter 11, Group 1, DMB L/C/2), noted above. The Gibson Hall was then a bank, and each shaft is *c.* 3.8-m high but more slender than those at Goldsmiths', weighing not much more than two tonnes.

2.7 Supporting the wrong side?

Logic, it seems, was also well out of the window when it came to marble and the 6th Duke of Devonshire. It was under the 5th Duke, William Cavendish (1748–1811) and then his son the 6th Duke, William Spencer Cavendish (1790–1858) that the Derbyshire Ashford Black Marble industry inevitably flourished, based upon mines and marble works on estate lands. This was the main competitor industry to Devonshire when it came to the smaller ornamental items such as specimen marble tables, turned and inlaid ornaments and ornamental versions of utility items such as thermometer stands and desk sets (Chapter 4).

The two industries had a lot in common, and in Chapter 4 we see how these portable marble items from the two industries can be distinguished. The 6th Duke held a particular passion for Italian marble work and he is known to have encouraged Derbyshire craftsmen to copy some of the Italian stone-inlaying techniques. There are many beautiful Derbyshire-manufactured ornamental stone items in the collections at the family seat, Chatsworth House, near Bakewell, but despite the Devonshire title there is nothing to be seen of Devonshire architectural stone at Chatsworth and there are no Devonshire marble tables or other ornamental items. For this great family of Derbyshire industry supporters it is as if the Devonshire industry did not exist. What can be found, however, is *Belgian Red* marble in some quantity, for example in some stylish marble fireplace bolections (Fig. 2.10c, d).

Despite what looks a lot like a giant snub from the aristocratic sponsors of the Derbyshire industry, an important vehicle for the promotion of the Devonshire marble brand must have been the smaller and portable ornamental stone items that came out of Devonshire. Far better than the use of marble samples, the architectural potential of Devonshire stones could be projected by a range of attractive marble objects, which extended to fire-

33

Chatsworth House, Derbyshire

St Peter's, Notting Hill

34

Figure 2.10. (facing page) *Red Ogwell*, St Peter's Church, Notting Hill, London (DMB L/W/9) and *Red Belgian*, Chatsworth House, Derbyshire. a: The chancel of St Peter's, Notting Hill and three of the *Red Ogwell shafts*. b: One of the *Red Ogwell* shafts. Two joints are visible that separate the shaft into three drums. c: 19th century *Red Belgian* marble bolection (17th century blue Delft C17 tulipieres and urns). d: *Red Belgian* bolection, stair hall, Chatsworth House.

places and the spectacular specimen marble tables (Chapter 4). The showrooms of the great marble works in St Marychurch and Plymouth offered the complete interior, from the marble pillared and panelled stair hall or parlour to the incidental ornamental marble objects to scatter within them. By contrast, the Derbyshire industry did not offer anything like the extensive range of architectural marbles that was available in Devonshire.

The Devonshire/Derbyshire rivalry must have come to its head in 1851, when the brand-leading ornamental products of the two industries met at the Great Exhibition at Crystal Palace in Hyde Park, London. Amongst the ten-or-so exhibitors of numerous Derbyshire vases, tables and tazzas, the most eminent craftsmen were probably J & T Hall of Derby, Thomas Woodruff of Buxton and John Tomlinson of Ashford. Exhibiting Devonshire marble items, on the other hand, were altogether just four, of whom John Woodley, owner of Petit Tor Quarry and the nearby marble works at Babbacombe, was displaying three specimen marble tables. The other exhibitors were J Bovey of Plymouth with an inlaid Plymouth marble fireplace, Henry Champerdowne of Dartington House Totnes, proprietor of a brown marble table, and William Stuart, a civil engineer from Plymouth, whose exhibits included a polished marble slab on two pedestals made of stone used in the then recently completed Plymouth Breakwater (Royal Commission, 1851, p.766 and Chapter 3). One other exhibitor of note was John Bradley of Exeter, a notable faux-marble painter, with "*a table painted on slate in imitation of Devonshire marbles*" (Royal Commission, 1851, p. 766).

The proving ground for craftsmanship was always going to be the intricate and sizeable inlaid tables, of which Woodley's three Devonshire ones were up against three Derbyshire ones by Woodruff and a further half dozen or so by Tomlinson. When the jury passed its verdicts Woodruff and Woodley, from the opposing industries, received Prize Medals (Royal Commission, 1852, pp. cx, 568, 569), whilst the others had to remain content with mere mentions. A magnificent, large round specimen marble table that closely resembles the original descriptions of Woodley's prize winning Great Exhibition exhibit is now housed anonymously at the London Natural History Museum, above the Exhibition Road entrance (Chapter 11, Group 2). Records are now lost regarding the acquisition and manufacture of this table, which are reconstructed and further discussed in Chapter 4.

2.8 Royal patronage and the coming of age

The 1851 Great Exhibition and other such high-profile events must have done much to promote the products of the two industries, but the most effective boost to trade was always going to be Royal Patronage. Queen Victoria probably knew the products of the Derbyshire industry quite well, at least partly through visits to the workshops whilst staying at Chatsworth, first as Princess, in 1832, then as Queen in 1843 (Tomlinson, 1996). It was not until after the Great Exhibition in 1851 that some of that interest was extended to Devonshire. Queen Victoria had a childhood friend living in Babbacombe Glen, whom she visited on two occasions (Pateman, 1980), but the first we learn of actual purchases comes in 1852 when there was an unannounced Royal visit to John Woodley's Devon Marble works by Prince Albert. In July that year a Royal Squadron of three ships appeared in Babbacombe Bay, from which Prince Albert landed anonymously and headed straight for Woodley's marble works. It is not known whether he took anything away with him, but the result of the visit was that Woodley soon supplied more than 30 Devon Marble

John Woodley's (Royal) Marble Works, St Marychurch

Figure 2.11. (facing page) John Woodley and his Royal Marble Works, 1840–2012. a: A figure, probably Woodley himself, faces the new Royal Coat of Arms over his showroom entrance, Fore Street, St Marychurch, *c.* 1862. b: The Coat of Arms, 2012. c: Fore Street, St Marychurch and Hillborough House with the Woodley name, *c.* 1851. Note the columns and urns on display, doubtless in Devonshire marbles. d: Hillborough House, the Marble works and Fore street, *c.* 1840. (*All prints are from Pateman (1980), with acknowledgement.*)

items to Osborne House for Her Majesty to select from (White, 1878; Western Daily Mercury, 1886). She retained all but four and the result of this success was that Woodley received the Royal Warrant. In about 1862 John Woodley was photographed outside his establishment in St Marychurch (Fig. 2.11a), proudly facing a giant carved Royal Coat of Arms he had just erected outside his marble works. This wonderful three-dimensional crest survives to the present day (Fig. 2.11b), set within the small neoclassical portico in Babbacombe town centre that is the only surviving remnant of the Woodley former factory and showroom. We need to know more about this great coat of arms. What is it made of; was it carved by Woodley himself or is it a concrete replica, like the modern pilasters?

Just how far reaching this Royal Patronage was in promoting Devonshire marble we can only guess, but the second half of the 19th century marked a huge expansion in the architectural uses of the stones (Chapter 5) and despite Woodley's death within only a few years of receiving his Royal Warrant, the name of the Royal Marble Works was proudly perpetuated by his successor and great marble entrepreneur, Andrew Blackler.

3. THE MARBLE MASTERS

3.1 Mason to Marble Master

A professional mason works with hard building materials and has long been a central part of the fabric of our society. In South Devon censuses in the mid 1800s the mason is there, along with carrier, scrivener, inn keeper, charwoman, dressmaker, mariner, blacksmith, nurse, shopkeeper, carpenter, labourer and many more. A mason could be a bricklayer or stoneworker—much in demand for the construction of durable buildings, walling and paving. Before the industrial revolution the mason was the nearest thing to an engineer. He was trained, skilled, numerate and could design work in advance of construction, but his mistakes could kill people. No wonder it became a jealously guarded profession with the appearance of 'guilds', 'lodges' and 'incorporations' and no wonder, too, that there evolved a parallel interest in becoming 'speculative' or non-professional masons, surrounded in 'Freemasonry' mystique. This chapter is about those who worked with marble.

Occasionally the professionals called themselves 'builder and mason', but a Marble Mason was a specialist and possibly a cut above. His work involved ornamental stone and he was more engaged in final preparation; cutting, shaping and, of course, polishing. Higher still in the hierarchy was a Master marble mason. These were often the artisans, usually in charge of others, perhaps as foreman, designer or even owner of the business. Master marble masons, marble masons, stone masons and masons form a descending hierarchy and are usually distinct in the censuses and local trade directories of the status conscious communities of the 19th century.

For the top flight of these early Victorian artisans, the Great Exhibition of 1851 came as a rare opportunity to bring their credentials before an international audience and John Woodley, Thomas Woodruff and John Tomlinson, figures already discussed (Chapter 2), did just that. Marble masons were not the only exhibitors of beautiful stone items, though, and their clients and even a few hands-off artistic designers also proudly displayed examples (e.g. Tomlinson, 1996).

3.2 Plymouth Masters

3.2.1 *William Stuart's legacy*

Great Exhibition exhibitor William Stuart had two separate exhibits that clearly demonstrated his stone working talent but he was actually a civil engineer. From Leith near Edinburgh, William Stuart began as a building mason, but his wider talents enabled him to become engineer to some major Scottish canal and harbour engineering projects (Hopkins, 1855). In 1811, William Stuart's knowledge of stone won him the task of contributing to the researching, opening and operating the 'Breakwater' quarries at Oreston, Plymouth, intended to supply limestone blocks for the forthcoming Plymouth breakwater (Chapters 1 and 6). This was a major Admiralty project and he was initially appointed as assistant to the project Superintendent, Joseph Whidbey, under the eminent pre-Victorian engineer John Rennie. As well as surveying and securing the large site on which the quarries were to be opened, this massive undertaking involved the clearing of waterways, the construction of barges and the preparation of wharves and narrow-gauge rail links into the quarries (Chapter 6). In 1830 William Stuart became Superintendent Engineer of the Breakwater project on the retirement of Joseph Whidbey.

Stuart's exhibits at the 1851 exhibition fully reflected his commitment to the project. Amongst several models and objects in his set of exhibits were both a "*polished marble slab on two pedestals composed of limestone from the breakwater quarries, Plymouth*" and a limestone model of the breakwater "*made for the exhibition under the direction of the Lords of the Admiralty*". Clearly, William Stuart was exploring the alternative potential for the dense, mostly grey limestones from around Oreston, by then very much less in demand owing to the recent completion of the project. He had certainly seen enough of it, having supervised the excavation and emplacement in Plymouth Sound of nearly four million tons of limestone from Breakwater Quarry and nearby. In recognition of his model of the breakwater, which was his own work, he received an honourable mention and the model was later deposited at Somerset House.

Back in 1828 Stuart was also briefly involved in researching a second Admiralty project involving the construction of a much larger breakwater across Torbay. How different the Torquay and Brixham coastlines would have looked today had this massive project, involving a proposed nine million tons of locally quarried limestone—more than twice the volume of Plymouth breakwater—been given the go ahead. William Stuart died of bronchitis in 1854 aged 81, still in full charge of the newly completed Breakwater project.

3.2.2 *The Goad Empire*

Living on the east side of Plymouth in 1851, brothers John and Edmund Goad probably acquired their masonry skills in a local stone works. Edmund, 23, was a granite works labourer, whilst John, 26, was a stonemason. There is no true 'granite' anywhere near so they must have been employed at a monumental stone works that used Dartmoor granite brought down to Plymouth. They lived almost next door to one another in the parish of Charles the Martyr where there were several mason families. Their father, a labourer, may also have been employed in the works. By 1861, John was a limestone merchant in Charles, employing seven, but the big venture for the two Goad brothers came in 1868 when they launched the "*Phoenix Steam Marble Works*" in Stonehouse, on the opposite side of town, not far from the famous Plymouth Hoe.

Judged by the name of the works, and the earlier and apparently adopted founding date of 1817, they may have taken over a statuary (carving) business from a William Brown, who appears on Phoenix Place in the East Stonehouse census of 1861. The new works ran in parallel with quarries at Oreston and a subsequent contract was the supply of stone for the marble pillars in the then Colonial Office in London, completed in 1868; now the Foreign and Commonwealth Office (Appendix: DMB L/W/5). The highly textured, grey to red stone was sourced from Radford Quarry, just south of Oreston (Chapter 9, Loc. Pl.6).

One success led to another when local architect Herbert Gribble got the contract to design the new Brompton Oratory, in west London (Chapter 11, Group 2) and specified stone from Radford. Probably on the strength of these two contracts John Goad was able to build a brand new showroom, also designed by Gribble, and this is pictured in a cartoon of 1883 (Fig. 3.1) by which time his Phoenix Steam Marble Works at the back was supporting 47 men, six apprentices and five women (1881 Census).

Goad is possibly the only Devonshire marble entrepreneur of whom we have a clear image, albeit a cartoon (Fig. 3.1). He became a local politician, building developer and steamboat company director, and died in 1886. He was predeceased by his younger brother, so it was his son, John Goad Jnr. the marble works foreman, who assumed control. Twenty years later, the Goad business was still operating from 4 Goads Buildings, Millbay Road as "*Quarry Proprietors*" (Pubhistory.com), but there is no reference to the marble works. In 1914 only Alfred John Goad, plumber, is left on Millbay Road so that the company seems to have become an early commercial victim of the First World War.

3.2.3 *The Cattedown Quarriers*

Cattedown was once an elevated limestone headland just south of Plymouth, overlooking Cattewater, otherwise the Plym Estuary (Fig. 6.4a). Opposite, on the east side of the estuary, was the site of the great Breakwater Quarry at Oreston (Fig. 6.4b). Today, Catte-

Figure 3.1. John Goad's brand new Phoenix Marble Works showroom, 1883 (Goad himself enlarged, inset, left). The building was designed by Herbert Gribble, architect at Brompton Oratory, London, where a lot of Goad's marble was used. Note the cart (bottom right and inset right) with pillar consigned for "*Oratory London per GWR* (Great Western Railway)".

down is a complex of large abandoned quarries that have been cut close to sea level, but it retains its identity as a location for industry. From 1820 or before, the Cattedown quarries are linked to the Sparrow family (Gill, 1993, 1997), of whom there were at least four generations named Benjamin from the mid 1700s onward. Over the years, the Sparrows developed and collaborated in businesses involving lead manufacture, manure, phosphates, gunpowder, shipping and especially limestone.

The second Benjamin Sparrow was a *"Limestone Dealer & Lime Burner"* at Cattedown in 1822, but he evidently had additional interests in Hooe Lake Quarry on the Oreston side of Cattewater, a further known source of specimen marble in the John Watson collection at Cambridge (Chapter 2). Prince Rock quarry, also a source of marble, is one of their Cattedown group and, for a brief period around 1877, the Sparrows called themselves *"Sparrow & Co, Limestone and Marble Merchants"*. By 1891 Benjamin Sparrow the fourth was living the family life of a country gentleman in a fine house near Ivybridge to the east of Plymouth (Taber, 2001), calling himself *"Limestone Merchant"*. He had already sustained a riding injury and died a couple of years later, probably as a result of it (Gill, 1993, 1997).

By the early 1900s ownership of quarries on both sides of Cattewater had fallen into the hands of Frederick Moore under the name of *"F.J. Moore Lime and Stone Merchant (Incorporating Sparrow & Co.)"*. Moore had acquired charge of Cattedown, Prince Rock, Pomphlett, Radford and Hooe, all known marble localities (Figure 2.1), and he also had Billacombe (at Oreston) and Elburton (now Moorcroft). Neither the Sparrows nor F J Moore were evidently ever manufacturing marble masons, but their quarries are significant in the Devon marbles story. The manufacturing side in Plymouth remained in the specialist care of the Goad family until the early 20th century, but it is likely that there were other companies taking on marble manufacture that were principally granite work specialists. Despite its undoubted industrial importance, Plymouth never emerged as the main centre of the Devon marble industry. That top spot went to St Marychurch, Torquay, which by the mid 1800s had developed an international market.

3.3 The east coast marble pioneers

3.3.1 Pioneers and founders

Of the numerous families on the east side of Devon who contributed to the industry and made it their livelihoods three stand out, the Woodleys, the Grants and the Blacklers. All appear on the scene at about the same time in the early 1800s, but it is likely that they would never have done so had it not been for the two original entrepreneurs whom we have already met. The entrepreneur is the one with the great ideas, the dogged vision, the raw determination and, equally important, the access to finance. One such person was Robert Fulton, canal pioneer, inventor of the horse-powered saw and steamship designer, but whose ideas on mechanisation may have exceeded his knowledge of quarrying. The other is John Hubbard, the one who could recognise a good business opportunity but whose vision may have exceeded his ability to deliver.

Hovering around Petit Tor Cove in 1793, though, is also a Mr Beale, stonemason of Exeter. He is captured in John Swete's (1793) description (Chapter 1) and Beale had apparently already removed some fairly spectacular slabs to Exeter where he had displayed them. Swete calls them *"beautiful"*, *"newly discovered"* and *"the subject of much admiration"*, and he notes colour and fossil contents in general terms, referring to a *"chimney piece"* made of the stone in his own local cottage. Given that Swete clearly knew Mr Beale, it is no great step to think that the fireplace was actually made by him, for he turns out to be John Beal, Stone Cutter, recorded at New Bridge, Exeter in 1791 (Taber, 2001). Beal has the distinction of being the earliest name connected with *Petitor* marble and it is sad that we know so little about him.

3.3.2 *Fulton makes his mark*

As for Robert Fulton (Fig. 3.2), he comes in a close second. We can pin him down in Torquay in the same year as Swete's visit to Petit Tor because Fulton wrote from there to fellow inventor Lord Stanhope in September that year (Dickinson, 1913). Swete's (1793) description of the *"ingenious"* Mr Fulton is the first appearance of the entrepreneur's name linked to Petit Tor and in view of the expensive factory that, by Swete's (1873) account, was already housing the miraculous sawing machine (Chapter 1), it is perhaps no coincidence that Fulton had invented the very thing that John Beal, stonecutter, might most have wanted. The hand sawing of marble was not much fun on Petit Tor beach, come rain, storm or tide, and it cried out for the talents of an inventor, but Fulton's ambitions went somewhat further than just cutting rock. They went as far as London in fact, where he was sure he could ship and market the beautiful finished stone. It did not last for long. In 1829, the Rev. Thomas Moore noted that *"some years ago a good deal of the Babbicombe marble was polished and sent to London"*, so the supply seems to have dried again.

What intervened, we do not know, but we might guess that the declaration of war on Britain by revolutionary France in 1793 did not help, a situation that eventually descended into the Napoleonic Wars of the early 1800s. It will have discouraged investment in coastal enterprises and demoralised businesses dependent on shipping, even taking away experienced seamen. On the 'Glorious First of June' in 1794 the British and French Fleets actually came to serious blows out in the Atlantic and, in 1798, with a real fear of invasion along the Devonshire coast, local regiments of volunteers were being raised and a fort on Berry Head (amongst others) was under construction. Taking with him his 1794 Society for Arts Silver Medal for his revolutionary sawing machine (Chapter 1), Robert Fulton seems to have departed the scene in this new climate of uncertainty. By 1796 he had gone north to finish work on canal navigation, dangerously popping up again in Paris in 1797 to experiment with submarines, torpedoes, explosives and steam propulsion, supplying his talents in favour of Napoleon Bonaparte.

We are left speculating that John Beal of Exeter might have been Fulton's 'man on the ground', charged with the day-to-day duties of quarrying and machining whilst Robert went about his business of moving the world on and backing the French Republic. If so, Beal was left in the lurch. Fulton's own American Republic was little more than a decade old and the option of staying in threatened Britain might have started to look

Figure 3.2. Robert Fulton, the *Petitor pioneer.* After an oil painting *c.* 1807 made following his return to the United States. (*From Dickinson, 1913.*)

quite unattractive. Furthermore, should revolution spread to Britain, it would certainly knock out the wealthy Aristocracy who were the best potential customers for a good ornamental marble sold in London. If it was not Fulton who was thinking this through, it will have been his backers and investors. The climate of fear must have receded a lot after the Battle of Trafalgar in 1805 but it was only after Waterloo in June 1815 that matters were fully resolved and the threat from France fully abated. Bonaparte was briefly held prisoner on board ship off the Devon coast (Chapter 6).

3.3.3 *John Hubbard's best endeavours*

From Hubbard's later account, we learn that the quarry was neglected after Fulton left so that John Beal, for one, might have been an indirect casualty of the troubles. Like Fulton he evidently does not show his face again. We have guessed that Fulton's departure was more about expedience than disappointment with the quarry but there is one more thing. In November 1795 there was a massive storm in the English Channel, one of hurricane force that caused havoc with a Royal Naval fleet in Lyme Bay with many tragic losses. Fulton's beach enterprise might also have been a casualty of the same storm. However, counting back from John Hubbard's description to the *Society of Arts* in 1809 (Chapter 1 and see below) the first abandonment of Petit Tor can be pinned down to two years earlier than the storm, in 1793, so the storm may simply have sealed Fulton's rejection of the marble business and encouraged his need to blow things up in the experimental safety of revolutionary France.

It was John Hubbard who was next to take up the challenge, the man with an eye for a good investment, and who also knew that the all-important ingredient was a knowledgeable and reliable workforce. Remarkably, owing to the discipline of scientific literature, we can read, in reported speech, the actual words that John Hubbard used as he described Petit Tor Quarry to the *Society for the Encouragement of Arts, Manufactures and Commerce* in the early 1800s (Society of Arts, 1809). In their trawl for samples of British marble in 1804 (Chapter 1) the Society set some specific requirements, including precise location and distance from road and water transport, as well as notes on quality both of the stone and any lime produced from it. Hubbard responded five years later with what became a page full of details (Society of Arts, 1809), including the following (author's brackets):

- *That the quarry which produced the different specimens* (Petit Tor quarry*) is twelve acres in extent.*
- *That marble similar to each specimen* (of the 60 submitted) *can be distinctly procured.*
- *That he had in his possession columns of red marble, eight feet long, and two feet diameter, and believed that they might be got ten feet long, and five feet diameter, and that blocks of other kinds might be got of large sizes.*
- *That he had at that time slabs six feet six inches long, by three feet six inches in width* (for marble panelling).
- *That the quarry is close to the sea, and a part thereof is covered by it at high water, and that he can load vessels direct from the quarry, having made a wharf for that purpose.*
- *That the quarry is situated about four miles from Teignmouth and was first opened about sixteen years* (previously) *and was afterward neglected; but that it has been now worked by him for two years.*
- *That the marble is harder in quality as the mine goes deeper and that some part of it rises fifty feet from the sea.*
- *That the sale price is about half that of foreign marble of similar appearance.*

- *That the general price is now about four shillings per superficial foot* (which at £41/m² in 2012 is remarkably close to the wholesale price of popular polished granite), *and will probably be so reduced as to be delivered at three shillings in London.*
- *That it will take a finer polish than any other marble found in the kingdom.*
- *That he supposes from sixty to one hundred workmen may be employed in the quarry next autumn.*
- *That chimney pieces made from this marble are not injured from the heat of fire applied near to them, nor liable to crack from alternate sudden changes of heat and cold.*
- *That great part of the refuse stones of the quarry will burn to lime, and that such lime is of superior quality to any other on that coast.*

John Hubbard had been through a lot but, whilst he clearly knew what he wanted, we have no evidence that he had the time-served practical experience of a marble mason. Indeed, if we have him right, the *"Watering Places"* guide (Anon, 1817) lists a John Hubbard as a local cabinetmaker, which makes sense, for such a man would have an eye for ornaments and interior décor. As for the factory on the beach, which might have been Fulton's original building, as well as its contents, these were apparently flattened by another storm that swept in some time in the early part of the 19th century. The *Western Daily Mercury* article of 1886 (Chapter 1), claims that Hubbard had *"prepared a quantity of polished stone for London and was anxiously waiting its shipment, when an easterly gale set in, destroyed all his workshops, and swept away the products of his labour"*. Known severe storms ravaged the coast in 1815, 1817, 1818, and 1824 (West, 2014), of which 1818 and 1824 seem to have been the worst. It is unlikely that Hubbard was still in charge in 1824, and there are other storms to account for (see below), but either might have rendered Hubbard unable to *"resume his favourite employment"*. The 1824 storm was of hurricane force, causing much damage around Lyme Bay and stripping substantial quantities of stone off the Plymouth Breakwater. Hubbard had lived through the military threat from the sea, but had perhaps failed to spot the danger of the natural one. This seems to have precipitated a second downturn to the Petit Tor business, perhaps coinciding with the post-Napoleonic depression, although others seem to have been in charge at Petit Tor by this time.

3.4 The east coast marble dynasties

3.4.1 *The rise of the Woodleys*
Daniel Woodley was born about 1770 and was already an experienced monumental mason when he arrived at St Marychurch in the early 1800s from Broadhempston, near Ashburton. Grave markers manufactured by Daniel Woodley are known to be widespread. Two, dated 1814 and 1828, are in Paignton and further carved headstones, two of which dated 1785 and 1795, from his Broadhempston years are as far away as Newfoundland in Canada (Pocius, 1981). Little more is known about him except that he allegedly took over the lease of the Petit Tor quarry in 1806 (Grant, 1922). Grant also refers to the establishment of a marble works in 1809. Given that by Hubbard's own account his resumption of production at the quarry was in 1807, it seems more likely that Woodley became foreman rather than operator around 1806. More uncertainty surrounds further early disasters to the company. Just how long Hubbard's 'wharf' lasted is not known, but there is a good chance that it got destroyed in the same gale that wrecked his factory, noted above. Alone this would not have crippled production because vessels at the time were commonly loaded and unloaded at a beach or 'strand' at a time when quays and harbours were an expensive or fortuitous luxury. In order to do this boats needed to be fairly flat bottomed, but the

downside of that was instability at sea. The second disaster involved just that. It is said that the ship rolled heavily during a storm that lasted several days, leading to a massive loss to the cargo of "*some thousands of pounds*" that had to be absorbed by the business. What a terrifying experience it must have been for the crew, and we know nothing of their fate. The third calamity was the collapse of a two-storey storage warehouse. Overfilled with finished goods, the warehouse walls were forced apart as the upper floor descended upon the lower.

From this bleak beginning, Daniel Woodley is said to have built the business up, clearly acquiring ownership at some stage in the early 1800s (Grant, 1922). He is listed in the 1841 census as living in Coombe Pafford, less than a mile from Petit Tor Quarry. He is already 71, having retired and handed the business to his two sons around 1836. Daniel the younger was also from Broadhempston, born about 1801, arriving in St Marychurch with his father not long after. In 1841 he occupies his own household with his wife Margaret and there appear to be no children. His younger brother, John Woodley, was born locally in 1813, and also lived separately with his own wife, Elizabeth and no children. The exact roles of the two brothers in the business are unclear. By 1851, both describe themselves as employers. Daniel is a builder and marble mason with a workforce of 27 including marble masons, masons, carpenters and labourers, whilst John is a marble mason employing 25 marble masons and labourers. These are substantial numbers of employees. Could they be different businesses, or do their separate descriptions in the 1851 census reflect their specialist roles within a joint business? Either way, they evidently turned the Petit Tor around, quite literally, from the original seaward-facing enterprise shipping directly from the beach, to a landward one, based on a new factory in St Marychurch. Starting around 1836, and until after the disposal of the business in 1865, their premises were located on Fore Street, St Marychurch although perhaps not at the same address.

According to local understanding, a house near St Mary's Church, originally known as "*South Villa*", was built in 1835 for the younger Daniel Woodley. It sold in 1841 for £460 when it became "*The Hermitage*". However, Daniel Woodley's address in the 1841 census is given as Coombepafford. This is some distance from South Villa, but in 1851 he was at "*Church Hill House*" which could have been nearby. Daniel, with his workforce of masons, carpenters and labourers was probably what we would today call a speculative builder. He may well have moved from property to property as projects were completed and sold, and "*South Villa*" sounds like a temporary site name. Daniel Woodley Jnr is listed in Pigot's Directory (1844) as "*Builder*", and then in Billing's (1857) as "*marble merchant, Fore Street*", probably at number 40 where he appears in 1861. By then, Daniel Woodley Jnr had evidently overstretched himself, or else his side of the business was not doing so well. Bankruptcy had loomed and he had been obliged to sell land to local estate owners, James Peake and Isambard Kingdom Brunel (Pateman, 1991 p. 125).

3.4.2 *The pre-eminence of John Woodley*

Daniel's younger brother John Woodley had moved to St Marychurch by 1851, and lived with Elizabeth at the marble works, possibly at Hillborough House (Fig. 2.11). John Woodley was the skilled artisan, who sold his magnificent specimen marble tables (e.g. Fig. 4.1) and ornaments to Royalty and Aristocracy. At the 1851 Great Exhibition, John Woodley's prize-medal-winning specimen marble tables were judged as of "*very great merit*" and their "*execution excellent*" (Royal Commission, 1852). He was evidently a superior craftsman and artist, and of all his contemporaries in similar marble industries, he is one of only two to be recognised as British sculptors in their own right. *The Biographical Dictionary of Sculptors in Britain, 1660–1851* (Roscoe *et al*., 2009) gives details of four of his 'signed' works together with their locations. The most important of these is a relief of a woman leaning on a broken column, with its Corinthian capital lying at her feet.

The name of John Woodley was well respected and appears next to his products in marble collections of the time. Four specimen marble columns and carved pilasters attributed to Woodley were held at the Museum of Practical Geology at Jermyn Street, London after 1851 (Graham Lott, pers. comm.) and a further nine attributed pieces were in the private collection at Hendersyde Park, Kelso in the mid 1800s (Hendersyde, 1859 and Chapter 1). John Woodley was proprietor of the St Marychurch marble works in 1852, when there was the surprise visit by Prince Albert (Chapter 2). Only a little later, Woodley was evidently photographed there facing a recently erected Royal Crest (Figure 2.11) following his supply of stone items to Queen Victoria at Osborne House on the Isle of Wight. This was now the 'Royal Marble Works' and Woodley's prizewinning Great Exhibition exhibits were apparently still on show there when he was listed by Billings (1857) as "*marble chimney-piece, urn & vase manufacturer*". It is interesting that there is no hint there of an architectural side to the business.

There are precious few Woodley items now known, partly because his principal hallmark design has had to be rediscovered for this book (Chapter 4). The man himself is even less well known, but by chance we have a copy of his signature (Fig. 3.3). On 23rd March 1849 John Woodley wrote to William Kitson, Chairman of the Building Committee for the new church of St Mary Magdalene at Upton, central Torquay. He was offering to supply

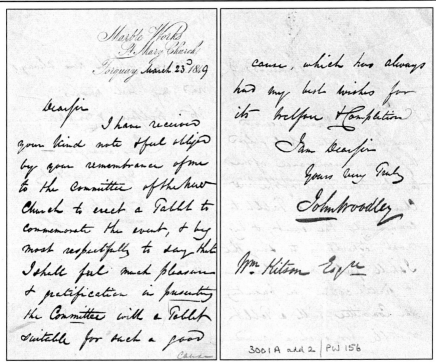

Figure 3.3. A letter bearing Woodley's only known written signature reads, "*Marble Works St. Mary Church, Torquay, March 23rd 1849 Dear Sir I have received your note & feel obliged by your remembrance of me to the Committee of the new Church to erect a Tablet to commemorate the event, & by most respectfully to say that I shall feel much pleasure & gratification in presenting the Committee with a tablet suitable for such a good cause, which has always had my best wishes for its welfare & completion I am Dear Sir Yours very Truly John Woodley Wm. Kitson Esqre* "(original punctuation).

the commemorative plaque for the forthcoming Consecration on 12th April, but had given himself just 19 clear days to complete the work! There must be a lot behind this story, including the fact that when Devonshire marbles were eventually installed in the chancel 30 years later, much to its advantage (Chapter 11, Group 7), the work went to the St Marychurch works, but by that time Woodley was dead. The letter is noted in Seymour (1963, p.66) and survived with a bundle of old church papers, now in the Devon Record Office.

The Woodley era seems to have come to an end after the death of John in 1862 and he is buried in a well-marked grave near his father, Daniel, at St Mary the Virgin Church, St Marychurch. This family identity with the local parish church is unexceptional but for one thing. In 1857 the church was falling into disrepair and funds were being assembled for an extensive renovation (Billings, 1857). By 1861 the work had been completed, with a new Gothic Revival nave, aisles and chancel (White, 1878–9) designed by John West Hugall (Fig. 3.4). Sadly, most of this interior was lost when the church was bombed and almost destroyed on May 30th 1943 with the tragic loss of 26 children and teachers. Nonetheless, what remained of the chancel was incorporated into the rebuilt church in 1952–3, including six shafts of *Petitor* marble. The completion date of 1861 means that the marble came from Petit Tor quarry whilst it was still under the control of John Woodley. This makes St Mary's the only known Woodley church interior.

Neither John nor his surviving brother, Daniel had a son. In fact none of the St Marychurch Woodleys appears in the 1871 census returns. Daniel took charge of the marble quarries at Petit Tor in the early 1860s, but exactly what happened to the marble works in the interregnum is not clear. It all went to public auction in 1865 and the successful bidder was an outsider, Andrew Blackler, marking the start of a further 50 years of marble manufacturing under a new dynasty. Daniel Woodley Jnr died not long afterwards in 1870.

3.4.3 *The Sharlands of Torquay*

A marble works at Madrepore Place, Torquay, must have been an iconic address for a marble mason. "*Madrepore*" was the informal name given to a stony object resembling a

Figure 3.4. The pre-war interior of St Mary the Virgin Church, St Marychurch, with its *Petitor* marbles, completed in 1861. This is the only John Woodley church interior so far recorded.

coral, one of the Madreporaria, a little-used term for a zoological group of coral-like organisms. The term 'madrepore worker' was one who collected and polished fossil madrepores. It was Henry Sharland (Kelly, 1856) and then William Sharland (1881 Census), who held the prized location at Madrepore Place, close to their works in Tormoham, just above Torquay. These were the second and third of three generations of 'statuaries' or sculptors, John, Henry and then William. John Sharland, seal engraver and statuary, father of the brief marble dynasty, is a listed sculptor with the Henry Moore Foundation along with John Woodley (Roscoe *et al.*, 2009). According to Octavian Blewitt (1832) it was John Sharland who discovered and soon exploited a fossil coral bed in the "*Vale of Ogwell*" around 1830. It was "*a splendid mass of stone,*" he says, "*entirely composed of a congeries of many beautiful varieties of aggregated and branching madrepores*". Sharland had discovered the celebrated Ogwell *Featherstone*, small polished columns similar to which are still seen today in the reredos at East Ogwell Church (Chapter 9, Loc. T3.2). John Sharland was soon working quarries at Ogwell and the marbles he produced he made into "*vases, tablets, and other kinds of ornamental workmanship, which display all the beauties of* (Featherstone's) *character and composition*" (Blewitt, 1832).

A second son of John Sharland, another William and brother to Henry, disappeared from the record for 20 years, re-emerging in 1871 as a "*Retired Gold Miner*" in Dawlish. Whether he had tried his luck amongst the scattered gold deposits of Devon or Cornwall or made a fortune elsewhere has yet to be resolved. As for the prestigious address on Madrepore Place in Tormoham of William's brother and nephew, in the light of history, it looks as though this was named more by intent than luck. Madrepore Road and Madrepore Place are located in an elevated part of the town in the vicinity of some old quarries. It is likely that these were Sharland properties and that the address, which was in existence in the 1850s or before, was their own contrivance for developments on their own land. If John Woodley in St Marychurch could have the badge of Royalty, the Sharlands could at least flag their own iconic discovery. *Featherstone* is an enduring mark of Devonshire marbles and appears in ornamental tables and ornaments, including ones not native to Devonshire (Chapters 2 and 4).

3.4.4 *The Blackler succession at St Marychurch*

Andrew Blackler, who won the Woodley's St Marychurch business at auction in 1865, was by no means new to the ornamental marble business. His immediate family were all stonemasons and there are at least ten further Blackler masons within the Ashburton/Teignmouth/Brixham area (Fig. 2.1) in the mid-to-late 1800s censuses, with more in Plymouth (Taber, 2001). Andrew Blackler was born in Broadhempston (Fig. 2.1) but his father, Thomas, soon moved the family to Berry Pomeroy, near Totnes, where by 1841 he had re-established a successful marble mason business. By 1851 Andrew was 23, married, and had moved a considerable distance away to Dawlish, the other side of Teignmouth (Fig. 2.1). Striking out on his own, and a further decade later, he was a successful marble mason at 19 Strand in Dawlish employing six men and four boys. An inscribed floral inlay thermometer stand by Blackler in Torquay Museum dates from this time (Fig. 4.15a). Given Andrew Blackler's considerable experience and apparent dogged initiative, it is no surprise that in 1865 he seized the once in a lifetime opportunity to take on the celebrated but ailing concern built by the Woodleys in St Marychurch. This was the prime location on the map of marble (Fig. 2.1), drawing from the most celebrated quarry of them all, Petit Tor.

In 1871, the Blackler family, Andrew (43) and his wife Sophia (45), together with their six children were living by the newly acquired Royal Marble Works, and Thomas (17) is an apprentice. Andrew Blackler invested substantially to modernise the business, tokens of which were planning applications made in 1874 and 1875 for improvements to works and showrooms. Perhaps in response to the increasing size of the workforce, in May 1880

Thomas Blackler, Andrew's oldest, made a planning application for a workmen's club and coffee tavern on Fore Street. By 1881, much had changed in the Blackler family. Andrew Blackler had remarried; the elder sons were living independently and there was a further young child. The marble works was bustling. Young Thomas Blackler was busy there, now a time-served marble mason, and there were 25 men in addition.

3.4.5 The Blackler dominance

By 1886 there was a vigorous new workshop at the junction of Fore Street and Torquay Road, later St Marychurch Road (Fig. 3.5). This was featured in the *Western Daily Mercury* of that year (Pateman, 1980), trumpeting a new 20-horsepower steam engine that powered a substantial range of belt-driven machinery, including a 15-ton multiple-bladed steel saw that used sand as a cutting abrasive. There was an automated flat polisher, capable of placing a fine finish on large pieces with little supervision, and a range of other impressive sanders and polishers. The greatest marvel of all was a great machine by which stones of four tons or more could be shaped and polished into finished marble columns.

This was expensive equipment, requiring a substantial throughput of stone to justify it. It is not clear at what stage all their quarries joined the Blackler portfolio, but the Ogwell Quarries, formerly part of the Sharland 'empire', were certainly included by the late 1800s, as was Ashburton (Fig. 3.6), so that a chain of quarries at Petit Tor (Fig. 3.7), Ogwell and Ashburton were all supplying the workshop. An agreement dating from 1887 licenses the Blacklers to work East Hill Marble Quarry in East Ogwell (essexcc, 1887). This is Ransley Quarry, later worked right into East Hill, north-east of the village, from which came the famous *Red Ogwell* and *Pink Ogwell* marbles. The transport distance from there to the works at St Marychurch was about seven miles and Ashburton was about as

Figure 3.5. Andrew Blackler's redeveloped Royal Marble Works *c.* 1886. Woodley's original entrance is on the right, with its Royal Crest above, and survives to 2015 (Figure 2.11). The stone-built extension was demolished and there have been two subsequent buildings on the site.

Figure 3.6. Ashburton quarry (one of 3 possible sites) with some very large marble blocks below the sheer leg lifting apparatus. A steam traction engine is positioned nearby. The block beneath the sheer leg could weigh as much as 8 tons. Six or so labourers face the camera.

Figure 3.7. Blackler's Quarry on Petit Tor Hill, St Marychurch. A Mr Moase faces the camera. Note the confused jumble of stone blocks in the face, characteristic of this one site.

much again. Both were across the grain of the turnpikes and over difficult terrain. Such supply routes, necessarily by horse and lorry, might be a token of Blackler's determination to succeed but they were also an indication of his confidence both in the marbles he was sourcing and the improving roads.

The later part of the 19th century saw a lot of marble contracts on the go for embellishing church and other interiors (Chapter 5). Blackler bought the business at a good time evidently landing a number of them. His enlarged and re-equipped factory, oriented towards major architectural projects, was a response to this booming market, but it was already tailing off (Chapter 5). This is thought of now as the era of high Victoriana, following the death of Prince Albert but at the 'acme' of Empire. Both in the colonies and at home, construction of public and communal buildings was burgeoning and there was a need to project wealth, fashion and prestige by the use of marble. We know of a number of important marble building interiors completed by Blackler at this time, both in Britain and abroad (Chapter 5) but one of the best is right on his doorstep. Although under the more visible name of its architect, the great decorator of Victorian churches William Butterfield, it is the colourful interior (and also the exterior) of All Saints Church at Babbacombe (1874, DMB SW/TQ/1. Chapter 11, Group 8, Fig. 11.21). Other interiors attributed to Blackler include St Augustine's Church, in West London (1870–76, DMB L/W/3. Chapter 11, Group 2), St James's Church, Paddington, London (1881, DMB L/W/4. Chapter 11, Group 3), and Birmingham Art Gallery and Museum (1881–5, DMB ME/B/1. Chapter 11, Group 4).

Blackler's work also went overseas. Uses of Devonshire marble outside the UK have not been systematically researched for this book, but there is one outstanding example. In the late 1870s Architect William Butterfield received the contract for St Paul's Cathedral in Melbourne, Australia. As Butterfield's style dictated, he specified stone to add natural colour and texture, and a lot was Australian, but several European stones were also used, including *Pink Peterhead Granite*, *Red Cork* marble from Ireland and *Rouge Belge* marble from Belgium. The centrepiece was to be the marble-framed reredos above the altar with its panels of shining glass mosaics by Antonio Salviati of Venice (Fig. 3.8a), and Andrew Blackler was asked to supply it. His *Red Ogwell* framed structure is spectacular and the importing of the crated ready-made stone kit was overseen from a Sydney address by his second son, Charles. The reredos is described in Cathedral records as made of "*Babbicombe marble and alabaster at a cost of some £1100*". The marble was shipped from Liverpool in 44 cases on 3rd December 1889 on the three-masted square-rig sailing ship *Aigburth* (Figs 3.8b, c).

Blackler's concentration on architectural products, which he clearly did extremely well (Chapter 5), might have been at the expense of the sort of smaller ornamental items that were the core of the earlier John Woodley enterprise, but there is evidence to the contrary. First is the way he continued to advertise himself, for example in local directory entries such as *White's History, Gazeteer and Directory of Devon* (White, 1878–9) that lists him as a "*Stone mason and quarry owner, marble chimney-piece, urn, vase and church column &c. mnfr*". Second is a pair of magnificent vases donated in 1930 to Torquay Museum by a 'Mrs. Blackler' (Chapter 4, Fig. 4.8). We cannot be sure, however, that these are not inherited Woodley items.

Andrew Blackler died in 1892, aged 65, and perhaps All Saints Church at Babbacombe is his unofficial memorial. His son, Thomas Andrew Blackler soldiered on. In 1906 he had a skirmish with the law for allegedly intimidating his workforce at a Parliamentary election, but the charges were thrown out. In 1911 he and his wife occupied Hillborough House, the Fore Street mansion that was once owned by John Woodley. He lists himself as "*Managing Director of the Marble Works*". There is no family but there are relatives and guests, plus a retinue of three domestic servants including a nurse. Hillborough House is believed to have become the Hampton Court Hotel, run by the Blacklers. The marble

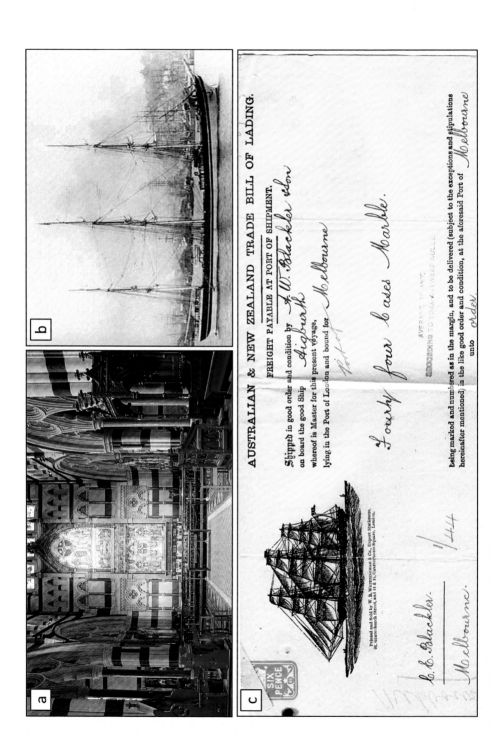

Figure 3.8. (facing page) Blackler's reredos in Melbourne Cathedral, Australia. a: The chancel of St Paul's Cathedral, Melbourne with Blackler's two-tier reredos behind and above the altar. The pilasters and base are *Red Ogwell* marble and the tracery is English alabaster. b: The sailing ship *Aigburth* that took the consignment from Liverpool to Australia. c: Part of the signed international Bill of Lading that accompanied the freight consignment. (*Acknowledgement: Dorothea Rowse, Melbourne Cathedral for photographs and information, with thanks.*)

business generally entered a recession in the 1900s and the Blackler enterprise faltered and was wound up in 1915, announced in the *London Gazette* on 25th May of that year. The final straw was probably the start of the First World War, which sounded the knell for many such labour-intensive luxury businesses. Thomas died in 1929, following which the factory buildings were sold off for other uses.

3.4.6 *The remarkable Grant dynasty*

World War one was certainly a trying time for the greatest of the South Devon Marble dynasties, the Grants, as we shall see, but it could have been a lot worse. Five generations of Grants, overlapping with two later generations of Hallidays from the female line, came through thick and thin for more than 200 years. The Grant's Marble business entered the 21st century, revamped under the Halliday descendants. The original business was variously into manufacturing, wholesaling and retail, for the most part concentrating on small items for the non-architectural side of the ornamental stone market. Their stock-in-trade included polished fossil specimens, jewellery made from pebbles found on beaches and a wide range of inlaid or veneered (termed mosaic) objects for domestic and presentational use. They were also making and engraving monumental items.

This was a business that had to compete with the Woodleys, later the Blacklers, and it was achieved by diversifying the product range into objects made of imported stones such as black marble, malachite and onyx in addition to the traditional local stones. The range of products included desk sets, thermometer stands and mantelpiece ornaments. In the early years of the business, whilst there was still a workplace shared with the Woodleys, the Grants had access to stone from Petit Tor but there is no sign that the Grants ever had their own quarries. Malachite from Russia became a particular speciality in the late 1800s, described by perhaps the greatest Grant entrepreneur, third generation William Henry, as "*a beautiful... very costly material, ten shillings to twenty shillings per pound, according to quality*" (Grant, 1922). Malachite work became a speciality and was headlined on the shop front and factory in the late 1800s (Fig. 3.10).

Generation 1. The founder of the Grant dynasty (Fig. 3.9a) was Joseph Grant (1777–1868) who, like Daniel Woodley Snr. and Andrew Blackler, was already an experienced stone-mason when he moved to St Marychurch parish from Broadhempston. They were of similar age and must have known one another from childhood. Initially, Joseph Grant worked at Petit Tor Quarry with the first Daniel Woodley. In 1836 he seems to have established his own stone-polishing workshop, the year soon adopted for the establishment of the Grant's Marble business and quoted in the 21st century. Clearly, Joseph Grant had no idea he was to become the founding father of a marble dynasty spanning 200 years, but as he moved into old age his decision about the line of inheritance would address the same key questions as with each succeeding generation. Technically the first in line for inheritance was Joseph Jnr, but by 1851 he was aged 39, unmarried and still living at home. He had no children of his own, nor evidently any real prospect of presenting any. He was nonetheless a skilled "*marble engraver*", making stone seals at his father's premises. These personalised carved and engraved items went back millennia and were used for embossing wax security seals on personal documents, particularly letters. They fell out of use in mid-Victorian times as gummed envelopes gained usage.

Figure 3.9. Harry Grant & Sons employees outside the works and showroom *c.* 1874. The first three standing on the left are William Henry Grant (WHG, tallest), later the 'Grand Old Man' (Fig. 3.10b), with sons on either side. Leaning, is possibly the disabled Harry Frank. On the other side of WHG may be William Henry Godfrey

Figure 3.10. Two outstanding members of the Grant dynasty a: Founder: Joseph Grant 1777–1868 b: Most famous: William Henry Grant, the 'Grand Old Man' 1836–1924 (*Acknowledgement: Mark Halliday with thanks.*)

Generation 2. Joseph Grant Jnr's special skills were not enough by themselves to secure the future of the Grant business. In 1851 Joseph senior was 73 and his wife, Elizabeth, was 68. He was still 'Head' of the household and a 'marblemason' in his own right. After Joseph Jnr, was second son Henry Grant (37), who lived separately in St Marychurch with his wife, Mary, and their three children. He was listed as *"Marblemason (Master employing 6 men & 3 boys)"*. Third son William Grant (35) lived in the 'Village' in 1851, with his wife, plus 5 children all under the age of nine. William was a *"Master Marble Mason Employing 4 Men"* and went on to have 3 further children. He was clearly a good businessman with a big family, but he was the youngest son. It had to be Henry, the second son, with a healthy family including his own teenage son and running the largest of the three family enterprises, who was best placed to take on the business. By 1861 the younger William had distanced himself, moving some 5 miles away to Tormoham (now Torre, part of Torquay), where, in 1871, he was pursuing a separate and successful family marble mason's business.

As the second-generation successor, Henry Grant (1813–1871) was well trained. He had received his apprenticeship under Daniel Woodley, subsequently striking out on his own, polishing fossil specimens and making jewellery. Following an advantageous marriage to Mary Pearce, daughter of a local quarryman, Henry Grant rented a house next door to his father-in-law, Christopher, in Combepafford (St Marychurch). He is listed there in 1841 where he had a workshop with several employees. Eventually outgrowing this a few years later, he joined his brother, Joseph Jnr, in a new venture in 1847 (Grant, 1922) on a freehold plot at Watcombe on the main road to Teignmouth. They developed the site, establishing a house, six cottages and a workshop. This joint venture became a success, soon attracting the Watcombe Terracotta Clay Company Ltd to the vicinity, exploiting recently discovered substantial deposits of red clay found in pockets in the nearby limestone both at nearby Watcombe and immediately behind the Grant workshops. Only the former showroom of the subsequently renamed Watcombe Pottery survived the later redevelopment of this row of buildings. The story of the highly collectible Watcombe Pottery could fill a separate chapter.

The 'Golden Age' of the Grant business arrived with the latter half of the 19th century. In 1861, second generation Henry Grant (1813–1871) had a workforce of ten. His father Joseph was now 83, a widower and retired. Henry was 47 in that year and his own children were already grown up and making out for themselves. In the subsequent decade, we find brother, Joseph on his own in one of the Watcombe cottages and in an ironic turn of fate a further decade later, in 1881, 69-year-old Joseph Jnr, still an active *"stone engraver"* according to the census, has married Ellen, 52.

Generation 3. The oldest of Henry Grant's three children, the third generation of the Grants, was William Henry Grant (1836–1924), both ambitious and very successful. In 1861 William Henry was 24, married to Mary (28) with youngsters, Emma (5), Eva (3), Harry Frank (2) and William H Godfrey (3 months). Three of these names would reappear towards the turn of the century. In the 1871 census, to add to the confusion of names, those of William Henry are reversed. His father, Henry, had just died, aged 58 and we may guess that this was a son's way of honouring the succession. He had two further children and a workforce of 13.

An 1874 planning application reveals the addition of a new showroom to the Watcombe development. This may be the reason for a celebrated photograph from around the time showing members of the Grant Family and 15 or so employees on the pavement outside a smart-looking and well-stocked showroom (Fig. 3.9). By 1881, burgeoning on all fronts, William Henry Grant had a seventh child and a workforce of 18. Business was booming in the late 1800s and William Henry Grant (Fig. 3.10b) became the most respected name in the Grant lineage. He was elected a local councillor in 1880, later chairing the St Mary-church Urban District Council in 1900. In his own brief memoir (Grant, 1922), William Henry recalls collecting *"geological fossils"* with his father on Babbacombe beach in 1852 when Prince Albert came ashore to do some shopping at Woodley's marble works (noted above). They must have been a bit put out by Albert's exclusive mission, but it may indicate that they were not selling the sort of high-end local marble objects that Albert was after. William Henry also visited the new Plymouth Breakwater with his father, in order to measure it up for the manufacture of marble models. One of these may be a model in the Oxford University collection. He noted that they were also producing marble models of the Eddystone lighthouse.

The name of the Grant establishments went through several revisions through the 19th and 20th centuries from *"The Watcombe Marble and Mosaic Works"* in the 1850s to *"Grant's Marble Works and Watcombe Pottery"* 100 years later (Grant, 1922). Potentially confusing is the name Harry, as in *"Harry Grant & Sons"*, used from the late 1860s to the 1920s. For example, the 1874 showroom (Fig. 3.9) bears *"Harry Grant Malachite and Mosaic Workshops"* whilst the gable wall behind has H. Grant. The first Grant actually christened Harry was 4th generation Harry Frank, born in 1859 and so just a child in the 'showroom' picture, but 'Harry' is also the traditional diminutive of 'Henry'. An informative variant emerges in *Kelly's Directory for the Watch and Clock Trade* (1880), under 'Madrepore, Malachite and Mosaic Workers'. It reads *"Grant Harry, Watcombe steam marble works"*. Like the 'Phoenix Steam Marble Works' in Plymouth, it presents us with a rare confirmation of how the late 19th century Grant stone works was powered. A fine photograph from before the turn of the century, shows such an interior with belt-driven machinery (Fig. 3.11) where at least 30 employees are hand working small stone items.

Much of the smaller produce from the Grant's Marble works was wholesaled to shops in Torquay and elsewhere. The Kelly's (1880) directory advertisement noted above summarises Grant products as *"works of art in marble malachite & floral mosaics including writing sets vases photo frames clock cases &c &c mosaic & malachite jewellery wholesale florentine mosaics repaired"* (original punctuation). This was by far the biggest entry in a long list of mainly Devon and Derbyshire names and is an important indicator of the product range and business ambitions of the firm.

After the death of one of the Grants' best local retail customers, Edwin Bradford, in 1874 (Chapter 4), the business established its own direct outlet in Torquay in 1880. Their first shop was up on Torwood Street, but it was soon relocated to Strand, on the waterfront not far from Bradford's former shop. It was managed by two of William Henry Grant's children, fourth generation Harry Frank and Emma. The shop sold their *"own manufactures, including marbles inlaid with floral mosaics on geometrical designs for table ornaments and stone jewellery... mounted in silver and gold"* (Grant, 1922). A photograph from around the turn of the century (Fig. 3.12) shows the exterior of this shop, with its proud manager, Harry Frank himself. In the windows there are rectangular picture frames, presentation shields and perhaps lighthouse models in stone. There also seem to be clocks, vases and many trinkets. Inside (Fig. 3.13), a breathtaking showroom with mirrors and fine furniture is filled with jugs, bottles, vases, figurines, models, boxes and diverse trinkets but a lot of it evidently ceramic rather than marble and probably Watcombe pottery. Seriously interesting objects fill the floor and wall cabinets, but despite all this ostentation, there are no classical specimen marble tables.

Generation 4. The line of inheritance once again became a problem as the fourth generation of the Grant dynasty grew up. The first two of William Henry Grant's seven children were girls and, in accordance with the times, the choice had to be made between the next two in line, Harry Frank and William Henry Godfrey. At the age of 60, in 1896, William

Figure 3.11. A marble factory interior around the late 1800s. Steam mechanisation has brought overhead belt drive to some of the machinery and a roof gantry provides the capability of lifting and moving heavy pieces around the workshop.

Henry Grant, the 'Grand Old Man of St Marychurch' (Fig. 3.10b) passed the business "*conditionally*" to both, possibly splitting it between them (Grant, 1922). He then lived on in retirement to the age of 88 in 1924. We can only guess what his condition of succession was in 1896, but it may have centred upon his oldest son Harry Frank (1858–*c*. 1913) who, like his great uncle Joseph Jnr, never married and had no offspring to inherit. In the early 20th century photograph of the Grant Shop (Fig. 3.12) he is lightly built and stands stiffly supported in the doorway, suggesting that he had mobility problems. This must also be the awkwardly posed youngster seen in an earlier photograph, perhaps aged 16, outside the Watcombe works around 1873 (Fig. 3.9).

Lacking today's sensibilities and financial buffers, inheritance then was about 'bread-winners', so that women, the disabled and the unmarried were, for practical reasons of the times, normally excluded. Whatever the story, physically challenged Harry Frank Grant is noted in 1911 as "*retired*" at the age of 52 and his fourth generation brother William Henry Godfrey was evidently in charge, bypassing the two older sisters. WHGG calls himself "*Marble Worker, Jeweller and Silversmith*" in 1911, living in St Marychurch with his wife and family, and the shop is evidently staffed by his older sister Emma, merely listed as 'shop assistant'. Four of WHGG's five children, aged between 16 and 22, are listed as "*assist. in the business*" which may include the manufacturing side. Amongst them, receiving their training for future management, are yet another Harry Grant and a Godfrey Grant, promising the future fifth generation of owners.

In 1913 the family turned Grant's Marble into a private limited company, with a board of directors and controlled share ownership. William Henry Godfrey along with his fifth generation son, Harry, were amongst the founding directors. Interestingly, another director was an 'Ernest Betjemann', a manufacturing cabinetmaker from Highgate, London. He

Figure 3.12. The Harry Grant & Sons shop at 10 Strand, Torquay, around 1900. This building survives into the early 21st Century.

Figure 3.13. The interior of the Harry Grant & Sons shop with its mirrors, showcases, furniture and small goods.

58

may have been a wholesale supplier to the shop, but he is better known as father of the subsequent Poet Laureate, Sir John Betjeman. The new company closed the shop in the lean times of 1916 and returned to their core business of manufacturing and wholesaling (Grant, 1922).

Generations 5 and 6. Fifth generation Harry Grant (1890–1958) made little early impact on the business, but for good reason. A post-war photograph shows him in a World War 1 Officer's uniform, with medals, from which we can reconstruct a pretty good account of his war record (Malcolm Hole, pers. comm.). Harry evidently volunteered for the 1/5 Battalion Devonshire Regiment and his initial deployment to Karachi in late 1914 was followed by the Mesopotamia campaigns in 1917. He then volunteered for the brand new Royal Flying Corps, soon to be the RAF, and as an Officer Observer he flew reconnaissance and bomb-aiming missions in 1918 in an Armstrong Whitworth biplane. After contracting malaria he was repatriated and then discharged in 1919.

Harry was 29 when he finally returned to St Marychurch. His father WHGG, at 58 was still actively in charge and his 19-year old brother, Godfrey, was waiting in reserve, just in case. Soldier Harry's stint in charge of the company lasted until 1958 when he died aged 67, leaving the business to Godfrey. After a further 18 years Godfrey also passed it on, selling to his nephew, Gregory G Halliday, son of his sister Jessie Grant and Torquay Borough Librarian Richard Halliday. The latest owner of Grant's Marble, Mark Halliday is Gregory's son and Jessie Grant's grandson, marking the sixth generation of the family to hold the business.

3.4.7 *The talented Messrs Jenkins*
Henry Tozier Jenkins, the founder of HT Jenkins & Son and the last of the Devon marble dynasties to be reviewed, was the son of a shoemaker (Jenkins, 1973). That is an unexpected start for an account of a great marble mason. His birthplace in 1842 was Broadhempston, Devon (1871 census). This was also the birthplace of Daniel Woodley in 1797, Joseph Grant in 1777, Thomas Blackler Snr in 1800 and Andrew Blackler in 1828. Each was the entrepreneurial founder or successor to one of the principal marble dynasties of south-east Devon and clearly this must be more than just pure coincidence. Here, by dint of four local stonemasons, was the founding centre of the south-east Devon marble industry.

The Broadhempston connections. In the first part of the 19th century, the Parish of Broadhempston was a thriving rural community, with about 800 people, mostly deriving a living from agriculture or retail and handicrafts (visionofbritain.org). Occupations in Broadhempston Village in 1841 included shoemaking, weaving, carpentry, cooperage and the navy. A few shallow quarries, probably linked to agriculture and building, are still identifiable, but there was only one stonemason family in the village itself, and little to indicate a thriving parish- or district-wide marble industry. Richard Polwhele (1793–1806, p. 53) records a black marble quarry in the parish of Broadhempston *"with which many houses in the neighbourhood are built,"* he says, but an earlier glimpse of marble comes from the late 1700s when Daniel Woodley was still living there. His Newfoundland (Canada) grave markers (Pocius, 1982) not only tell us of an active monumental mason business somewhere in the parish of Broadhempston, but also that it was technically an international one.

There were seafaring links surviving from the 16th century along much of the Devon coast, especially between Broadhempston and Newfoundland. These were established by the first coloniser of Newfoundland, Sir Humphrey Gilbert (1539–1583), half-brother of Sir Walter Raleigh, who belonged to Broadhempston parish. The Newfoundland trade remained important on the Devon coast and even in the 18th century shoes were still being exported to Newfoundland contained in Broadhempston-made fish barrels that were then relayed back to parts of Europe filled with salted fish (Jenkins, 1973). In this light, it is less perplexing that the occasional grave marker should also have found its way to Newfoundland from Broadhempston and it is likely that some of the exported shoes were made by Henry Jenkins' father.

Broadhempston is credited with supplying stone for the churches at Ipplepen and Torbryan (Pateman, 1980) and it may not be necessary to seek special reasons why the parish became the cradle of the industry. Every profitable business has to start somewhere and perhaps the skills of marble masonry on the back of an existing and well-tried transport route via Totnes to Dartmouth and beyond were the key. When this declined and the coast became a more secure and attractive alternative then perhaps the locus of the industry simply moved there in the late 1700s.

Nonetheless, there could be a far more pragmatic explanation for the St Marychurch 'Marble Rush'. Neither of the earliest entrepreneurs at Petit Tor, Robert Fulton or John Hubbard, could conjure up a fully staffed stone-quarrying and shipping enterprise from nothing. In particular, and at about the right time, we know that John Hubbard told the *Society of Arts* that he supposed "*from sixty to one hundred workmen may be employed*" in Petit Tor quarry by the autumn of 1809 (Society of Arts, 1809). Numbers of that sort would have required a substantial recruitment effort and in particular some experienced quarriers and master masons were needed to organise them. For example, it is more than likely that Daniel Woodley from Broadhempston, already at Petit Tor by 1806, was a widely known and respected figure in the industry, and if the best available marble masons happened to be those Woodley knew from his Broadhempston days, perhaps he and John Hubbard simply went there to get them.

The Jenkins family. Henry Jenkins arrived from Broadhempston much later, however, and his connections with the honourable birthplace were perhaps more by chance. He became apprenticed to a marble firm in Torquay around the 1850s and was a marble mason in his own right by 1871, established on Lower Union Street with six employees. A decade later he describes himself as a "*Statuary and marble mason*". A statuary is a sculptor and this is a hint of the family genius yet fully to unfold amongst his five young sons, Frank, Wilfred, Walter, Gilbert and John. Frank studied art, first in Devon and then in London (Jenkins, 2010). He became an international prizewinning sculptor, working mainly in London, and amongst his several prestigious commissions was a spectacular frieze for the interior of Lloyd's Register in the City of London. Dating from 1901, this is one of the city's great Devonshire marble interiors (DMB L/C/3. Chapter 11, Group 1) where his father, Henry, supplied panels in *Petitor*, arches in *Ashburton* and columns in *Red Ogwell*.

Further work followed in collaboration with the Lloyd's architect Thomas Colcutt and in particular with his fellow student, artist Gerald Moira, during which they produced the magnificent Arts and Crafts cupola over the stage at the Wigmore Hall, London (built as part of the Bechstein piano manufacturer's showroom and still an important musical venue). Their best known collaboration was a series of wall-panel reliefs for the iconic J Lyon's & Co. Trocadero Restaurant on Piccadilly Circus. Good sources of further information on Frank Lynn Jenkins are Jenkins (2011 and 2013).

Wilfred, Henry Jenkins' second son became a society photographer in London, whilst his fifth and youngest became a naval engineer (Jenkins, 1973). Henry's fourth son, Gilbert, became a leading architect, and worked with his father on some prestigious projects, including the design of their new marble works on Lymington Road in Torquay. Gilbert undertook work at the Tate Gallery, London and at Chatsworth House, Derbyshire as well as completing several major landscape architecture projects. He became president of the Architectural Association in 1927 and of the Institute of Landscape Architects in 1935.

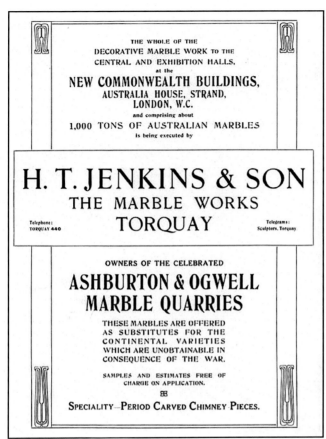

THE WHOLE OF THE
DECORATIVE MARBLE WORK TO THE
CENTRAL AND EXHIBITION HALLS,
at the
NEW COMMONWEALTH BUILDINGS,
AUSTRALIA HOUSE, STRAND,
LONDON, W.C.
and comprising about
1,000 TONS OF AUSTRALIAN MARBLES
is being executed by

H. T. JENKINS & SON
THE MARBLE WORKS
TORQUAY

Telephone:
TORQUAY 440

Telegrams:
Sculptors, Torquay

OWNERS OF THE CELEBRATED
ASHBURTON & OGWELL
MARBLE QUARRIES

THESE MARBLES ARE OFFERED
AS SUBSTITUTES FOR THE
CONTINENTAL VARIETIES
WHICH ARE UNOBTAINABLE IN
CONSEQUENCE OF THE WAR.

SAMPLES AND ESTIMATES FREE OF
CHARGE ON APPLICATION.

SPECIALITY—PERIOD CARVED CHIMNEY PIECES.

Figure 3.14. An advertisement by HT Jenkins placed in an architectural supplies catalogue. Australia House was built 1913–1918. The advertisement refers to the difficulty in obtaining continental marbles because of the First World War. (*Picture courtesy of John Woolf.*)

The Jenkins succession. It was Walter, the second son, who was destined to take over the Jenkins marble business (Jenkins, 1973). Marble-work collaborations between father and son include the grand marble staircase at Oldway Mansion, Paignton and the Chapel at Dartmouth Royal Naval College (DMB SW/PL/5, noted in Chapter 5). Walter received commissions from Edwin Lutyens, the great 20th century country house architect and the firm worked on the Queen Victoria Memorial outside Buckingham Palace. In 1911 the Jenkins business is listed in a business directory under "*Marble Works and Monumental Masons*" (McKenzie, 1911) along with the Blacklers, Grants, Sharlands and two others. This is close to the last time that they would appear together.

The Jenkins business survived the First World War when import of foreign stone became difficult (Fig. 3.14) and they went on to supply work for the Cenotaph in Whitehall and prestigious contracts worldwide. Although undertaken by a Devonshire marble specialist, much of this demand was not for marble but was for die-cut masonry using building stone from other British and worldwide sources. From the advertisement, however (Fig. 3.14), it is clear that Jenkins had taken over the Ashburton and Ogwell quarries from the Blacklers and, in an ironic twist of circumstances, were actually offering these Devonshire stones as substitutes for presumably more popular continental ones. The Jenkins business survives today under the name of Walter W Jenkins & Co. Ltd, but there are no continuing direct links to the original Jenkins family.

3.5 Ipplepen—nothing on paper

One of the so far unsolved mysteries surrounds the working of *Ipplepen* marble. The stone is widely used and in large quantities, for example locally in Torbay Town Hall (DMB SW/TQ/6. Chapter 11, Group 7), and far away in a castle and church at Todmorden, Yorkshire (DMBs NY/OL/1-2, Chapter 11, Group 11). Ipplepen even supplied 80 *Red Ipplepen* columns and pilasters at the Gibson Hall, London (DMB L/C/2. Chapter 11, Group 1) where they are amongst the biggest single pieces of Devonshire marble known, measured at 3.8 m. There are numerous other examples of the use of *Ipplepen* marble and it falls into two distinct types, *Red Ipplepen* and *Grey Ipplepen*. From the samples in the national stone collections the quarry names are known and include Ipplepen (Barton) Quarry and Beltor Quarry at the scattered settlement of Ipplepen (Fig. 2.1). Barton Quarry is not extensive but is unusually deep and to this day there remains an isolated single, very large piece of *Red Ipplepen* marble at the bottom, possibly the last one to be extracted.

But where were such large pieces machined? Who extracted it and how did they get such lucrative contracts? There are no obvious industrial remains at Ipplepen apart from a surviving Quarry Cottage. Local references to quarrying commonly conflate Ipplepen with the nearby Broadhempston area and/or the even closer Stoneycombe quarry which has been a site of aggregate extraction ever since the railways were introduced (Chapter 9, Itinerary S1). Contemporary trade and other directories for Ipplepen reveal little to nothing about quarrying (e.g. White, 1850), but White (1878–9, p. 502) lists "*Poole & Co., limestone and marble quarry owners, Devonshire Marble works*" at Ipplepen, whilst Kelly (1889, p. 305) lists "*Marble quarries belonging to Mr W.G.Thorpe and limestone quarries the property of Mr R Maddicott*". These are missing names in the marble firmament, and perhaps there are more. The Ipplepen mystery remains.

3.6. Madrepore manufacturers

The line of buildings that once contained the Grant's shop on Strand, Torquay originated around 1806 as a row of stone houses—a notable feature of the waterfront both then and later (Fig. 3.15). A few of these original buildings still survives in the row of modern shops. The street was named "*Strand*" after the working shoreline it was built over and its buildings became a small goldmine for retailers of fossils, jewellery and marble items right through the 19th century. In the 1830s there was James Braham, madrepore worker and jeweller at no. 8 (Blewitt, 1832). In the 1840s there was Alexander Jacobs, madrepore worker and jeweller at no. 14 (Pigot, 1844). In 1851, Edwin Bradford, "*Marble Mason, Goldsmith and Jeweller*" took on no. 8, then no. 9 to 1871 (Taber, 2001). Finally, the Grants had their shop at no. 10 from 1880. This closed in 1916, the year after the demise of Blackler's Royal Marble Works at Babbacombe, and probably through the same cataclysmic circumstances.

The beaches around Babbacombe Bay, between Torquay and Teignmouth were continually yielding fossil coral and sponge specimens derived from pebble deposits overlying the Devonian limestones. We know that the Grants were not beyond collecting good beach pebbles (see above), and the tables manufactured by John Woodley contain certain stones that could only have come from the beaches. A 2012 replica table now in Torquay Mu-

Figure 3.15. Torquay from Park Hill in the 1830s. The row of houses on the Strand (inset) was built at the previous turn of the century and housed several stone-orientated businesses.

seum, made by Mark Halliday of Grant's Marble (see above and Chapter 4) was almost entirely made of these. The polished pebble business first became a speciality in shell or mineral shops, but jewellers were also making exquisite items from local stones (Chapter 4). White (1850) lists seven "*madrepore manufacturers*" in Torquay. James Braham, Alexander Jacobs (both jewellers) and Henry Sharland, (a marble mason) have already been met; William Nichols, Pratt & Putt, Thomas Thornton and William Widger were others. One of the earliest was Mary Wyatt who operated from Torwood Road in Torquay (Blewitt, 1832). John Heggerty, Old Quay, Torquay was a shell and mineral dealer in 1832 and was the guide at the already famous Kents Cavern nearby who introduced William Gladstone to the caves in that year (Chapter 4).

By far the most prolific of the madrepore dealers in the marble triangle (Fig. 2.1) was Alfred JR Sclater, Bank Street, Teignmouth and later his son, Thomas. AJR describes himself as a "*Naturalist*" and a "*Mineralogical Conchologist*" in the censuses, but he was also a substantial collector and dealer of fossils and shells, developing a local museum in the 1890s. Both of the Sclaters advertised regularly for exchanges of specimens in *Hardwickes Science Gossip*, an "*Illustrated medium of Interchange and Gossip for Students and Lovers of Nature*" (Hardwicke, 1865–93). Alfred Sclater's most remarkable entries offered "*500 slabs of polished madrepores*" in exchange for other fossils or shells in 1877, and "*1000 sections of corals for microscopists*" in 1879. Sclater's specimen labels are a familiar sight on old fossil collections in many modern museums (e.g. Fig. 3.16).

Figure 3.16. A specimen of Devon coral with an AJR Sclater label. (*Acknowledgements to Wolverhampton Arts and Museums Service where this specimen is located.*)

4. MARBLE MASTERPIECES 1: THE PORTABLE ITEMS
DEVONSHIRE MARBLE TABLES, ORNAMENTS AND JEWELLERY

4.1 Introduction to Devonshire marble tables and decorative items

The products of the Devon marble industry range from imposing colonnaded masterpieces, intended to impress, right down to delicate jewellery, intended to delight. They were manufactured over a period of more than 100 years by successions of skilled marble masons often from the dynastic families who treasured their expertise and passed it on, as we have seen in Chapter 3. This chapter looks at the smaller end of the spectrum—the 'portable items' such as decorated ornaments and utility pieces that comprised the non-architectural output of the marble workshops. Once merely unusual, and sometimes of dubious style, they are now all valuable antiques provided they are not too damaged or incomplete.

These are the objects that once lined the floors and shelves of south Devon shops and showrooms (e.g. Fig. 3.13), intended to adorn the homes of aristocrats, wealthy middle classes and trinket-seeking tourists. They range from items of staggering showmanship or beauty such as specimen marble tables (Fig. 4.1) to complex machine-turned bowls and vases (Fig. 4.8) or useless items such as mantelpiece obelisks (Fig. 4.12). The full range included brooches, bracelets, cutlery handles, trinket boxes, paperweights, ink stands, picture frames, bowls, vases, tazzas, ewers, trays, thermometer stands, whole desk sets, whole dressing-table sets, mantlepiece obelisks and, of course, the spectacular specimen marble tables (Figs 4.1 to 4.21). The utility items such as thermometer stands and writing sets reflect a bygone age of low technology, but no less style conscious.

Few of these items feature a single variety of stone. Although the Devonshire marble palette included many richly textured stones that could be used on their own, most of the Devonshire items were manufactured as composites, usually as inlay work or mosaics using a plain black background. Inlays were placed into prepared sockets in the backing stone whilst mosaics were prepared as individual pieces laid next to one another. It was partly through the fashion of the time, in the period of mourning in the post-Albert Victorian era, that the backing stone was usually a sombre pure black, but it provided a superb contrast, setting off the brightly coloured Devonshire specimen pieces.

There was problem, though. Pure black marble was not available in Devon. It is not that there was a shortage of actual black marble, particularly in the Plymouth area, but one of the hallmarks of Devonshire marble is the presence of calcite veins, usually white, which would appear as flaws in backing pieces. Pure black marble without veins had to be brought in from elsewhere which meant one of two alternatives. The first was the black Carboniferous limestone quarried in abundance in parts of Belgium, mainly used for architectural purposes, and the second was the almost indistinguishable black Carboniferous limestone from near Ashford in central Derbyshire already noted in Chapter 2. *Ashford Black* marble is a soot-black textureless limestone that was mined rather than quarried at sites near Bakewell. If the Devon industry was to respond to fashion it had to import plain black marble, but both sources were equally difficult. Plenty of Belgian stones were reaching Britain in the mid 19th century, but even the direct route by ship from Ostend to Devon was about 250 miles (475 km). The alternative, in the pre-railway era, was a full 200 miles (320 km) from Derbyshire by horse and cart, but worse than that, Derbyshire was the centre of its own *Ashford Black* marble inlay industry, already noted in Chapter 2, in direct competition with Devonshire marbles and producing some very similar ornamental items.

In fact, so similar are certain designs of Devonshire and Derbyshire items that they can be hard to distinguish and it is necessary to establish some criteria for doing so. At the time of the Great Exhibition of 1851, the Report of the Judges (Royal Commission, 1852) noted that the products of the Derbyshire industry had "*become very important*" whilst those of

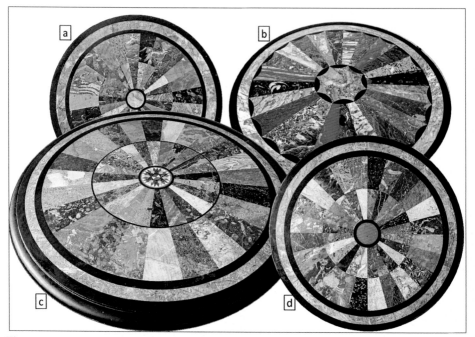

Figure 4.1. Typical Woodley-style Devonshire marble tables. a: Torquay Table 2 (465 mm), Torquay Museum No. V6583. b: Torquay Table 1 (690 mm), Torquay Museum No. V6584.1. c: Sedgwick Table 1 (1.2 m), Sedgwick Museum, Cambridge. d: Sedgwick Table 2 (*c.* 700 mm), Sedgwick Museum, Cambridge.

Devonshire were "*rising into importance*". It is a useful calibration for the time, for if we compare the two industries now, that of Derbyshire is still well recognised whilst that of Devonshire is almost completely eclipsed. This is even reflected in museum collections nationally, such as Buxton and Derby, where there are fine collections of Derbyshire ornamental objects, but there is only one museum, Torquay, that separately recognises Devonshire ornamental items. Even the county museum at Exeter has no Devonshire items catalogued as such and nor, apparently, does the Victoria and Albert Museum in London.

Perhaps this reflects confusion between the products of the two manufacturing centres, with Devonshire objects being catalogued as Derbyshire, and that is certainly the case amongst most antique dealers, but worse, perhaps it means that the entire British ornamental stone genre is not being recognised. In its heyday, the Devonshire industry was thoroughly well advertised and there were several well-stocked retail outlets in Plymouth and Torquay that were marketing highly recognisable Devonshire objects. Clearly, plenty of items passed into private hands for the best part of a century, but they are now either unrecognised or lost. In order to recover what we can, we should first look at what we can learn from the unquestionably Devonshire products, starting with the easiest and most iconic of these, the Devonshire marble tables.

4.2 The Devonshire marble tables

There are Devonshire marble slab tables and Devonshire specimen marble tables. Three examples of slab tables have been encountered in these surveys and they perhaps ought to be the most common because of their relative ease of manufacture. All three were encountered in Saltram House, Plymstock, where they are believed to be part of the original furnishings dating from the mid to late 18th century. Two are large slabs of typical black Plymouth stone *c.* 1.6 m and 2.1 m by 0.8 m, on early Georgian style mahogany bases (*c.* 1730–1740, online, see ref. National Trust Collections), and one is a typical variegated Radford marble on an Adam-style painted wood base (*c.* 1760, not online). Assuming these tops are original, and they seem to be in remarkably good condition for their age, they may be the earliest dated uses of ornamental Devonshire marble encountered.

Only 13 specimen marble tables have been encountered and photographically recorded in this study and two further examples are experimental reproductions. Most have a black marble backing that may have come from Derbyshire but the supporting pedestal, if in stone, is made of a faceted or turned piece of Devonshire marble set on a matching circular, square or octagonal plinth. Some tops, perhaps most, were designed without a pedestal so that they could be fitted to a base of the customer's own choosing, usually wood.

All the tables have a rich display of varied rock and fossil types, but these stones do not register exactly with the marbles used in building interiors. Table manufacturers were not limited by the need for volume and consistency as was necessary in buildings, and in fact contrasts in colour and texture from stone to stone in the smaller items were a desirable feature. Inlay marbles were treated more as semi-precious stones where curious fossils, strong colours and unusually rich rock textures were the most sought after characteristics. They could use small offcuts from standard decorative marbles, but in particular the restricted sizes required meant that a whole new source could be brought into play, using Devonian limestone cobbles and pebbles taken from local beaches. The obvious source of these was beneath the sea cliffs in Devonian limestone, but perhaps more commonly stones came from the overlying Permian conglomerates which include abundant limestone pebbles (Chapter 8). For the purpose of obtaining small pieces of stone rich in colour and texture that were easily sliced into thin plaquettes, such loose beach pebbles, requiring no quarrying or complex problems of land ownership, were even preferable. Several small businesses thrived on collecting and polishing such pebbles and selling them as individual specimens in their own right (Chapter 3). The result is that the range of stones used in ornamental objects differs greatly from that used in buildings. A contemporary newspaper article from the 1880s claimed that there were more than 50 varieties of *Petitor* marble that came out of the St Marychurch works near Torquay (Pateman, 1980). That is clearly true, given John Hubbard's experience (Chapter 3) but the number would have been increased by the diverse inlay stones that came from the surrounding beaches that were collected for the tables and ornaments. A separate guide is offered (Chapter 13) to stones used in the smaller artefacts of both the Devonshire and Derbyshire manufacturing centres.

4.2.1 *The Woodley Group*

The most common table-top design is a radial arrangement of elongated stone plaquettes (Fig. 4.1) with carefully separated contrasting colours and textures. This 'sunburst' style is typically from John Woodley's Royal Marble works at St Marychurch in the years prior to 1865, and might be said to be ahead of its time, becoming a popular motif in the later Art Nouveau and Art Deco movements. The design was inlaid as a mosaic assembly into a wide depression cut into the black marble base which usually consisted of a single piece of limestone. The edge was therefore without joins and so very robust, but everything inside it consisted of thin butt-joined slices of stone a few mm thick. Next to the outside rim, or not far away, is usually a band of *Yellow Petitor* (Fig. 4.1) with perhaps a further black band inside this. Additional concentric rings of black stone towards the centre can be either upstanding parts of the base or else separate pieces of applied mosaic. Further design hallmarks of this type of table include a central array of specimen stones in a circular, hexagonal or octagonal arrangement and/or a single-stone centrepiece. Surrounding this, between the central array and the outer radial tier there might be a zone of randomly fitted angular scrapwork (Fig. 4.3) or a second tier of radial stones (Fig. 4.1). Eight tables of this general type have been recorded, of which two (Fig 4.1) are in Torquay Museum (Chapter 11, Group 8). The larger of these, the *Torquay table 1* (Fig. 4.1b) has its own marble pedestal and the specimen marbles celebrate reef- and near-reef rock types, just about all of which can be matched to a reference collection made in recent years from beaches around the Petit Tor area. Some identical ones are used in the reproduction *Halliday tables* to be described shortly (Fig. 4.7). Formal documentation on the Torquay table is lacking, but its radial panels include typical 'shadow rock' and pieces of red and grey reef mud that are famously Petit Tor. The centrepiece is a scalloped specimen of brightly coloured and highly fractured and veined reef rock that would classify as *Yellow Petitor* like the peripheral band. An octagonal plinth suggests an early design and the table has the hallmarks of a Woodley piece.

Another pair of tables is held by the Sedgwick Museum in Cambridge (Fig. 4.1). Of these, the larger *Sedgwick table 1* (Fig. 4.1c) is in private daily use and is described in the Buildings guide (Chapter 11, Group 6. Fig. 11.15). Both consist of reef or near-reef rock types, and a further table in Cambridge, on public display in the Fitzwilliam Museum (Chapter 11, Group 6), is analysed in a bit more detail in Fig. 4.2. The stones in this *Fitzwilliam table* include the rare green *Kitley* from near Plymouth and the famous Bradley Woods *Featherstone* from near Newton Abbott, but most of the stones could have been sourced within 200 m of Petit Tor Down at Babbacombe. Even the outer band of brown Pleistocene flowstone of Kents Cavern type, placed where *Yellow Petitor* is found in other tables, can be found in fissures and small cave systems in and around the Petit Tor quarries.

How do we know these five designs studied so far are by John Woodley? It all hinges on a further well-documented example of the type, the *Fillongley table* (Fig. 4.3). More than 1-m diameter, it is an octagonal table with a fossil collection in its own right, featuring many of the corals and stony sponges seen around Babbacombe, together with pieces of the reef rocks themselves. The style and stones are a close match for the group already discussed and it is the only table recorded so far with full documentation giving the details of manufacturer and method of delivery to its 19th century purchaser (Sotheby's Fine Furniture & Decorative Arts Sale, 13th April 2011). The table was supplied to George Adderley, 1st Baron Norton, from the marble works of John Woodley of St Marychurch in Torquay in 1844 at a cost of £25 to include the pedestal. It went directly by sea to Chamberlain's

Figure 4.2. (facing page) The Fitzwilliam Table, Fitzwilliam Museum Stair Hall, Cambridge. Catalogued as: "Italian or Derbyshire, 19th century Red figured marble with *pietra dura* top Lent by the Master and Fellows of Trinity College (AAL.2-1971)". This is a *c*. 1-m diameter typical Woodley table with radial design in mainly coarse reef and near-reef sediments. The rock types are typically Woodley, many from the St Marychurch vicinity. 1: Green *Kitley* marble. 2: Brown muddy lagoonal sediment. 3: Red reef mud, Petit Tor. 4: Coral and stromatoporoid (strom.) reef sediment. 5: Limonite-altered reef cement (*Yellow Petitor*). 6: Dolomite-altered coral trash. 7: Grey reef mud with gastropods. 8: Veined reef cement, (*Pink Petitor*). 9: Limonite and hematite-altered coral/strom. reef trash (*Fossil Petitor*). 10: *Thamnopora cervicornis,* Bradley Woods (*Featherstone*). 11: Red, laminated reef mud, Petit Tor (as 3). 12: Coral/strom. reef trash (*Fossil Petitor*). 13: Coarse crinoid/coral sand, Petit Tor Breccia. 14: Part-dolomitised brachiopod shell rock, Petit Tor Breccia. 15: Limonitised reef sediment. 16: Coral/strom. reef trash with *Renalcis* shadows and white replacement cement, Petit Tor. 17: Dolomite-altered coral trash (as 6). 18: *Amphipora* (strom.) rock, Oddicombe Breccias. 19: Indeterminate sand. 20: Dolomite-altered coral/strom. trash, Oddicombe Breccias. 21: *Periphacelopora* sp. Bradley Woods (*Featherstone*). 22: Limonite-altered reef cement (*Yellow Petitor*) (as 5). 23: Dolomite-altered coral/strom. trash (as 16). 24: Growth-banded stromatoporoid in coarse strom. sediment. 25: Circular band of reef mud (*Grey Petitor*). 26: Centrepiece *Favosites*. 27: Circular band of Pleistocene flowstone of Kents Cavern type, probably Petit Tor Beach.

Wharf in London where it was forwarded on to Fillongley Hall, near Nuneaton in War-wickshire, care of Baches Canal Boats. This was the pre-railway age, a time of poor roads and reliance on horse power, so that transportation by sea and canal were the securest and most convenient methods.

Appropriate for its octagonal layout and large size, the whole of the top has been ve-neered onto slate and the black marble and *Yellow Petitor* around the margin are all applied pieces, perfectly mitred at the angles. The radial arrangement of the larger stone plaquettes is common to the group of five tables so far studied and can be taken as a Woodley hall-mark. Underneath, the substantial turned column is embellished with carved lotus leaves and supported on a substantial but plain three-pointed socle with bun feet. It is made of *Grey Fossil Petitor* marble only available to John Woodley from his quarries at Petit Tor. Today, Woodley is a recognised sculptor of his age with several fine carved and signed funerary objects to his name (Chapter 3).

A collection of fossil specimens of the quality seen in this table top would be difficult to assemble from available localities today. There are rare specimens of red stone containing orthocone fossils, early relatives of ammonites, also noted in the **Kensington table** (Fig. 4.4, see below). Unobtainable today, the orthocones came from marginal pockets found in the reef rocks at Petit Tor. Stones from further afield include green marble from Kitley and pieces of the very rare red oolite (here termed *Avon Oolite*) also found in the Queen Victoria goldfinch platter yet to be described (Fig. 4.9) that is also a known Woodley item.

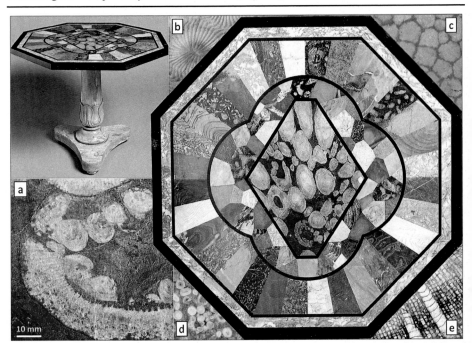

Figure 4.3. The Fillongley Table (1.1 m), private collection. This was delivered to the first Lord Norton at Fillongley Hall in 1844. The pedestal is in typical *Grey Petitor* reef rock and the top has 32 radial segments containing reef and near-reef sediment textures and fossils. The scrapwork centre surrounds a unique centrepiece with a cross section through a branching colony of the rugose coral *Cyathophyllum* sp., some pieces of which show budding juveniles (a). Other inlay examples are (b) the rugose coral *Haplothecia* sp., (c) the tabulate coral *Favosites* sp., (d) the Carboniferous Oolite from Bristol, used in the Woodley Goldfinch Platter (Fig. 4.9) and (e) the tabulate coral *Heliolites* sp.

Figure 4.4. The Kensington Table (1.67 m), Natural History Museum, London. There are 24 main radial stones in *Petitor*-type reef and near-reef rocks with a further 72 outer tier plaquettes, many featuring fossils, each separated by a bar of black marble. The centrepiece has a six-fold 3D box motif set in *Alveolites* coral, outside which is a garland of 12 rare Petit Tor orthocone (fossil cephalopod) pieces framed in a circle of black marble. The table has a stout pedestal and socle in probable *Ashburton* marble (inset) and is inscribed "DEVONSHIRE MARBLES" (inset). The significance of this table is captured in the text. The background image is one of the coral pieces featuring *Haplothecia ogwellensis*.

The most spectacular of all the currently known tables, the last in the Woodley group and one that will take a lot of beating, is that held by the Natural History Museum in South Kensington, London (Fig. 4.4). The **Kensington table** is in the former Geological Museum wing on Exhibition Road and takes centre place on the landing of a stairway made in a range of British marbles constructed as a showpiece within the building in 1935 (Chapter 11, Group 2). The table is nearly a century older than that, however, and is likely to have been in the collections for some time, perhaps an intended centrepiece on the new marble stairway. The table shares much in common with both the Cambridge and Torquay Museum examples but goes one better by combining both typical reef-rock marbles and a range of commonly occurring fossil corals and stromatoporoids, then known as madrepores. It has the ring of scalloped black marble seen in the Torquay table and the typical narrow black rim with the band of *Yellow Clouded Petitor* marble inside it. Unusual stones include a central 12-fold radial egg-and-dart arrangement with chambered orthocone fossils in red matrix (noted above). One of these is analysed in Chapter 8 (Fig. 8.3) for its complex preservation history. Some of the madrepore specimens in this table are identified in the Fossils Guide (Chapter 12). Sadly, there are no catalogue records matching this table, although a search of publications around 1935 when the building was finished might yet reveal some photographic clues.

All seven of the tables figured so far share significant similarities that collectively point to a particular quarry or area and a single manufacturing style. Anchored by the known Woodley item amongst these, the *Fillongley table*, we may confidently attribute the undocumented remainder to John Woodley of Babbacombe. In fact, it cannot be discounted that the *Kensington table* is the one exhibited by John Woodley at the Great Exhibition in 1851. His exhibit was a *"circular marble table (on pedestal) inlaid with choice and rare specimens of marbles and madrepores of the different varieties found in Devon"* (Royal Commission, 1851). Awarding him a Prize Medal for his work, the judges found it *"of very great merit"* and in a brief critique noted that the table was *"of the kind called specimen tables and the forms... geometric but the execution is excellent and the selection of marbles admirable"* (Royal Commission, 1852). The black marble ogee-moulded edge of the table is inscribed with the words "DEVONSHIRE MARBLES" (Fig. 4.4), something that appears in none of the other examples, and only likely to have been added to an exhibition piece.

The final table of the Woodley type is worth noting. This is the *Gladstone table* (Fig. 4.5), formerly in the Gladstone family seat, Fasque House, Kincardineshire, not far from

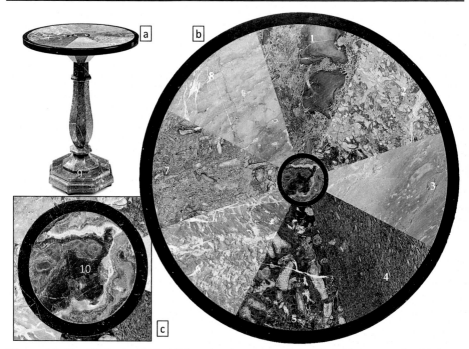

Figure 4.5. The Gladstone Table (595 mm), private collection. This table went to the Gladstone family seat in Kincardineshire in the late 1830s. a: The table with octagonal pedestal and base. b: The circular top with eight large pieces of Devonshire marble, mostly known types. c: The modest centrepiece that may have been collected by the young William Gladstone (see text).
Stones as follows: 1: Stromatoporoid (strom.) limestone, Petit Tor Breccia. 2: Coral-bearing piece with branching rugose forms. 3: Grey muddy reef rock (*Grey Petitor*). 4: Coral/strom. reef trash with *Renalcis* (a bacterium) 'shadows' (*Fossil Petitor*) (as 9). 5: *Thamnopora* corals from Bradley Woods, Newton Abbott (*Featherstone*). 6: Highly veined muddy sediment (*Pink/Yellow Petitor*). 7: part-dolomitised coral/strom. reef trash. 8: Red laminated reef mud, Petit Tor. 9: Coral/strom. reef trash with *Renalcis* shadows (*Fossil Petitor*) (as 4). 10: Typical local Pleistocene flowstone.

Balmoral in north-east Scotland. The table was dated as *c.* 1835 by Christies of London prior to auction in 2008, and the probable reason will become clear. The specimen marble pieces are unusually large, inlaid into a round black marble slab, rather than the whole surface being veneered. Comprising just eight radially arranged pieces around a circular central insert, the design is deceptively simple, but the large plaquettes will have been a challenge both to prepare and to insert with precision. The baluster-style base is made of Petit Tor 'shadow rock', identical to the stone used in other Woodley-type tables, but the historical interest of the table focuses on the relatively small and modest centrepiece which is a very plain piece of stalactite flowstone of Kents Cavern type.

The table probably arrived at Fasque as one of three, of which the author has seen two. The puzzle is why such an unnecessarily plain central insert should have been chosen (Fig. 4.5) to be set against some of the best *Petitor* and *Featherstone* panels that could be manufactured. Far better-figured pieces of flowstone are seen in the ***Fillongley table*** (Fig. 4.3) and the ***Fitzwilliam table*** (Fig. 4.2), and the incongruous Gladstone centrepiece seems understated, especially against some of the spectacular centrepieces displayed in other tables.

The key seems to lie in the few weeks the young William Gladstone, destined to become Queen Victoria's least favourite Prime Minister, spent in 1832 with his parents on a visit to Devon. The Gladstone diaries (Foot, 1968) tell us that in August that year, aged 23, the young Gladstone was fresh from graduating with a first in mathematics and classics at Oxford University. He had completed a six-month Grand Tour through Italy and was hoping to take up a career in politics through a forthcoming Parliamentary by-election at Newark on Trent. That summer, he took a five-week 'gap' in Torquay, joining his mother Lady Anne and father Sir John Gladstone, a wealthy Liverpool merchant. Characteristically, he was never idle, passing the time reading, writing, arguing, riding, visiting, sailing and sightseeing, including a visit to Kents Cavern. This had been the site of the discovery beneath cave flowstone of some controversial human artefacts and was much in the news. Having earlier seen some fossil remains from Kents Cavern at Torre Abbey, William visited the cavern on 19th September where he "*spent some hours... in digging and hammering*", later complaining that it was already much knocked about and that no good stalactites remained. More significantly, he took home some specimens of stalactite which the following day he spent time "*scrubbing and gumming*" but not, he notes, to their advantage. They were clearly not very good specimens.

William had to leave Torquay soon thereafter to attend to some election matters in Lincoln, but it seems possible that, before departing themselves, his parents had ordered this table (along with the two others) requesting that their talented son's indifferent flowstone souvenirs from Kents Cavern should be cut and placed at the centre. Why else should the ***Gladstone table*** centrepiece be so plain, unless it holds some greater significance than its mere appearance? Often the best way to display an indifferent rock specimen is to cut and polish it. Many years later, in 1889, William Gladstone was to reconnect with the Devon industry, receiving a presentation casket in onyx from the Torquay Liberal Working Men (Pateman, 1980). This was made at Grant's Marble Works—Woodley's main local rival in earlier times. It takes us full circle to know that William Gladstone's bust presently occupies a plinth of fine *Petitor* marble in the sculpture hall at Manchester Town Hall (Chapter 11, Group 11, Fig. 11.33).

4.2.2 *Some very different table tops*

By complete contrast, there are two large, rectangular Devonshire marble tables at Ugbrooke House near Chudleigh (Figs 4.6a-c). Chudleigh is one of the known earliest centres of ornamental marble manufacture (Chapter 1) and the ***Ugbrooke tables*** are thought to have been made from stones collected on the estate of the Lords Clifford of Chudleigh in the immediate vicinity. Handwritten keys (e.g. Fig. 4.6c) name and show the positions of marbles used, many of which are credible, but the stones include a specimen of Bradley Woods *Featherstone* (Fig. 4.6b) and a foreign green onyx travertine, so that these two tables, now somewhat degraded, are more complex assemblies than previously believed. They are a very traditional specimen marble design featuring stone squares of equal size in a diagonal pattern, a border of oblong pieces and divides in white Tuscan marble.

Two further rectangular Devonshire specimen marble tables are in country houses. One, a cleverly inlaid array of Devonshire stones edged with Tuscan white *Carrara*, all set into a one-piece black marble base a little over 1-m wide, is at Saltram House (Figs 4.6d-e). It is on a wooden base of later design than the slab tables noted above from Saltram and is thought to be 1850 or earlier (online, see ref. National Trust Collections). The second example is at Sherbourne House, Dorset and is a more complex design with mixed stone provenance. It has rectangular and octagonal pieces that include some white Tuscan breccia types and is edged with black and yellow *Portoro* marble from Liguria, Italy.

Equally distinct and anonymous is the **Gardner table** (Figs 4.6f-g), a circular specimen marble panel set in an ebony frame and stand, sold through Richard Gardner Antiques of Chichester. This is centred with a chessboard made in dark grey and light pink Devonshire stones surrounded by a field of Devonshire scrapwork and a margin of egg-and-dart plaquettes. Thin bands of black marble separate these fields, but the outermost black is an ebonised frame. The stones are all high quality fossil and rock types, with good representation of Petit Tor and Bradley Woods types. The small stones are a deliberate design feature rather than reflecting limited availability, so that a lot may be beach pebbles derived from Permian conglomerates and breccias in the cliffs along the stretch of Babbacombe Bay, north-east of Torquay. If so, a manufacturer in the small-stones capital Teignmouth, or even further north-east at Dawlish, where Andrew Blackler was established prior to 1865, cannot be discounted.

Methods of manufacture of these tables have been referred to several times. In order to test these, the author has collaborated with local south Devon stonemason Mark Halliday in the creation of two reproduction Devonshire specimen marble tables (Fig. 4.7), the first to be made in well over a century as far as we are aware. Mark Halliday is a direct descendant of the Grant family, the name of which has been prominent in local stone manufacture for 200 years (Chapter 3). Using stones mainly sourced from Petit Tor beach, our first table, **Halliday table 1** (Fig. 4.7e), was presented to Torquay Museum in 2012. Many of the incorporated pieces are fossils or examples of reef or near-reef limestones (see Chapter 7) identical to those used in the 19th century by Woodley, Grant and Blackler (Chapter 3). The tables were inlaid using the time-honoured mosaic technique, where thin plaquettes of rock were shaped and close fitted, but they were attached to a slate base using modern resins. The thin, circular bands of black marble were not hand cut but were prepared using modern water jet cutting techniques. The finished assembly was then machined flat and polished.

Several clear conclusions arose from the experiments including how lengthy and laborious the process was, even allowing for modern machinery. The larger table took at least 100 man-hours to complete. Back in the mid 1800s, though, this time might have been doubled or even trebled owing to the limitations of the cutting and polishing materials

Figure 4.6. (facing page) Some less usual Devonshire specimen marble tables. a: One of the 2 UgbrookTables. Ugbrook House, Chudleigh. b: Enlargement with *Featherstone* and a *Petitor* 'shadow rock' type. c: The original hand-written key to the marble types. d: The Saltram specimen marble table, Saltram House, Plympton, Plymouth. e: Enlargement of a specimen of 'shadow rock'. f: The Gardner Table - a chessboard top set in an ebonised table. g: Enlargement - stones are uniformly small and include many known fossil and rock types, some probably from beach pebbles. (*Photos f and g courtesy of Richard Gardner Antiques.*)

Selecting the stones on the beach

a

b

Preliminary layout after slicing the stones

c

Fitting shaped plaquettes to a slate back

e

Version 1: The Torquay Halliday table

d

Version 2: The Banchory Halliday table

76

then available. Today we rely on diamond and carborundum as our abrasives, set in copper alloy, fibreglass or resin, whilst only a generation ago and earlier, rock saws consisted of steel blades and the abrasive was beach sand, poured in by hand. Exmouth beach sand, angular and straight off the Dartmoor granite, was particularly good, and it could be recycled a few times. Sawing large blocks in this way went at the rate of 20–30 mm/hour. Today, it is up to 100 times faster using modern abrasives. It is one of the key reasons for the modern resurgence in the use of ornamental stone slabs, for example in kitchens. As regards scrapwork, where pieces are shaped and assembled apparently randomly, it is a lot more difficult than it looks and not random at all. Ideally, pieces should meet corner-to-corner at Y junctions and not T junctions, pieces should be four- or five-sided and not triangular, and colours need to be carefully separated, especially the greys. The advantage of scrapwork is in the name—it provides a use for smaller irregular pieces, but it actually takes longer than tiling regular radial pieces and needs a lot of careful planning.

4.3 Three important machine-turned Devonshire stone items

In the same way that the pedestal beneath a table could be made from one or more pieces of machine-turned solid stone, it was possible to produce entire decorative pieces in this way as well. Most of the smaller turned items such as pen or ink holders use anonymous black marble so that turned items in high-quality Devonshire stone are very much more unusual. Just three pieces are noted here, a pair of vases in *Petitor* marble (Fig. 4.8a) and a tazza in Bradley Woods *Featherstone* (Figs 4.8b–d) that may be the sole survivor of a pair.

The two **Torquay vases** are in the collection of Torquay Museum. A large (c. 500-mm tall) vase such as this may be outwardly simple, but it is a substantial challenge, and making two identical ones adds to, rather than reducing the technical demands. They were each manufactured in at least three separate pieces using a lathe, but large size can increase the manufacturing problems. The bigger the intended object, the greater are the difficulties of holding and stabilising the stone in a lathe, hollowing out the interior and matching the separate machined pieces so that they fit together perfectly as if made from a single block of stone. These two elegantly proportioned classical-style vases are a great rarity, especially since there are still two of them, but we can readily recognise the stone that was used (Fig. 4.8a). This is a *Petitor* variety for which the term 'shadow rock' has been introduced. Petit Tor quarry was in the ownership of the Woodleys from the early to mid 1900s and the stone commonly appears in the inlays and supporting pedestals of tables made by or attributed to them. The vases might also be from the Woodley workshops, but for two small details. They were donated to Torquay Museum by a Mrs Blackler in 1930, and they are catalogued as having been manufactured around the turn of the century. In fact the style seems much earlier than the suggested 1890–1910 date range and these are surely a lot older. The Blacklers took over Petit Tor quarry from the Woodleys with the purchase of the business in 1865. Given the name of the donor of the vases we may guess that they were a Blackler product, but the Blacklers might have purchased and cherished a few earlier Woodley items. Perhaps the vases were part of the Woodley stock that Blackler acquired with the business in 1865, retaining them as show pieces. It would be quite unfair, though, to imply that Andrew Blackler was unable to produce skilled items such as this. Some of his carved reredos work for churches is superb and the vases are well within the range of his capabilities.

Figure 4.8. Some machine-turned artwork items. a: The Torquay Vases (*c.* 500 mm) Torquay Museum specimen no. V6587. b: The *Featherstone* Tazza (275 mm). Private collection. c–e: Details of the turning and inlay workmanship in b (see text). (*Photo 4.8a courtesy of Torquay Museum.*)

The second example is a single tazza made from turned Bradley Woods *Featherstone* (Figs 4.8b–d). This is the rock that contains the fine-branching coral *Thannopora cervicornis* that came from a now overgrown and worked-out locality in the Lemon Valley, near Newton Abbott. This ***Featherstone tazza*** is another compound piece, consisting of a broad inlaid bowl (*c.* 275 mm diameter), a short pedestal and a rectangular base. This was the ultimate test of the skilled baubler (inlay worker), because the upper surface of its elegant beak-moulded rim (convex above and concave below, Figs 4.8c, d) contains 24 blocks of impeccably fitted inlay in alternately facing wedge shapes (Fig. 4.8c). This band of inlay nonetheless matches the dual curvature (radial and centric) of the beak-moulded rim with no perceptible gaps. It is breathtakingly clever. The inlay specimens in the rim are corals and stromatoporoids that also appear in the flat centre of the dish. The free use of *Featherstone* suggests Sharland, the man who found it, whilst the lack of malachite or any other foreign stone, a Grant hallmark, suggests that it is not by them. The radial design and 3D cubes are known Woodley devices and the stones used are very similar to those in known Woodley products. The impeccable execution of this item suggests that it was always intended as an artwork piece of the highest quality, of which Woodley was certainly capable.

4.4 The Royal Goldfinch Platter

This is a 360-mm diameter black marble plate with a moulded rim (Fig. 4.9). It bears a radial pattern of specimen marbles, at the centre of which is the image of a goldfinch. On the back is a Buckingham Palace label, and lightly etched into the polished surface is "FROM JOHN WOODLEY'S Marble Works *ST MARYCHURCH* TORQUAY". The platter was donated to the Museum by a Twickenham man in 1971, and might be one of the several items sent by John Woodley around 1852 to Queen Victoria at Osborne House on the Isle of Wight. Woodley had been visited by the Prince Consort in July of that year and was invited to submit a few small items for the Queen's selection (Chapters 1 and 2). From an attached label it is clear that the platter had been housed at some stage at Buckingham Palace, and an implicit connection to Albert is through the Goldfinch, his favourite bird, of which he had his own captive pet. If this tray was part of the Osborne House consignment then the date of 1866 is problematic. By this time the St Marychurch Works had held the Royal Warrant for more than 10 years as the 'Royal Marble Works', and ownership had finally passed to Andrew Blackler. The date may mark the year the item was catalogued, perhaps on transfer from Osborne House to Buckingham Palace.

This tray has Woodley's radial pattern and the stones are all local, but those in the central image are by no means exclusively Devonshire. The extensive brown/orange stone field behind the bird is made of several pieces of the unnamed oolitic limestone (made of many tiny spheres) from Carboniferous rocks in the Avon Gorge, Bristol, here termed *Avon Oolite* (noted above). This stone was used by Woodley in his *Fillongley table* of 1844 (see above), whilst the moss-covered branch is in green *Connemara marble*, rare in other Devonshire products, but common enough alongside Devonshire marbles in building interiors. The *pietra dura* goldfinch is vivid, somewhat stiff and stylised, but nonetheless accurate. Indeed, we can tell that it is a female—it all has to do with whether the red coloration stops in front of the eye or just behind it! At least some of the stones making up the bird itself are Devonshire, including the bright red in the bird's head and probably also its breast. The Woodley Platter is the only 'signed' Woodley item encountered in this study.

4.5 Standard inlaid ornaments

These are the most numerous items, sought after by the trinket-hungry visitors to the south Devon coast, and their diversity has already been noted. They are the smaller ornamental items, commonly utility objects such as thermometers and desk ware, but there are three distinct styles. One has geometric or abstract (scrapwork) mosaic or inlay designs using a range of local marbles, similar to some of the tables, another uses only green malachite in geometric patterns and a third extends into foliar and floral images using green malachite and white shell or bone. They are all normally bedded in black marble.

4.5.1 *Devonshire marble mosaics and scrapwork*

Six items are described here, a desk tray, a finger-ring holder, an ink stand, an obelisk, a thermometer stand and a paperweight. The first two are accompanied by identifications of the stones used in order to set a baseline for comparisons.

The **Gothic desk tray** (Fig. 4.10) is a *c.* 305-mm-wide artefact in flamboyant 'Batman' style. It has a black marble base with bun feet and a 'deck' of diverse yellow, pink, red, grey and white stones, all either Devonshire or non-British. Plaquettes are fitted in scrapwork style, and their edges are exposed on the moulded edges of the tray. Thickness shows clearly and each plaquette is 2 mm (1/16th of an inch) deep. The tiled deck is pierced by an elongated, dished recess to take pens and a circular recess, flat bottomed, to take an inkwell (glass with brass lid, Fig. 4.20). The stones are identified in Fig. 4.10 and a general identification guide to such stones is given in Chapter 13 (Volume 2). The yellow stones are problematic, including an even-textured lemon yellow likely to be Italian and identified as such in Fig. 4.10. The maker is not known, but the range of stones, which are at least mostly Devonshire, is quite sufficient to identify the general provenance.

The *finger-ring holder* (Fig. 4.11) is much smaller (95-mm wide) and the stones are inlaid within a black marble rim and adopt the double curvature of this—both centric and radial. The stones are very precisely chosen for their colour—white, grey, yellow, orange

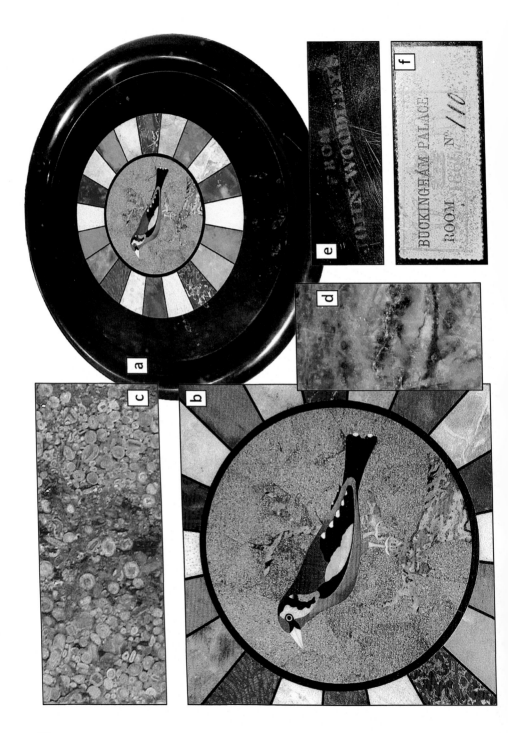

80

Figure 4.9. (facing page) The John Woodley Royal Goldfinch Platter (360 mm). Torquay Museum specimen no. V5047. a: The radial design. b: The goldfinch on a *Connemara* branch and a background of '*Avon Oolite*' - not a Devonshire stone. c–d: Details of *Connemara* and *Oolite*. e-f: Etched inscription and label on the rear (see text). (*Photos e-f courtesy of Clare Jones.*)

and red. Their identities are shown in Fig. 4.11 and they are very much the same as in the Desk Tray (above), but lacking malachite. The acorn head of the shaft is a small turned piece of green *Lizard Serpentine*. This ring holder may be a survivor from a fuller set of dressing table items. The maker is not known but the exclusive range of stones identifies the piece as Devonshire.

A *Torquay scrapwork paperweight* (Fig. 4.12a) is 106-mm wide and has a tiled deck of local and imported stones, taken to the edge, on a backing of black marble. The interlopers are green malachite and a two white pieces that could be Tuscan marble or *Strombus* shell. The paperweight has a flat base with no feet.

A *Torquay inkstand* (*c*.150-mm wide, Figs 4.12b, c) shows similar inlaid construction to the ring holder but on a larger scale. The base is a turned and elaborately moulded piece of black marble with bun feet, and the inlaid ring of scrapwork around the margin has double curvature once again. It is executed in a similar range of stones to the desk tray (Fig. 4.10) and all except the malachite were sourced in Devon. The inkwell is in moulded glass and, unusually, its lid is embellished by further pieces of scrapwork rather than the more usual brass. The manufacturer is not known, but there is a likelihood that all these first three items were made by Harry Grant & Co. at their St Marychurch works at Watcombe.

A *Torquay obelisk* more than 700-mm tall was repaired at the works of Grant & Co., Newton Abbott in 2014 (Figs 4.12d, e). It has a plinth in black marble, a 'dado' and needle in inlaid black marble, and the inlay stones are in geometric and scrapwork patterns. Amongst the exclusively Devonshire stones there are several *Petitor* varieties and some

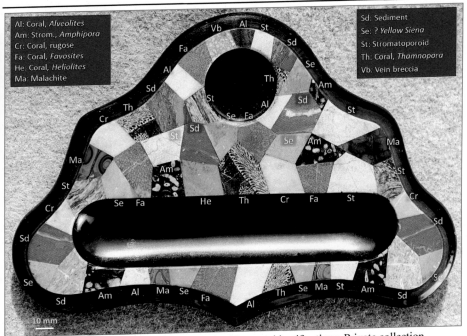

Figure 4.10. The Gothic Desk Tray (305 mm) with stone identifications. Private collection.

81

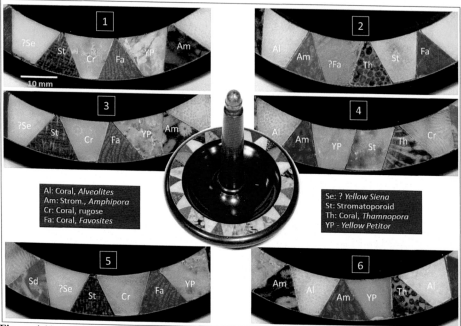

Figure 4.11. A Devonshire ring holder (95 mm) with stone identifications. Private collection.

Al: Coral, *Alveolites*
Am: Strom., *Amphipora*
Cr: Coral, rugose
Fa: Coral, *Favosites*

Se: ? *Yellow Siena*
St: Stromatoporoid
Th: Coral, *Thamnopora*
YP - *Yellow Petitor*

Figure 4.12. Three Devonshire scrapwork items. a: Torquay paperweight (106 mm). Torquay Museum specimen no. V5046. b: a Torquay inkstand (*c.* 150 mm). Torquay Museum. c: Enlargement of stones used in b. d: A Torquay obelisk (*c.* 700 mm), Private collection. e: Enlargement of stones used in d. (*Photos a and b courtesy of Clare Jones and Torquay Museum.*)

82

Figure 4.13. Devonshire boxes and thermometer stands. a: An *Ashburton* cigar box. Private collection. b-c: Specimen stone thermometer stands, (165 mm and 210 mm respectively). Torquay Museum, specimen nos. V5042 and V6586. d: Trinket box (100 mm) in *Featherstone*. Private collection. (*Photos a and c, courtesy of Clare Jones. Photo b courtesy of Torquay Museum.*)

pieces of Bradley Woods *Featherstone*. The pointed top is also *Featherstone*. Obelisks became popular stone items in the mid to late 1800s after the presentation and eventual transport to Britain of 'Cleopatra's Needle', a genuine hieroglyph-bearing Egyptian classical monument made in red granite. After a disastrous journey to London by sea in 1878, when several crew lost their lives and the ship itself was abandoned and nearly lost, the monument was finally erected on London's Victoria Embankment. The fame that the story brought to this mysterious antiquity ensured that obelisks became a common device amongst Derbyshire stone items but this is the only Devonshire example so far recorded.

The Bradford mosaic thermometer stand (Fig. 4.13c) consists of a base and upstand of black marble, both faced with plaquettes of Devonshire fossils and reef rocks, together with green malachite and an uncertain yellow stone. The plaquette shapes are simple, orthogonal or radial, and the upstand is tiled to the edge so that the thickness of the plaquettes is visible. The item is marked 'BRADFORD BRˢ TORQUAY', of whom there may have been three (Kelly, 1856). The best known is Edwin Greenslade Bradford, "*Marble Mason, Goldsmith and Jeweller*" who was at 8, The Strand in the 1850s, moving to no. 9 in the 1860s. There was also a James Bradford at 7, Victoria Parade in 1856, and a further 'Bradford Brother' is listed at 4, Victoria Parade (Kelly, 1856). The *Bradford mosaic thermometer stand* may have been manufactured by the only known marble mason amongst these, Edwin Bradford, but we also know that he bought in ready-manufactured items from Harry Grant & Sons at nearby St Marychurch. Alongside this thermometer stand is a further example (Fig. 4.13b) tiled with thicker Devonshire pieces, given a bevel at the edges, separated by thin strips of black stone. The base has large rectangular feet that may be exclusive to Devonshire designs.

83

4.5.2 *Devonshire malachite work*

Malachite work, using stone imported from the Siberian Urals (Grant, 1922; Royal Commission, 1852), was one of the specialities of the firm of Harry Grant. Malachite products commonly lack any local stones and the black marble and malachite five-piece ***Bradford desk set*** (Fig. 4.14) is an example. Indeed, were it not for the inscription on the thermometer, we would overlook this set as Devon altogether. The engraved inscription on a disk of ivory, secured by a corded gold circlip, reads "EDWIN BRADFORD STRAND TORQUAY" (Fig. 4.14g). He was an important wholesale customer of the Grants (Chapter 3) and inlaid stone 'blanks' are likely to have been supplied by them which Bradford finished with gold, ivory, glass and brass embellishments, including the instruments. The items (Figs 4.14a–e) are a set of scales (the brass mechanism of which is by S Mordan & Co., London), a spill vase, a pen dish, a thermometer plate (fitted with a challenging semicircular glass tube) and an inkstand with a plain glass inkwell with brass lid. The dramatic keys design is executed in carefully matched Russian malachite and the motif changes to an orthogonal scroll on the scales, which may have been added separately. The thermometer, the mercury tube of which has been replaced at some time, is graduated in both Fahrenheit and Réaumur (Fig. 4.14f). Réaumur was widespread in Europe until the mid 19th century, and was based on a 0°–80° scale proportional to the expansion of alcohol between the freezing and boiling points of water (80° represented 8% expansion at the boiling point of water). No desk of a well-appointed and knowledgeable gentleman should have been without a desk set like this!

4.5.3 *Devonshire malachite* **pietra dura** *inlay*

Two pieces of rare known Devonshire foliar/floral inlay are noted here (Fig. 4.15). As

Figure 4.14. The Edwin Bradford Desk set (item d is 165 mm). All items are black marble with malachite inlay. There is no Devonshire stone here. Private collection. a: Letter balance. b: Spill holder. c: Pen dish. d: Thermometer plate. e: Inkwell holder. f-g: Inscription details on the thermometer dial.

with the desk set above the stones tell us nothing about provenance and without the vendor's names engraved on their ivory plates we might never attribute them to Devon. In fact one of these, the upright stand, was actually purchased in Derbyshire where many similar objects were made. Once again they are black marble, now inlaid with flower designs; their petals in white bone or ivory (not shell) and their foliage in malachite.

The ***Blackler floral thermometer and compass plate*** is a 145-mm diameter flat thermometer stand featuring immediately recognisable white Jasmine flowers, symbols of amicability, sensuality and attachment (Figs 4.15a, b). It is engraved 'Blackler Dawlish' which not only pins down manufacture to south Devon, but narrowly constrains the date of manufacture. Andrew Blackler had moved to Dawlish by the time of the 1851 census and he left there for St Marychurch in 1865 when he took over the Royal Marble Works. The Blackler factory was substantial, with the capacity to shape and finish polished marble columns, and it was probably located behind his retail premises at 19, Strand, Dawlish where he is known between 1851 and 1856. This provides an unusually good date constraint for this item. The stand now requires a properly calibrated replacement for its lost semi-circular mercury thermometer, something that is hard to get made in the 21st century. The ivory thermometer scale once again shows both the Fahrenheit and Réaumur scales.

The second floral item is the ***Bradford floral thermometer stand*** (Figs 4.15c, d). This has representations of white Jasmine on the upright and Lily of the Valley (symbol of happiness, purity, sweetness) on the base. The address is given as 8, Strand, Torquay where Edwin Bradford was located between 1851 and 1861 according to census data. This is an elegant item, with an ogee-moulded edge to the upright stand and a pyramidal form to the base, with squat bun feet. It is likely to have been manufactured at the Grant's factory at

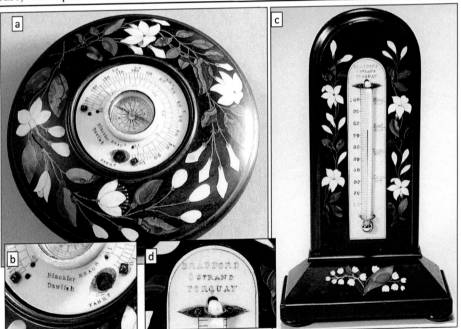

Figure 4.15. Two floral inlay items from Devonshire. The leaves are malachite, the petals are ivory or bone and the base is black marble. There is no Devonshire stone here. a: A Blackler thermometer and compass plate (*c.* 150 mm). Torquay Museum specimen no. V5063. b: A Bradford thermometer stand (195 mm). Private collection. (*Photo 4.15a, courtesy of Torquay Museum.*)

Watcombe. The use of malachite for the leaves in both the Blackler and Bradford thermometers is discussed in the section below on distinguishing between Devonshire and Derbyshire items.

4.6 Devonshire marble boxes

Returning to Fig. 4.13, two Devonshire marble boxes are illustrated. The first (Fig. 4.13a) is a *Cigarette box* in *Ashburton* marble with a brass-hinged lid. The second is a small *Trinket box* (Fig. 4.13d) in Bradley Woods *Featherstone*. Other examples of this latter design are known, made with cut pieces that might otherwise have served as inlay plaquettes. A similar one is figured in Price (2007, p.8).

4.7 A Devonshire marble landscape piece

The *Babbacombe* pietra dura *landscape* (Fig. 4.16) is a near-complete mystery. It was donated to Torquay Museum by Mrs Blackler in 1930 along with the two vases noted above. The image is a 'hardstone picture' in typical Florentine style, i.e. done entirely in stone, using expert artistic workmanship. Stones were selected by tone and content to portray colour, light, shadow, depth and surface texture. The sun shines from the south-west, lighting the trees on the south side of Babbacombe Glen, but not the north. The back of the beach is also in shadow, whilst sunlight plays over the rocks on the headland. Whitewashed and stone buildings glow as if in an Italian scene. There are light blue tints in the

Figure 4.16. The Babbacombe *pietra dura* landscape. Torquay Museum specimen no. V6587. a: The image in its black marble frame (240 x 180 mm). b: The *pietra dura* image. Many of the stone types used could have been found on the beach. Only the green *Connemara* marble used for the woodland is imported.

sky and sea, a rare colour in stone and achieved by staining. The small, shaped stones used for the trees might be Devonshire *Kitley* but are more likely to be green *Connemara* whilst the headland rocks are fossil-bearing *Petitor* types. The beach with its cuspate forms is done using a single piece of fine white fossil coral (*Alveolites*) with growth bands and the rocks in the foreground correspond to stone types of various identities that can be found on the same beach today, the purple ones resembling *Lizard Serpentine*.

We know nothing of the date of manufacture of this familiar scene or the artist. The image shows relatively advanced building development above Babbacombe Beach but not the pier, built by public subscription in 1889 (Pateman, 1991). The piece might date from *c.* 1860 but a more detailed analysis of the buildings would pin it down further. This is a unique item of Devonshire manufacture of which there is no other known example.

4.8 Devonshire marble jewellery

Between the 1850s and 1870s Edwin Bradford's Shop on Strand, Torquay had a large staff of jewellers working on malachite designs for mounting in gold (Grant, 1922). In the late 19th century the nearby Grant's shop in Torquay, which specialised in malachite products, was selling "*stone jewellery for wearing-apparel mounted in silver and gold*". Malachite was thus an important component in Devon jewellery and the only signifi-cant non-Devonshire stone used, but it is not characteristic of Devonshire jewellery. It is the local stones that give away this beautiful jewellery, often featuring corals and stony

Figure 4.17. Devonshire marble brooches. Typical rectangular, oval and round forms are set in white metal, mostly with complex assemblies of several coloured stones. White pieces are coral, either fine textured *Alveolites* or coarser *?Mariastrum*. Dark pieces are either cellular-looking coral *Thamnopora*, or rounded stems of the branching stromatoporoid *Amphipora*. Reds include coral *Favosites*; yellows are possibly *Yellow Petitor* marble and green is Russian malachite. Brooches are from the Nick Crawford collection, with grateful thanks to Heather Crawford.

sponges ('madrepores'). From business directories of the time, we know that a number of madrepore workers operated in Torquay, Teignmouth and elsewhere in the mid 1800s and there was also a good trade in polished specimens for fossil collectors (Chapter 3). The sources of specimens for these jewellery and fossil items were normally beach pebbles. Brooches are the commonest form, bracelets are known, but necklaces and pendants have yet to be recorded.

Devonshire brooch designs (e.g. Fig. 4.17) can be square, round or oval, up to 50 mm across, and finished in a domal cabochon or a hollow-centred doughnut. There can be a single stone or many, flush fitted and worked as if a single stone. Multiple stone arrangements are geometrical and symmetrical, with radial patterns, chequerboards or diamond arrays, stones commonly separated by black bars. Known bracelets comprise single stones set in silver and chained together or, more rarely, the stone itself is riveted and the individual pieces are chained together (Fig. 4.18).

Devonshire jewellery is briefly described in Jones (2012). Nick Crawford was a notable collector before his untimely death in 2015 and it is some of his brooches that are shown here (Fig. 4.17). Commonly used stones are named in Fig. 4.18 (see also Chapter 13).

4.9 Distinguishing Devonshire and Derbyshire products

4.9.1 *The two industries*

The ornamental products of the Devonshire and Derbyshire industries, the table tops, vases and small items appealed to the same market and were in direct competition. It was inevitable that there would be some design overlap, particularly amongst the utility objects such as thermometer stands and inkwell holders where convergence was simply a response to fashion. The backgrounds of the two industries were very different, though, as are many of their raw materials.

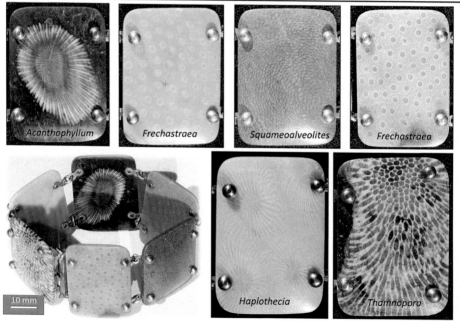

Figure 4.18. A Devonshire marble bracelet. The stones all comprise fossils (identified) and are held in the assembly using rivets. The metal is pinchbeck, an alloy of copper and zinc (brass).

The Devonshire small-items industry was a natural development of an already success-ful architecture-orientated ornamental marble industry dating from the 18th century. It was the diversity in colour and texture of the stones themselves that created the opportunity for a parallel industry specialising in the smaller items. Clearly land and quarry ownership were major constraints but between Plymouth in the west and Torquay in the east, and as far north as Ashburton and Chudleigh (Fig. 2.1), there was plenty of opportunity to find and exploit a suitable and presentable stone, but the beaches in particular, noted above, extended the potential sources of good stones as far north as Teignmouth (Fig. 2.1).

The Derbyshire story was very different. The abundant mineral veins within the lime-stone outcrop area held a diversity of appealing stone types with a long history of exploita-tion, not least amongst which was *Blue John*, the unique semi-precious blue fluorite mined in the vicinity of Castleton. The host rocks themselves were less attractive. Local Carbon-iferous limestone is much less varied and more flawed than its lightly metamorphosed De-vonian equivalent, so that architectural demand was limited, but paradoxically it was this very drabness that became a secret for success. The Derbyshire industry was first centred within the bounds of the Chatsworth estate, the family seat of the Dukes of Devonshire. We have already noted their minimal connections to the eponymous County of Devon, but the 6th Duke had a personal passion both for minerals and ornamental stone and he quickly became aware that the well-known Italian stone inlay industry, mostly based in Florence, used a background stone of plain black marble of a type he had in abundance on his own estate back at Chatsworth.

Around the 1830s the 6th Duke started to encourage local Derbyshire manufacture of Florentine-style stone inlay work, establishing a water-powered factory on the River Wye at Ashford, near Bakewell (Tomlinson, 1996). Italian Florentine inlay items were already a familiar 'must have' souvenir for those wealthy enough to embark on the European 'Grand Tour' (e.g. William Gladstone, noted above) and, after some Royal encouragement for the genre, the Duke's sponsorship of Derbyshire-produced Florentine inlay (e.g. Figs 4.19b, c) became a great success, establishing a 'standard' to which the rest of British stone manufacture would aspire. Manufacturing spread across Derbyshire and elsewhere and thousands of inlay items were produced, from spectacular tables to simple paper-weights. Associated with these was always the manufacture of an even greater volume of the less-demanding and therefore less-expensive objects using a range of stones inlaid in geometric or abstract patterns (Figs 4.19–4.21). These required less time and skill and fell more within the reach of the then 'ordinary' pocket.

There was a problem though, that whilst black marble could be mined in abundance in Derbyshire, suitable inlay materials were not as common. All of the hallmark inlay materi-als for Florentine work had to be imported and even local specimen stone types for inlays were restricted in their colour palette. It was quite the reverse in Devonshire. There was no suitable black marble for the backing pieces, but coloured inlay stones were there in abundance, including red, yellow, orange, green, grey, black and white, as we have already established. The stones around the two centres were geologically, tonally and texturally very different and the obvious solution was to do a few exchanges. When we examine the artefacts themselves, it is obvious that, one way or another, this is exactly what happened, but an open trade between the two centres is never hinted at or acknowledged.

4.9.2 *Distinguishing the tables*

At their extremes, the tables of the two industries are very different. Both typically use a base of black marble, but Florentine-style floral inlay work in *tables* (e.g. Figs 4.19c, d) is probably exclusive to Derbyshire. Inlaid *Ashford Black* marble table tops from Derbyshire are nearly always a single slab, generously endowed with a wide border outside the inlay design (Figs 4.19a–d). The inlay is set directly into the black stone, single pieces or small

Figure 4.19. (facing page) Three Derbyshire table tops for comparison. a: A rectangular specimen table by Joseph Hall Spar and Marble Works, Derby, *c.* 1840. Sedgwick Museum, Cambridge. Unusually, this contains numerous stones from the Bristol area, including *Cotham* marble and '*Avon Oolite*' but it includes good examples of Derbyshire regulars. It could have been made to order or to suit a South West market, but definite Devonshire stones are few. b: This is a typical Florentine floral design table with an engraved plate beneath stating: "MANUFACTURED BY T. WOODRUFF INLAYER TO THE QUEEN". Private collection. c: Detail of inlay in b. d: A mineral specimen table top from Derbyshire, the pieces random-fitted with spaces filled by resin incorporating crushed galena. e: Detail of some specimen pieces including clear calcite, brown barite, white/red banded barite, grey fossil coral and *Rosewood* marble.

assemblies being perfectly fitted into carefully excavated sockets. Detail was superbly executed (Fig. 4.19c) even down to texture and shading that uses the minor natural variations in the inlay materials themselves. This is true *pietra dura*, sometimes rivalling the best Florentine work of the time.

Derbyshire also produced round and rectangular specimen marble tables which had random-fitted or geometric designs and no Florentine work (Figs 4.19a, d). These were primarily intended as displays of rock, fossil or mineral specimens rather than artwork. The commonest have simple arrays of equal-sized rectangular pieces in diagonal or orthogonal patterns (Fig. 4.19a). Many northern country houses open to the public have one or two of these. Chatsworth has several. Nonetheless, this style was produced by both industries, and probably by others as well, so that they are best differentiated through the stones they use.

Characteristic Derbyshire stones are shown in Chapter 13 and include translucent white banded calcite (Fig. 13.9a), vivid *Blue John* (Fig. 13.8d), or opaque brown-banded *Rosewood* marble (Fig. 13.8b). Other mineral types such *Oakstone*, a brown, growth-banded barite (Fig. 13.9b), and silvery galena were also used. Local coral is common in Derbyshire items, characteristically with small, round, clean white outlines in a plain uniform grey or black matrix (Figs 13.7b–d).

The bright reds, oranges, pinks and yellows associated with corals and other stones from Devon are unusual in Derbyshire, and Derbyshire workers used the more expensive local mineral specimens noted above as well as foreign semi-precious stones such as green malachite, blue lapis lazuli, and red carnelian or agate. They even put blue or red coloured glass into floral inlays to brighten things up. When a red stone was at last found in Derbyshire, named *Duke's Red*, (Fig. 13.8a) it was hoarded at Chatsworth House and only released in controlled quantities. It is still there in the basement today, the bottom having fallen out of its market!

Derbyshire tables commonly show:

* Circular, rectangular or polygonal black marble
* Broad black marble borders
* Florentine inlay, geometric inlay and/or scrapwork inlay
* Stones typically occupying recesses in the black marble base
* Mixed stones provenance from Derbyshire, rest of UK or elsewhere, including:
  * hallmark local *Blue John*, *Rosewood marble*, *Oakstone* barite, Monsal Dale corals, *Duke's Red* or crinoidal stone (see Chapter 13 for these)
  * occasional Devonshire stones
  * common non-British stones include white *Tuscan*, yellow *Siena*, green malachite, green *Connemara*, variegated *Portoro* and Belgian red/pink/grey limestones (mostly illustrated in Chapter 13).

Typical Devonshire tables also employed black marble but they show a much less generous border and the base beneath the visible stone is sometimes not marble at all, but black slate. This used up much less black marble and added strength. No floral inlay designs have yet been recognised and specimen stones are commonly tiled onto a marble or slate base rather than being set into it.

Devonshire tables commonly show:

- Circular, rectangular or polygonal black marble and/or black slate backing stones
- Narrow black marble borders
- Geometric and/or scrapwork patterns only. Florentine styles not known.
  - Radial arrangement with centrepiece common
  - Simple orthogonal and diagonal arrays probably also common
- Stones typically tiled onto the surface
- Thin plain or scalloped strings of black marble separating different tiers of stone
- Exclusively Devonshire types, with:
  - bright colours; white, grey, orange, red, pink and black (see Chapter 13 for general types)
  - strong textural variation
  - a wide range of Devonian fossils (see Chapter 12 for fossil types)
  - perhaps a few non-British stones
  - never any Derbyshire stones

The more economical use of black marble in Devonshire items (e.g. slate backs and narrow borders) must reflect restricted availability. It raises the question of why Devon manufacturers needed to bother with black marble at all as they could have used white *Tuscan* marble, as seen bordering and backing contemporary non-British specimen marble tables (e.g. Fig. 11.17). One answer is that black stone looks better, and they followed the popular Derbyshire and Florentine style. There were increasing numbers of Florentine items coming into England as 'Grand Tour' trophies so that the discerning customer might have been attracted to something that looked a bit like one. An alternative connection is that the choice of black was a deliberate attempt to appeal to the 'political correctness' of the time associated with Queen Victoria's preferences and her lengthy mourning.

4.9.3 *Distinguishing the smaller ornamental items*

It is amongst the smaller items that there is the greatest convergence between the two industries and distinction can be tricky. Both industries produced small items with Florentine-style floral inlay or with geometric or scrapwork designs using specimen stones. Even where there are specimen stones distinction can be difficult, not because the stones are hard to recognise, but because some items have a mix of Devonshire and Derbyshire stones. It is best to start with some specific artefacts and thereby reveal some provisional rules to aid distinction.

a) *Distinguishing basic geometric or scrapwork designs*

There seem to be two ways of distinguishing these, first through their design, and second through their stone varieties, but neither is straightforward.

Devonshire manufacturers were unafraid of revealing their tiled rather than inlaid style where they deliberately left exposed edges showing the full thickness of the tiles (e.g. Figs 4.12a; 4.13 b, c; 4.20a). Derbyshire manufacturers were much more coy about this, preferring that stone assemblies should occupy recesses (Fig. 4.20c) and be framed by black marble, but this is by no means a universal distinction and one fine Devonshire item reveals a superbly executed framed style (Figs 4.12d, e).

Figure 4.20. Distinguishing smaller items from Devonshire and Derbyshire. a: The Gothic desk tray (Fig. 4.10) - definite Devonshire. b: The ring holder (Fig. 4.11) – definite Devonshire. c: A Thomas Woodruff (Buxton) thermometer stand (245 mm) – definite Derbyshire. d: A test-piece IN/OUT paperweight of unknown provenance.

More secure is a distinction using the inlay stones themselves, but in an unexpected way. The figured Devonshire small items helpfully show almost exclusive use of Devonshire stones (Figs 4.10–12). In Fig. 4.20 a, b the two analysed Devonshire examples (Figs 4.10–11) are set beside a known Derbyshire item (Fig. 4.20c) and one with unknown provenance (Fig. 4.20d). It is the Derbyshire items that break a potentially simple rule. Figure 4.20c is a Derbyshire *Ashford Black Marble* thermometer stand sold by Thomas Woodruff of Buxton, Derbyshire with 47 pieces of scrapwork, all but one identified in Fig. 4.21. Remarkably, only eight are Derbyshire stones, whilst a surprising 25 are from Devonshire. The Derbyshire stones include *Duke's Red, Rosewood* marble, some white crystalline travertine and several pieces of Carboniferous coral (Fig. 4.21). A further 13 stones are from neither Derbyshire nor Devonshire, including Russian malachite, Italian white marble, an uncertain onyx and some pieces of Cornish serpentine. Of the Devonshire stones, 17 are obvious pieces of Devonian coral or stromatoporoid, including two that are the iconic Bradley Woods *Featherstone*, and the remainder are pieces of hematite-stained Devonshire limestone. Only 17% of the stones in this signed Derbyshire item have a local Derbyshire provenance whilst 53% are from Devonshire. Such a small proportion of Derbyshire stones in a pedigree Derbyshire piece is unexpected.

Figure 4.21. (following page) Analysis of the stones in the Woodruff thermometer stand (Fig. 4.20c). Stone inserts are numbered serially. Figure numbers in brackets relate to Volume 2, Chapters 12 and 13 that offer comparable stones but not always the same colour. Blue: Derbyshire stones. Pink: Devonshire stones. Grey: other British and non-British materials. Note that arrows from labels at the sides visibly pass behind inner labels. Just 8 of the 47 stones are from Derbyshire in this known Derbyshire item.

A Derbyshire Thermometer Stand

1. Malachite (13.11b)
2. Devon coral (13.1a)
3. Derbs. white Calcite (13.9a)
4. Derbs. *Duke's Red* (13.8a)
5. Devon coral (e.g. 13.1c)
6. Devon coral (e.g. 13.1b)
7. Uncertain ?non-British
8. Green Onyx
9. Devon stromatoporoid (c.f.13.12d)
10. Devon Coral (13.1a)
11. Devon coral (13.1b)
12. Devon sediment (13.3a)
13. Devon coral (13.1b)
14. Malachite (13.11b)
15. *Lizard serpentine* (13.6b)
16. Devon strom. (c.f. 13.2d)
17. Derbs Coral (e.g. 13.7.b)
18. Marine shell (13.9c)
19. Devon sediment (13.3a)
20. ?Devon *Yellow Petitor* (13.3c)
21. *Lizard serpentine* (13.6c)
22. Uncertain compound coral
23. Devon sediment (c.f. 13.3b)
24. Derbs Coral (e.g. 13.7b)
25. Green Onyx
26. Derbs. *Duke's Red* (13.8a)
27. Devon sediment (13.3b)
28. Marine shell (13.9c)
29. Devon *Yellow Petitor* (13.3c)
30. Devon coral (13.1d)
31. Devon coral (13.1b)
32. Devon coral (e.g. 13.2b)
33. Derbs. *Duke's Red* (13.8a)
34. Devon coral (c.f. 12.14c)
35. Devon sediment (c.f. 13.3b)
36. Devon Coral (13.1a)
37. Malachite (13. 11b)
38. Devon Coral (13.1b)
39. Derbs. (13.8b) *Rosewood marble*
40. Derbs. *Duke's Red* (13.8a)
41. Tuscan marble (13.11c)
42. Devon coral (13.1d)
43. Devon sediment (13.3b)
44. Malachite (13. 11b)
45. Italian *Siena* (13.11a)
46. Devon coral (e.g. 13.2b)
47. Devon coral (13.1b)

6. Serial number. (13.1b) comparable Fig.

Sourced elsewhere

Sourced in Devonshire

Sourced in Derbyshire

10 mm

1. ? *Yellow Siena* (13.11a)

4. Devon sediment (e.g. 13.3b)

1. ? *Yellow Siena* (13.11a)

2. Devon sediment (13.3a)

2. Devon sediment (13.3a)

2. Devon sediment (13.3a)

10. White marble (cf. 13.11c)

18. Likely *Yellow Petitor* (13.3c)

7. Devon coral (13.1bii)

10. White marble (cf. 13.11c)

1. ? *Yellow Siena* (13.11a)

5. Derbs. (13.8a) *Rosewood marble*

11. Green Onyx

12. Derbs. White Calcite (13.8c)

3. Malachite (13. 11b)

13. Devon coral, (small in 13.1d)

14. Devon coral (12.10a)

15. Probable serpentine

12. Derbs. barite (13.9b)

17. Devon Coral (13.1c)

9. Derbs. Coral (e.g.13.9a)

8. *Lapis Lazuli, Afghanistan*

10. White marble (cf. 13.11c)

12. Derbs. barite (13.9b)

16. Unknown sediment (13.10a)

2. Devon sediment (veined) (13.3a)

13. Devon coral (13.1d)

12. Derbs. White Calcite (13.8c)

7. Devon coral (13.1bii)

6. Derbs. *Blue John* (13.8d)

5. Derbs. (13.8a) *Rosewood marble*

22. Devon coral (13.1d)

2. Devon sediment (13.3a)

9. Derbs. Coral (e.g.13.9a)

5/13. Devon coral (e.g. 13.1d)

2. Devon sediment (13.3a)

2. Devon sediment (13.3a)

3. Malachite (13.11b)

13. Devon coral (13.1d)

19. Devon coral (13.1b)

2. Devon sediment (13.3a/b)

12. Derbs. barite (13.9b)

14. Devon coral (12.10a)

11. Green Onyx

Figure 4.22. (previous page) The poll of stones in the IN/OUT paperweight with unknown provenance. Stone inserts in this figure are numbered according to broad type, of which 19 are distinguished. Some arrow links between labels and respective stones pass visibly behind other labels. Blue: Derbyshire stones. Pink: Devonshire stones. Grey: Other British and non-British stones. There are several iconic Devonshire rock types yet this is almost certainly a Derbyshire item, with some signature Derbyshire stones.

In the case of the office paperweight of unknown provenance (Fig. 4.20d, analysed in Fig. 4.22) there are 43 pieces of inlay. The statistics are Devonshire 20, Derbyshire 10 and other 13. That comes to 23% from Derbyshire and 46% from Devonshire.

It is not that customers would necessarily have been misled, or even have been any the wiser had the stone varieties been pointed out to them. No one was being cheated because these were fascinating objects made of mysterious stones from somewhere out in the wild, and doubtless the important local varieties were all that mattered. Nonetheless these eclectic assemblies illustrate how we can make no assumptions over provenance no matter how accurate the stone identifications.

A likely explanation for dominance of Devonshire stone types in the definite Derbyshire object (Fig. 4.21) is that their greater diversity of colour and texture simply made products more attractive, but there was probably something else. Conveniently workable pebbles of corals, stromatoporoids and coloured sediment were being obtained in large quantities from Devon beaches by 'professional' pebble collectors and we know that Alfred Sclater, for one, readily dispatched material on order (Chapter 3). Perhaps it was just quicker and easier to order from Devon rather than go through the uncertainty of sending collectors to hammer outcrop or search quarries in the Derbyshire Dales.

Could we conclude that the Derbyshire manufacturers never intended their pieces to be made of exclusively local stone, and were content to get much of their material from wherever it was expedient? A clear rule emerges, which is that if specimen stones have mixed provenance then the item is likely to be from Derbyshire, whilst if the stones are nearly all Devonian types, perhaps with a bit of malachite included, then Devonshire is where the item is from. On that basis the IN/OUT paperweight is clearly a Derbyshire piece.

b) *Distinguishing Floral inlay items*

There may be no Devonshire floral tables, but there is a clear record of smaller items with Florentine inlay coming from Devonshire. Local St Marychurch historian Edna White (Pateman, 1980) describes items made by Joseph Grant (Chapter 3) as including "*black marble inlaid with floral designs*". This might apply to items manufactured at any time between 1836, when the business was first established, and the 1850s when Joseph Grant retired. William Henry Grant (Grant, 1922 and Chapter 3) described goods in their Torquay shop, established in 1880, as including "*marbles inlaid with floral mosaics*". The dates suggest that floral inlay items were made in Devonshire over a considerable part of the 19th century. Examples of such products are figured above (Fig. 4.15) and the Bradford item (Fig. 4.15c) is likely to have been wholesaled to him by Grant's. Since the provenance of floral inlay items cannot be determined using the stones, none of which were local, we can only be certain where a manufacturer has inscribed a name, and these two examples (Fig. 4.15) are the only ones known so far.

By studying the detail, however, we may begin to pick up some differences between northern and southern provenance. For example, both of the Devonshire items (Fig. 4.15) seem to use ivory or bone for white petals, rather than the much purer white and more stable *Strombus* (queen conch) shell typical of Derbyshire items (Chapter 13, Fig. 13.9c). Could that be a mark of Devonshire items? Then there is the use of the malachite in both items. Genuine Florentine *pietra dura* inlay was traditionally made using the more delicate *Verde d'Arno* (Chapter 13, Fig. 13.9d), found in the bed of the River Arno in Florence and nearby. This was adopted by the inlay industry in Derbyshire around 1850 to replace the use of Russian malachite (Tomlinson, 1996). The Devonshire items noted above (Fig. 4.15) all employ malachite and none has yet been recognised that uses the classical Florentine *Verde d'Arno*. Without hard evidence from a name-engraved plate we do not yet know whether the hallmark malachite continued to be used by Devonshire manufacturers after the mid 19th century by which time Derbyshire had stopped using it.

The following summarises what we now know about similarities and differences between Devonshire and Derbyshire smaller items:

- Both industries based their products on black marble
- Both industries produced items with Florentine inlay, geometric mosaic or scrapwork mosaic
- Some Devonshire items contain geometric inlays of malachite only
- Known Devonshire Florentine-style items contain malachite and ivory/bone in the inlay rather than *Verde d'Arno* and shell. These may be indistinguishable from early 19th century Derbyshire items.
- Some Devonshire designs show stone tiles with exposed edges
- Specimen stone items from Devonshire are almost exclusively tiled with local fossil and rock specimens with bright colour and strong texture. This is the most reliable distinguishing feature.
- Specimen stone items from Derbyshire can display many Devonshire stone types, some of them iconic Devonshire corals, and Derbyshire stones can be in a small minority
- Non-British stones are normal and abundant in Derbyshire items
- Non-British stones are found in many Devonshire items but they form a small proportion of the stones used.

4.9.4 *Distinguishing Devonshire and Derbyshire Jewellery*

British Victorian stone jewellery is very diverse, with a number of centres producing some very characteristic designs. These include Scottish agates, Scottish granites, Scottish Iona marble, Yorkshire jet, Derbyshire black marble, English flint, Tisbury coral and Cornish serpentine. Scottish items in particular share with Devonshire jewellery the round, radial and sectored inlay designs that are essentially Celtic inspired, and at any one time some romantically described and quite wrongly attributed Devonshire pieces can be found on sale as Scottish pieces both in specialist antique outlets and on websites. Items claiming to show 'Scottish coral' and even ones with green malachite need to be examined carefully. Scottish jewellery is commonly more elaborate than Devonshire, with much more working of the metal, usually silver. Most Scottish stones such as agates and granites are a lot harder than Devonshire ones and they are likely to retain brighter and smoother surfaces. Granites are usually coarsely crystalline, averaging pink or grey, whilst agates are brightly coloured and finely banded with clear, white, grey, brown, red or green colours in various combinations. Artificial stain is common in agate, for example blue.

As regards distinguishing Devonshire jewellery from Derbyshire, they are normally very different. Derbyshire jewellers preferred to create miniatures of the locally produced, full-size *pietra dura* Florentine-style designs featuring inlaid flowers and leaves and the Devonshire-type radial design in local stone is very unusual from Derbyshire. Derbyshire Florentine designs are commonly offered in local shops and antique fairs today and a far bigger problem arises in distinguishing Derbyshire from Italian Florentine work, which the Derbyshire 'baublers' were deliberately replicating. Both produced some superb work, and unfortunately they used the same inlay materials to create their designs. These included *Strombus* shell, light blue glass and green Florentine *Verde d'Arno*. Derbyshire stone sources were seldom used. The only recourse is to look at the base, and where slate is found an Italian origin may be inferred.

However, fine inlay work in jewellery was certainly not beyond the Devon manufacturers. In 1852, Devon items made by John Woodley of St Marychurch and offered to Queen Victoria included brooches with intricate "*lily of the valley, jasmine and orange blossom patterns*" (Western Daily Mercury, 1886) which certainly sounds a lot like some of the Derbyshire and Italian Florentine floral work. We do not know whether the base material used in Devon was black marble or slate, so that we cannot discount the possibility that some slate-based jewellery, that might otherwise be regarded as Italian in origin, might actually have come from Devon!

4.10 Conclusions

Devonshire marble portable items are a distinct genre. These have been almost universally unrecognised in the past, but with greater public awareness and more items to compare we should be able to make headway in identifying more manufacturers and in making clear distinctions from the competing Derbyshire and other known manufacturing centres.

There are sufficient numbers of known Devonshire portable items for us to be able to distinguish two clear styles. The first is the Woodley style, mainly seen in the tables, with spectacular arrays of local stones carefully arranged into radial and scrapwork designs. Stones are tiled onto and set within black marble and are dominated by bright colour and rich texture, reflecting the provenance of the stones, mainly in the St Marychurch area near Torquay. The second is the Grant style, generally the smaller items, again based in black marble, but showing a lot of malachite and even showing only malachite, in which the Grants had self-proclaimed specialisation.

There are certainly other styles but not enough is yet known of these to make generalisations. What is very obviously missing from this record is any sign of the west Devon manufacturers such as John Goad of Plymouth, whose premises were loaded with portable items according to an engraving in the contemporary architectural magazine *Building News* (Fig, 3.1). Plymouth items have yet to reveal themselves.

5. MARBLE MASTERPIECES 2: THE INSIDE STORY
THE BUILDINGS DECORATED WITH DEVONSHIRE MARBLE

5.1 Finding the buildings

There is no official list of the buildings in which Devonshire marbles have been used, and until work began for this volume only a dozen or so were known informally; even fewer with recognised varieties. The Devonshire marble quarries are, of course, completely silent and no records are known from the once hyperactive marble works themselves. Once recognised, some buildings have promising archives, especially churches and cathedrals, but these note stone types vaguely or even inaccurately and yield little more information than contained in the National Heritage listings that are often based on the work of Nikolaus Pevsner in his (now 53-volume) series of county-by-county guides, *The Buildings of England* (1951–2014).

Contemporary articles, company advertisements, technical texts and historical guides occasionally provide examples of a building where Devon marble has been used, but in many cases provenance is not detailed and variety names are not used. Nonetheless, it has been possible to locate, sometimes by sheer serendipity, more than 75 buildings in the UK (the 'Devonshire Marble Buildings', or DMB list, Appendix 1) that have significant design-led uses of Devonshire marble either inside or outside. There are a further dozen or so buildings awaiting confirmation and about the same again overseas in countries that were once a part of the British Empire. DMBs include cathedrals, churches, chapels, municipal buildings, corporate offices, banks, museums and mansions. Where these are referred to, their DMB number is shown (explained in Appendix 1) and where there is further description in the Buildings Guide (Volume 2 Chapter 11) a reference to that is given. There are enough Devonshire marble buildings now known to reveal a lot about a passing fashion for marble embellishment, the architects involved, the favourite stones used, the way they were used and, occasionally, why.

5.2 Matching the competition

The search for Devonshire marbles has shown up the diversity of ornamental stone used in British buildings and Devonshire is seldom the exclusive stone. British non-Devonshire ornamental stones are often encountered and it is common to find varieties from France, Belgium, Italy and further afield. The foremost of these companion and competing stones are described and discussed in Chapter 2. To an architect, regional or geological consistency mattered less than price, availability, effect and previous experience. Contacts probably also counted for a lot in what sometimes appear to have become fairly random marble selections. A fine example of a diverse and elaborate marble interior is Goldsmiths' Hall, London (Figs 5.4b; 5.6c. DMB L/C/1. Chapter 11 Fig. 11.1). This building is difficult to gain access to, but can be viewed in an online virtual tour that is sufficient to show some of its marble diversity. There are two varieties of Devonshire used in ground floor arches and panels but at first floor level there are tall Belgian Devonian columns plus a wealth of Italian panelling and detail.

Some architects had favourite palettes of marbles that they returned to on different commissions. Sir George Gilbert Scott is the prime example, regularly using polished ornamental stone in narrow shafts and he was remarkably consistent in his preference for British varieties. In St John's College Chapel, Cambridge (Fig. 11.16. DMB E/CB/2. Chapter 11, Group 6), Scott employed a favourite combination of red and green *Lizard Serpentine*, *Red Cork* and green *Connemara* from Ireland (British at the time), *Pink Peterhead* granite from north-east Scotland and two varieties of Devonshire marbles, *Red Ogwell* and grey

Ashburton. In this chapter we briefly examine another George Gilbert Scott building, Exeter College Chapel at Oxford (Fig. 5.11a. DMB SE/OX/1. Chapter 11 Fig. 11.12) where his use of stone was exclusively West Country, and we look for his reasons.

William Butterfield was another architect with a predisposition for British stone. In fact he liked to use local materials wherever he could. Two of Butterfield's churches are looked at here, St Augustine's, west London (Fig. 5.9d. DMB L/W/3. Chapter 11 Group 2, Fig. 11.7) and All Saints, St Marychurch, Devon (Figs 5.9a; 5.10a. DMB SW/TQ/1. Chapter 11 Group 8, Fig. 11.21). In these buildings the stones were almost exclusively Devonshire marbles, but for his earlier and perhaps most iconic church, All Saints, Margaret Street, London (Chapter 2 Fig. 2.7. DMB L/W/7), Butterfield widened his search in the absence of suitable local options. The nave is dominated by great clustered columns of *Pink Peterhead* granite from Scotland (but directly accessible by rail or ship). There is *Derbyshire fossil* with its masses of crinoid segments topping the pulpit, chancel screen and in the chancel steps and baptistery floor (some architectural terms are illustrated in Fig. 5.2). In fact there are not many marbles readily available at the time that are not used in All Saints, from the red *Lizard Serpentine* in the chancel side-arcade shafts and the masses of alabaster on the walls, to the numerous details throughout in green *Connemara*, Red *Languedoc* and white *Carrara*. When it came to the red Devonian marble in the plinth below the chancel screen and in the pilasters in the baptistery arch it was not *Red Ogwell* that was used, but the Belgian competition (Chapter 2).

5.3 The Victorian boom

The use of Devonshire marble certainly extends back into the 18th century, where it becomes lost in an uncertainty of date and indeed some demolitions. We know that John Fulton perceived a market for Devonshire marble in London in the late 1700s and that at about the same time the Reverend John Swete's cottage in the cliffs at Babbacombe had a fireplace in *Petitor* marble (Chapter 2), now lost. Fireplaces have not specifically been sought in this study. Many are eclectic mixes of stone, and salvaged Devonshire marble fireplaces can still be bought today. Church fittings such as pulpits and fonts are happily more permanent but can be no less mongrel. Again, these have not been sought systematically, but have always been noted and photographed where encountered. In most of the DMBs listed in Appendix 1 a bit of Devonshire marble holds something up, covers something over, or points something out, as deliberate architectural features. Sometimes we are lucky and it is all three.

Devonshire marble interiors peaked in Britain in the 1860s and 70s (Fig. 5.1). There was no obvious single reason for this. Better methods of manufacture, including steam power, made it cheaper; better transport links by rail made it more easily transported and the increasingly wealthy industrialist- and Empire-driven middle classes had more disposable cash. All of these may be reflected in the data shown in Fig. 5.1 where the start dates of nearly 90 known marble-embellished buildings, including around 75 with Devonshire, are plotted in 5-year groups against a measure of national wealth. The simple lognormal distribution shows building starts rising suddenly in the mid 1800s not closely tied to the longer term increase in national wealth, but triggered by something, and petering out in the early years of the 20th century, evidently finishing with the start of the First World War.

Perhaps what the peak shows best is the massive acceleration in building generally that took place in the mid-to-late 1800s (e.g. Wilkinson & Ashley, 2009). Housing and suburbs burgeoned (e.g. Bannergee, 2008) and where new stable populations became established, new or more assertive municipal and ecclesiastical provision was also required. It is into these two categories that many (but by no means all) of the 75 or so known DMBs actually fall, but does the general Victorian building boom decline at the same time as the marble

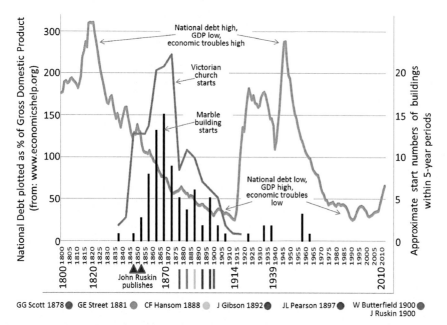

Figure 5.1. Marble building starts (black) and Victorian church starts (brown) plotted against a measure of national wealth (red). Dates of influential publications by John Ruskin are positioned, as are the date of Ruskin's death and those of some prominent architects who used Devonshire marble.

boom in the late 1800s, or does building continue with the steadily improving economy? For example, between 1880 and 1900 six of the most prolific marble embellishers passed away (Fig. 5.1) so did they take the predilection for marble with them? A more random selection of Victorian churches has been compiled by Roger Turner (2014) and a plot of his first 175 (Fig. 5.1), using start dates where shown, gives very much the same distribution as for marble buildings generally, with a broad peak around 1865 and a clear decline after the mid 1870s. Marble embellishment evidently tailed off with the Victorian church building boom, even though not all the marble buildings were churches. There must be a reason for that.

5.4 Gothic—from style to imperative

The use of start dates is important, avoiding the completion problems and in particular getting as close as possible to the design date. In Victorian times getting the style right was paramount and the sought-after style was the Victorian Gothic or Gothic Revival. This was about emulating the great medieval cathedrals with their pointed arches, clustered spires and elaborate decoration. The revival was not new. It had been going since the late 1700s, but in the Victorian era it became an art form and then edged one step further into being a token of faith. Once there it would take another revolution to close the show and its final curtain came with the deeply driven social, economic and political upheavals immediately following the end of the 19th century.

Given that ending, it is hard to view the gathering of the Gothic Revival in a balanced light, for the passions that got it going before the middle of the 19th century were those both of religious zeal and intellectual elitism, seeking answers to perceived current so-

101

cial problems in an utopian past. The principal driving forces behind the Gothic Revival were the Cambridge Camden Society from 1839, later the Ecclesiological Society, and the Oxford Movement dating from a little earlier, later known as the Tractarians. These were both intellectual pressure groups, originally based at their respective ancient universities. They were motivated by a perceived falling of spiritual and moral standards and increase in secularism, much driven by rapid urbanisation and societal redistribution already noted, and they sought a return to an idealised vision of a medieval age of grace and discipline. They differed in two ways. The Cambridge Camden Society started as a Cambridge undergraduate group promoting Gothic church architecture to provide an appropriate stage for spiritual practise and was strongly Anglican, whilst the Oxford Movement was a 'convocation' of senior Anglicans whose priority was to fix theology (belief and theory) and liturgy (conduct of worship) and were strongly High Church Anglican, leaning to Catholicism. Both came to have a profound influence on the styles and practises of their time.

Gothic architecture in the mid 1800s was not confined just to churches. It found expression in municipal, governmental and private buildings and was carried not by whim, but backed by a whole set of principles that inspired a complete generation of architects. Of particular relevance to the Devonshire marble story is that those principles espoused the use of natural stone for construction and carved ornamentation and encouraged the use of polished stone to provide decoration derived from nature. It was principally the doing of John Ruskin (1819–1900), who stood aloof from the contemporary intellectual movements that were channelling architectural style, preferring to promote his own passions, and he was not even an architect. Ruskin was essentially an artistic polymath, becoming an influential art and architecture critic and guru. He was also the pre-eminent supporter of the Pre-Raphaelite artistic movement, able through his own considerable charisma and determination to channel a considerable chunk of the artistic zeitgeist of the Victorian era.

Ruskin's clearest influence in the present tale came through his publication (Ruskin, 1849) of the *Seven Lamps of Architecture* (Fig. 5.1). Here, he stamped his mark on Gothic Revivalism and promoted the continued use of natural stone in construction for reasons of its naturalness, colour, texture and sculptural qualities. In the '*Seven Lamps*' (guiding lights) Ruskin wanted to see a 'marble' church in every town, and describes "*the true colours of architecture*" as being "*those from natural stone*" (4, Aphorism 14). He notes the availability of "*stained and variegated stone*" as unlimited. Marble and limestone are more or less synonymous in Ruskin's writing, so that it is notable that in '*Seven Lamps*' he was less enthusiastic about stone finished by "*chiselling and polishing*", suggesting that the sums involved could be spent instead raising a building one storey higher (4, Aphorism 17). Nonetheless in his "*Stones of Venice*" (Ruskin, 1851–3, ref. 5) he repeatedly praises the use of coloured marble, describing and figuring with reverential detail the coloured (and once polished) marbles in the arcades and "*spandrils*" of the Ducal Palace.

In the 1850s Ruskin's words came to some architects a little like the orchestral conductor's smile at the brass. These included the two already noted, George Gilbert Scott (1811–1878) and William Butterfield (1814–1900), to whom should be added George Edmund Street (1824–1881) and several others. Street became the great paneller, happy to cover walls entirely with flush panelled polished Devonshire and other marbles. Butterfield was the textures man, using stone in the strictest Ruskinian sense in his polychromic masonry, but very willing to add further colour and texture by the use of shafts of polished Devonshire and other British stone. Scott was the elegant shafts man, and incredibly prolific. He used granite and serpentine where extravagance permitted, both of them specifically blessed by Ruskin, as well as marbles from western Ireland and south Devonshire for added brilliance.

On seeing William Butterfield's All Saints Church, Margaret Street, London (DMB L/W/7), already noted, Ruskin wrote, "*It is the first piece of architecture I have seen, built in modern days, which is free from all signs of timidity or incapacity... It challenges fearless comparison with the noblest work of any time. Having done this, we may do anything; there need be no limits to our hope or our confidence*" (5, note 36 in Conclusion to Ch 4.). A footnote comment to this passage refers to "*precious and beautiful marble*" in the (unfinished) interior of All Saints, leaving us in no doubt of Ruskin's encouragement of its use. "*The London of the nineteenth century may yet become as Venice without her despotism,*" he declared. All Saints must have seemed like Heaven-on-Earth (and it still does). This was an outright victory for the Cambridge Camden Society whose pet project All Saints was, and it was praise indeed for the darkly sincere Mr Butterfield, yet Ruskin could not bring himself to name this greatest exponent of his architectural passion, five years his senior.

By no means all those who worked in Gothic Revival style embellished in marble. For example one of the style's most promising and influential practitioners and much disliked by Ruskin, was Augustus Pugin (1812–1852). He ornamented using rich colour, pattern and texture, much like Butterfield, but it is hard to find a building by him with polished marble. Pugin was great at detail and made his name through joint work on the Palace of Westminster with Sir Charles Barry where he designed ornament, furnishings and fittings. He is also credited with the clock tower, Big Ben, now the Elizabeth Tower. There is precious little ornamental marble at the Palace of Westminster and what there is, for example on the ceremonial stairs leading to Westminster Hall, is probably attributable to Barry rather than Pugin.

Not all marble building interiors of the mid-to-late 1800s were Gothic either. There are some fine Baroque interiors, of which Goldsmiths' Hall, noted above, is a good example, and the best encountered so far is the Fitzwilliam Museum, Cambridge (DMB E/CB/3) Chapter 11 Fig. 11.17). These are examples of buildings constructed with a different pastiche in mind, that of Classical Greece and Rome, their marbles used as assertions of power, wealth, influence and magnificence.

5.5 The decorative uses of Devonshire marble

The principal ways in which marble is used in buildings, together with some of the key terminology, are summarised in Figure 5.2. These include structural pillars, ornamental shafts, arches, stairways, wall panels, floor fittings and pavement. Ornamental stone is most commonly found in specific parts of churches and cathedrals and so a typical layout is also shown in Fig. 5.2.

The art of marble embellishment seems to have changed little in 2,000 years although manufacturing techniques have moved on fundamentally from the hand sawing, trimming and polishing of classical times that survived even into the 19th century, to the computer-controlled cutting and finishing of the present day. In stricken Pompeii, for example, suspended at 79AD when the effluence of Vesuvius entombed it, buildings around the forum had open colonnades of marble pillars two storeys high, set on sturdy plinths and topped by the usual carved capitols. External walls were generously clad with marble panels, probably polished, but a lot of these valuable and reusable facings were robbed out in the years following the eruption.

Displays of marble have changed little since then, with some exceptions. More sophisticated building engineering has made possible the theatrical marble Imperial Stairway, but where polished marble was exposed to rain and external industrial pollution, especially as its use spread to cities in northern Europe, it fared less well. It therefore comes as a considerable surprise to find a few British building exteriors panelled and/or colonnaded in Devonshire marble. Even more surprisingly, Devonshire has been used in renovation as a replacement for the very traditional and modest *Purbeck* marble shafts in the weath-

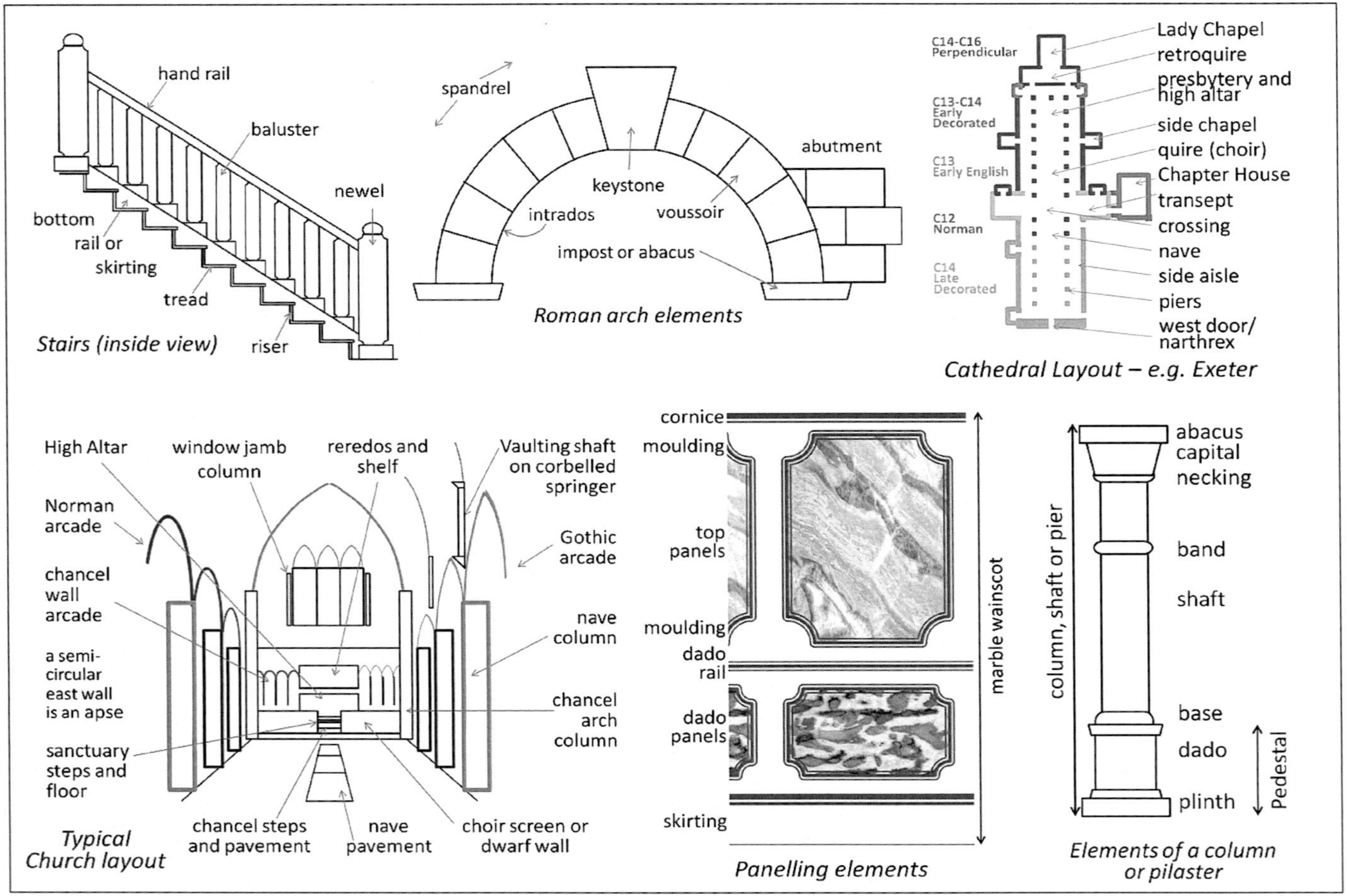

Cathedral Layout – e.g. Exeter

Lady Chapel
retroquire
presbytery and high altar
side chapel
quire (choir)
Chapter House
transept
crossing
nave
side aisle
piers
west door/narthex

C14-C16 Perpendicular
C13-C14 Early Decorated
C13 Early English
C12 Norman
C14 Late Decorated

Elements of a column or pilaster

abacus
capital
necking
band
shaft
base
dado
plinth

Pedestal

column, shaft or pier

Roman arch elements

abutment
voussoir
keystone
intrados
impost or abacus
spandrel

Panelling elements

marble wainscot
cornice
moulding
top panels
moulding
dado rail
dado panels
skirting

Stairs (inside view)

hand rail
baluster
newel
riser
tread
bottom rail or skirting
skirting

Typical Church layout

Vaulting shaft on corbelled springer
Gothic arcade
nave column
chancel arch column
choir screen or dwarf wall
reredos and shelf
nave pavement
window jamb column
High Altar
Norman arcade
chancel wall arcade
a semi-circular east wall is an apse
sanctuary steps and floor
chancel steps and pavement

Figure 5.2 Marble architecture and ornament – some essential terminology

ered exteriors of some of our medieval cathedrals. Ornamental shafts in the west front of Salisbury, for example, (DMB SW/SP/1) were extensively replaced in the 1860s and 70s by George Gilbert Scott, using a definite Devonshire stone that may be *Ashburton* marble.

5.5.1 *Columns and pilasters* (Fig. 5.3)

Columns (round, usually freestanding) and pilasters (rectangular, attached to a wall) must be the most cherished of all the architectural elements. Columns are staple diet in classical architecture where a row of them is united by a flat capping architrave to create open space beneath. Then came the round Roman arch to link columns, producing an arcade, and in medieval times the round one was superceded by the more streamlined and capable pointed Gothic arch.

The more slender decorative shaft also came in with the Gothic. This was placed beside external windows and doors as at Salisbury cathedral and around internal structural columns also seen there, where the decorative *Purbeck* shafts actually bend in sympathy with the *Purbeck* masonry piers they are attached to. There is a surprisingly substantial terminology for the seemingly simple column, pillar or pier (Fig. 5.2) of which the shaft is the central element and the part most commonly made in polished marble.

Some of the finest Devonshire marble pillars, not featured elsewhere in this guide, are in the Officers' Wardroom and Mess, HMS Drake, Plymouth, Devon (Figs 5.3a; 5.3b; 5.9e. DMB SW/PL/5). Specified by Superintendent Engineer Major Monro Wilson and completed in 1898, the building has 18 single-piece, slightly tapered shafts, up to 2.4-m tall distributed between four state rooms and a hallway. Unexpectedly, all the marble shafts and pedestals used in HMS Drake come from the east side of Devon (*Ashburton, Ogwell* and *Petitor*) rather than from any of the numerous local Plymouth sources in the west.

Fine examples of Plymouth marbles are however seen at Brompton Oratory in Kensington, London (Figs 11.4; 11.5. DMB L/W/1. Chapter 11 Group 2) where *Radford* and *Mill Quay* marbles feature in the substantial columns, pilasters and pedestals. Further examples of fine internal uses are in Yeoville Thomason's (1881) Birmingham City Museum and Art Gallery (Figs 5.4a; 5.5c. DMB EM/B/1. Chapter 11 Group 4 Fig. 11.10) and the Gibson Hall, London (Fig. 11.2. DMB L/C/2. Chapter 11 Group 1) by John Gibson (1865). The Gibson Hall is a former bank building where the 80 *Red Ipplepen* columns and pilasters have some of the tallest recorded single pieces of Devonshire, measured at 3.8 m.

Carved ornamentation such as fluting (vertical grooves) has not been noted in Devonshire examples. Perhaps the intrinsic variegated colour and texture of the stone did away with the need for surface treatment or, more likely, fluting was just not a Gothic device. The somewhat coarser clustered (compound) form does occur in Devonshire columns, where a quatrefoil or even 'octafoil' cross section has been machined into the stone. An eight-fold clustered cross section is seen in the nave arcade in George Edmund Street's (1864) St John's Church ,Torquay (Fig. 5.3c. DMB SW/TQ/4. Chapter 11 Group 8 Fig. 11.23). Here, *Petitor* runs down the left of the nave and *Ashburton* down the right. The shafts are built upwards in separate drums, which would have presented significant advantages in manufacture and handling, and *Black Ashburton* is used as a fillet between each drum. Simple cylindrical drums are seen in William Butterfield's (1874) All Saints Church, Babbacombe (Fig. 11.21. also Figs 5.9a; 5.10a. DMB SW/TQ/1. Chapter 11 Group 8), where six nave shafts have five drums each. Drums are a common Butterfield device that provided opportunity for his polychromic decoration by alternation of colour and/or texture.

One of the finest external uses of Devonshire marble is on the entrance bay of the Town Hall at Tiverton, Devon (Fig. 5.3d, DMB SW/EX/10) by H. Lloyd (1864). There are eight columns and four pilasters here, all sturdy, with shafts some 2.4-m tall. The stone is now significantly weathered and pitted so that much colour contrast is lost, but a bit of wetting soon restores this. These external shafts have the fossils and textures of *Red Ogwell*, al-

a Officers' Mess, HMS Drake, Plymouth

Pink *Petitor* shaft

Grey *Petitor* pedestal

b

Red *Ogwell* shaft

Ionic column

Black *Ashburton* pedestal

c St John's Torquay

Drums in *Petitor* varieties

Compound column

Black *Ashburton* fillets

d Town Hall Tiverton – exterior

Probable *Ogwell* shafts

Corinthian column

Corinthian pilaster

106

Figure 5.3. (facing page) Devonshire marble shafts and pedestals. a & b: Officers' Wardroom and Mess, HMS Drake, Plymouth (DMB SW/PL/5). c: St John's Church Torquay (DMB SW/TQ/4). d: Town Hall Tiverton, Devon (DMB SW/EX/10).

though not the colour. Their Corinthian capitals (carved acanthus patterns) are done in a non-Devon limestone. Other examples of external uses of Devonshire marble are on the face of the County Chambers building in Exeter (Fig. 11.31. DMB SW/EX/10. Noted with Chapter 11 Group 10) by an unknown architect. *Red Ogwell* here is more obvious than at Tiverton, in columns and panels at first floor. A dark fossiliferous stone used in second floor columns and pilasters is possibly *Ashburton*.

George Gilbert Scott's external use of Devonshire was a surprising choice as the replacement for the subdued blue-grey *Purbeck* decorative shafts in the west face of Salisbury Cathedral (1860, noted above and Fig. 5.14). Replacements using *Purbeck* were expensive and he used a somewhat cheaper light grey Devonshire stone flecked with pink, later claimed to be *Ashburton*, and he was obliged to tone it down using resins and oils (Ayers, 2000). It was the same story at Westminster Abbey (DMB L/W/6) (Rodwell & Mortimer, 2010). The Galilee Porch at Ely Cathedral (Fig. 5.14, DMB E/CB/5) is another such substitution job for *Purbeck* where Scott replaced all fifteen of the decorative shafts at the west door with Devonshire. Scott used varied and unusual Devonshire stones in some of his renovations and it has yet to be determined whether any of his own or perhaps church records can tell us exactly where some of these are from.

At St John's College Chapel, Cambridge (DMB E/CB/2. Chapter 11 Group 6 Fig. 11.16) Scott's (1863) internal decorative shafts include some very easily recognised Devonshires amongst his multi-coloured clusters below the transept arch and as individual shafts marking windows and window bay arches throughout (Fig. 11.16). There are nearly 200 individual decorative shafts altogether at St John's including Devonshire, Irish and Cornish stones, and if we take a conservative estimate of 2.5 m for each we emerge with a prodigious 0.5 km of polished shafts in this one single building. Up to a fifth of this is Devonshire and is the only English limestone marble used. Scott also used Devonshire at his elegant Exeter College Chapel, Oxford (Fig. 5.11a. DMB SE/OX/1. Chapter 11 Group 5 Fig. 11.12) which is further discussed below.

The smallest shafts, sometimes referred to as colonnettes, are usually of no structural significance. They appear in ornamental blind arcades lining walls in churches and also around pulpits and fonts. Examples are seen in Figs 5.4 and 5.9. Ornamental colonnettes show the greatest diversity in marble types, perhaps because they can use up odd smaller blocks of stone that just happen to be lying around, but more probably because they can affordably feature more unusual stones that supply colour or texture for added richness and emphasis. If there are imported coloured stones in a church, it is in the colonnettes that we can most often find them.

5.5.2 Arches and arcades (Fig. 5.4)

Sometimes technically very difficult, larger arches in ornamental stone are usually done as fans of separate, shaped blocks (voussoirs, Fig. 5.2), perhaps ornamented with mouldings confluent from one piece to the next. An alternative method is to use thin marble facings clad to plain masonry. The most striking examples encountered in this study are the lofty arches in Yeoville Thomason's (1881) Industrial Hall at Birmingham City Museum and Art Gallery (Fig. 5.4a. DMB ME/B/1. Chapter 11 Group 4 Fig. 11.10). The arches are sprung from capitals of *Yellow Petitor* resting upon pilasters of *Red Ogwell*. They are faced either side with several wide-radius hood-moulded (a contoured cornice) voussoirs of *Red Ogwell*, whilst the inside curvature of two of the three arches is shaped by intrados (inside panels, Fig. 5.2) of coffered (recess-panelled) *Ashburton* (Fig. 5.4a). This is one

a Coffered intrados in *Ashburton* marble, voussoirs and pilaster in *Red Ogwell* capital and key in *Pink/Grey Petitor*

Birmingham Art Gallery and Museum

b Goldsmiths' Hall, London

Spandrels, intrados: *Red Ipplepen*. Voussoirs: white *Tuscan*

c Voussoirs and keystone in green *Kitley*, abutments in green *Connemara* and *Pink/Petitor*, coping and entablature *Ashburton, Kitley, Purbeck.*

Natural History Museum, London

d Communion rail arcade in Plymouth marbles with *Rose Red Radford* colonnettes. Steps in *Ashburton*

St John's Church, Hooe, Plymouth

Figure 5.4. (facing page) Devonshire marble arches. a: Birmingham City Museum and Art Gallery (DMB ME/B/1). b: Goldsmiths' Hall, London (DMB L/C/1). c: Natural History Museum, London (DMB L/W/2). d: St. John's Church, Hooe, Plymouth, Devon (DMB SW/PL/7).

---

of the most demanding pieces of manufacture an architect could call for and it reflects the theme of the hall itself, highlighting industrial genius.

More extensive are the flush-panelled *Red Ipplepen* arch spandrels (outside, Fig. 5.2) and intrados (Fig. 5.2) embellishing the sturdy Roman arches in the Philip Hardwick (1871) interior at Goldsmiths' Hall London (Fig. 5.4b. DMB L/C/1. Chapter 11 Group 1 Fig. 11.1), noted earlier. The voussoirs themselves are solid chunks of moulded white *Tuscan* shaped similarly to those at Birmingham, but inside these is a fully panelled semicircular 'tunnel' where the intradoses are not planar, but gently curved to form the inside lining.

Where smaller scale permits, an entire arch can be formed in just two juxtaposed carved pieces. The strongest method is to shape each of the piers together with a half-arch on either side from a single piece. This method commonly applies to blind arcades and reredoses and the example here (Fig. 5.4d) is the communion rail at St John's Church, Hooe, Plymouth (DMB SW/PL/7) by William White (1855).

The great arch through the stairway at the Exhibition Road entrance of the Natural History Museum, London (Fig. 5.4c. DMB L/W/2. Chapter 11 Group 2 Fig. 11.6) is by Allison and Markham (1935) and is a rare example of Art Deco Devonshire. The voussoirs and keystone are rare green *Kitley* marble from south Devon and the copings are in green bivalve-rich *Purbeck* marble, much more unusual than the blue. The copings across the entablature at the top are *Ashburton*. The side abutments (side masonry, Fig. 5.2) are 'geologically' stratified with green *Connemara* and pink/grey *Petitor*. This display of green British stone, very difficult to pull together at the time, is a magnificent evocation of the 'greenness' of the Earth. It was done before space shots revealed that it is actually all blue! Perhaps it was more about our "*green and pleasant land*". The visitor emerges onto the floor of the main exhibition hall from subterranean darkness, where the panelling is in dark grey fossil-rich *Ashburton* marble.

5.5.3 Stairways (Fig.5.5)

Stairways can be tricky as they contain many elements. The 1904 remodelling of the interior at Oldway Mansion, Paignton (Fig. 5.5b, not a DMB) by George Soudon Bridgman got it wrong. Given more space and more restraint, the complete opposite can be achieved as in the Baroque double stairway at the Fitzwilliam Museum, Cambridge (Fig. 5.5d. DMB E/CB/3. Chapter 11 Group 6 Fig. 11.17). Edward Middleton Barry introduced an abundance of colour here (*c.* 1875) including Devonshire *Red Ogwell*, Italian yellow *Siena,* and Italian green *Genoa*. There is even *Pink Peterhead* granite in the towering pillars, but there is enough space, and flow (for example the clever sweeping *Siena* handrails), as well as use of plain colour, (for example the stairs themselves which are plain *Hoptonwood* from Derbyshire) for it all to be just about perfect.

Yeoville Thomason's (1881) stairway at Birmingham Museum and Art Gallery (Fig. 5.5c. DMB ME/B/1. Chapter 11 Group 4 Fig. 11.10) has more modest proportions but uses the same *Red Ogwell* marble for balusters, rails and pillars. The Edwardian stairway by Thomas Collcutt at Lloyd's Register, London (Fig. 5.5a. DMB L/C/3. Chapter 11 Group 1 Fig. 11.3) beams elegance with flush-panelled marble on all walls. The pale solid balustrades and side walls are *Grey Petitor* and the dark handrail with its gooseneck risers is made of dark grey *Ashburton*. Beneath the carpet, the stairs are white *Carrara*. Both this stairway and the one at Birmingham rise past a colonnaded stair hall but the stairways could hardly be more different, the Birmingham one remaining in the classical groove, the London one rising out of it into a new century.

Oldway Mansion, Paignton

Rails and steps in Belgian Red. Panels in French *Cippolino Rubolotto*.

Fitzwilliam Museum, Cambridge

Balusters, newels and panels in *Red Ogwell*, shafts in *Pink Peterhead*, rails in Italian yellow *Siena*.

Lloyd's Register, London

Steps and risers in white Tuscan, panels in *Grey Petitor*, pilaster in *Pink Petitor*. Rails, arch and pedestals are in grey *Ashburton*.

Birmingham Art Gallery and Museum

Balusters, rails and shafts in *Red Ogwell* and *Pink Petitor*.

Figure 5.5. (facing page) Some Devonshire marble stairways. a: Lloyd's Register, London (DMB L/C/3). b: Oldway Mansion, Paignton, Devon. c: Birmingham City Museum and Art Gallery (DMB ME/B/1). d: Fitzwilliam Museum, Cambridge (DMB E/CB/3).

5.5.4 Wall Panelling (Fig. 5.6)

Simple flat bits of marble can have a remarkable effect on a wall, converting it from a mere boundary into a striking feature, all down to the colour and texture lent by stone. Frames and mouldings in polished stone are common. Stone panels generally match the geometry of the surrounding space, for example the triangular space beneath a flight of stairs (Fig. 5.5b). The Chapel of St Cyprian's at Ugbrook House is the earliest dated interior on the DMB list, embellished in 1835 (Fig. 5.6a. DMB SW/TQ/10). Here the panels are a mix of Italian and Devonshire, but the Devonshire varieties took the lead, with Italian ones either carefully matched or deliberately contrasted. The style has Classical simplicity, with rich, mostly Devonshire dado panels framed by unadorned flat strips of Tuscan marble, whilst above the dado there are pilasters with interposed framed and panelled niches and artwork.

At St James's Church, Sussex Gardens, London (Fig. 5.6b. DMB L/W/4. Chapter 11 Group 3 Fig. 11.8), noted above, George Street's (c. 1881) design is ostensibly more minimalist with its flush panelling, but his layout and diversity of stone types, especially in the baptistery (strangely placed at the east end) is no less complex. Entire walls to ceiling height are banded in *Petitor* and *Ogwell* marbles with thin strings of green *Connemara* (Fig. 5.6b). Two rows of diagonally patterned *Yellow Petitor* panels are mirrored above and below in the baptistery dado to create a herringbone effect (Figs. 5.6b; 11.8). Sweeping anticlockwise right round the baptistery, the herringbone arrows direct us from this true east end of the building, to the opposite and ritual east end.

At St Mary Magdalene Church, Torquay (Fig. 5.6e. DMB SW/TQ/5. Chapter 11 Group 7 Fig. 11.18) there are richly panelled marble wall wainscots (c. 1879) by George Gilbert Scott junior. These are mainly in *Ogwell* and *Petitor* and his choir screen (1881) is also panelled (Fig. 5.6e). Everywhere, there are matching (i.e. mirrored or butterfly) pieces of *Pink Petitor* done by using adjacent cut slabs, opened out in book style. In the screen they are set within lightly embossed frames of black *Ashburton* marble.

Taking some secular examples, in Robert Hesketh's (1871) Goldsmiths' Hall London (Fig. 5.6c. DMB L/C/1. Chapter 11 Group 1 Fig. 11.1), noted above, there are some full height panels of *Red Ipplepen* recessed within frames of grey *Ashburton* and green *Genoa*. These are tucked away behind the arches at ground floor level. The Great Ballroom at the Grand Hotel Birmingham (Fig. 5.6d. DMB ME/B/3. Chapter 11 Group 4 Fig. 11.11), completed in 1883 by John Chamberlain, has a sweeping and encircling dado of *Red Ogwell*, bordered by black *Ashburton*.

5.5.5 Altars and reredoses (Fig. 5.7)

The altar, the spiritual and ritual focus of a church, is usually deliberately emphasised by the surrounding architecture and ornamentation. The reredos is the panelled or carved backdrop to the altar, sometimes termed the altarpiece, often set with religious icons or artwork that emphasise the focus. Traditionally, the area was lit by candles and in some designs a shelf below the reredos or attached to the altar, sometimes referred to as a retable, provides space for candles, the holy cross and ritual items. Altars, reredoses and retables commonly feature marble or alabaster and in a few examples this is in Devonshire marble, where red, pink and yellow are the preferred colours as they convey warmth and light.

Figure 5.6. (following page) Devonshire marble panelling. a: St Cyprian's Chapel, Ugbrook House, Chudleigh, Devon (DMB SW/TQ/10). b: St James's Church, Sussex Gardens, London (DMB L/W/4). c: Goldsmiths' Hall, London (DMB L/C/1). d: Grand Hotel Birmingham (DMB ME/B/3). e: St Mary Magdalene Church, Torquay, Devon (DMB SW/TQ/5).

a St Cyprian's Chapel, Ugbrook House

Ipplepen pilaster, Ashburton frame, Petitor panel. Tuscan (Italy) elsewhere.

b St James's Church, Sussex Gardens, London

c Goldsmiths' Hall, London

Red Ipplepen panel, Ashburton upper pilasters, green Genoa lower pilasters, Breche Nouvelle (France) skirting

d Grand Hotel Birmingham

Dado of Red Ogwell, rail and skirting in Black Ashburton.

Flush panelled wainscot of Petitor and Ogwell marbles with strings of green Connemara Red Ipplepen font in foreground.

e St Mary Magdalene Church, Torquay

Matched panels of Pink Petitor in Ashburton frame

a. Reredos arcade in *Pink Petitor*, side arcade in *Red Ogwell* with pietra dura panels

Reredos, wall arcade and altar, St James's, Sussex Gardens, London

b. Red *Ogwell* moulding and shelf, *Yellow Petitor* panel

Reredos and shelf, St Mary Magdalene, Torquay

c. Alabaster reredos, *Red Ogwell* shelf and retable

Reredos and retable, St John's, Torquay

d. Altar top, retable shelves and side panels in *Ashburton*. Black dolerite, white *Tuscan*, green *Connemara* and green Swedish elsewhere

Altar and retable, Sidney Sussex College, Cambridge

113

Many churches, especially high church Anglican or Catholic ones, have more than one altar with a reredos, and some Catholic buildings have a wealth of marble ones. Where a single architect has been responsible for the whole building, the altar and reredos usually came as part of the package, but some are later additions, even recycled from elsewhere.

Possibly the finest Devonshire reredos is that at GE Street's (already noted) St James's Church, Sussex Gardens, London (Fig. 5.7a. DMB L/W/4. Chapter 11 Group 3 Fig. 11.8) The central scene of the Last Supper, carved in white *Carrara*, is framed by an elaborate suspended arcaded hood with flanking buttresses in carved and moulded *Pink Petitor*. The forms of the reredos arcade are picked up again either side in a subsidiary three-fold blind arcade with mullions and tracery in carved and moulded *Red Ogwell*. This is panelled with delightful floral designs done entirely in bright stone inlay on a black marble base (*pietra dura*). The designs were probably all by Street, whilst the marbles were supplied and carved at Andrew Blackler's Royal Marble Works, St Marychurch (St James, undated). These are further discussed below.

The Street/Blackler team emerges again to complete the sanctuary at St John's Church, Torquay (Fig. 5.7c. DMB SW/TQ/4.Chapter 11 Group 8 Fig. 11.23). There is a carved and inlaid alabaster-framed reredos with painted carved images inside, all resting on a *Pink Petitor* ledge (Fig. 5.7c). A double retable shelf in *Red Ogwell* lies immediately beneath. Some fine pieces of polished *Red Ogwell* ashlar provide the wall beneath the shelves.

We have already noted the Devonshire marble panelling in the walls and chancel screen at St Mary Magdalene church at Upton, Torquay (Fig. 5.7b. DMB SW/TQ/5. Chapter 11 Group 7 Fig. 11.18). The lower part of the reredos here (1889) is framed with *Red Ogwell*, matching the shelf below. There is an intervening *Ogwell*-framed panel of rare *Yellow Petitor* (Fig, 5.7b). Modifications to this church interior may have been influenced by both George Gilbert Scott senior and George Gilbert Scott junior but only after the initial shell was completed by Anthony Salvin in 1849. The lower reredos seems to be the design of GG Scott Jnr, but yet another Gothic Revival architect, Temple Lushington Moore, took final control as the chancel was completed in the latter part of the 19th century. Exactly who designed what and when is not clear from the account in Seymour (1963). It is likely that most of the extensive chancel marble (wall panels, see above, and sedilia, see below) was executed by Blackler, but at different times, as the money became available.

A final example is the stately and subdued altar at Sidney Sussex College, Cambridge (Fig. 5.7d. DMB E/CB/4). The side panels and altar top in black *Ashburton* are appropriately splendid, with rare gastropods and branching stromatoporoid colonies. This panelled Baroque interior and similarly styled altar are by Thomas Henry Lyon, 1910–12, a local Professor of Architecture, whom we shall meet again.

5.5.6 Marble screens (Fig. 5.8)

The use of church interiors for both religious and secular purposes has changed quite a bit over the centuries, and continues to do so. The design and arrangement of furnishings and fittings have reflected these changes and polished marble screens have proven just as dispensable as wooden or metal ones. A fine marble chancel screen installed with the Victorian interior of Plymouth Cathedral, for example (Fig. 11.24, DMB SW/PL/1. Chapter 11 Group 9), is now nowhere to be found.

Figure 5.8. (facing page) Mainly Devonshire chancel screens. a: St Matthias Church, Torquay, Devon (DMB SW/TQ/8). b: St Bartholomew's Church, Kitley, Devon (DMB SW/PL/8). c: Worcester Cathedral (DMD MW/W/1). d: St Peter's Church, Shaldon, nr Teignmouth, Devon (DMB SW/TQ/15).

a

Fine *Red Ogwell* rests on Derbyshire alabaster

Choir screen
St Matthias,
Torquay

b

A local *Kitley* marble, probably worked at nearby Plymouth

Choir screen
St Bartholomew's,
Kitley, Plymouth.

c

Mainly *Grey Petitor*, with a plinth in veined grey *Ashburton* or Plymouth

Choir screen
Worcester
Cathedral

d

A fine *Grey Ipplepen* cope rests on green probable *Val d'Aosta* from Italy

Choir screen
Shaldon St Peters,
nr. Teignmouth

115

George Gilbert Scott's design for a Devonshire *Petitor* marble screen at Worcester Cathedral (Fig. 5.8c. DMB MW/W/1), part of his renovations of 1871–5, might be mistaken for Baroque, but on top of it rests a tall and typically Gothic gilt timber arcade more easily recognisable as the work of Scott. Two of his other favourite marbles, the Irish green *Connemara* and *Red Cork* are not far away in his spectacularly carved alabaster pulpit. Scott's classical structure at Worcester contrasts with the obviously Gothic one at St Bartholomew's, Kitley (Fig. 5.8b, DMB SW/PL/8) with its double-pitched (roof-like) cope, probably the design of William Butterfield although his drawings were lost in an early fire. The Kitley screen has all the carved and pierced Gothic trimmings and is made in what may be a very local Devonshire marble, similar to that seen in the drum-built nave piers. This is a reef rock, with pockets of abundant small brachiopods, and is *Ipplepen*-like in many respects, but of *Green Kitley* for which the locality is famous, there is no sign. It is only detectable in the stone walls outside.

The other two screens in Fig. 5.8 are alike and both date to the 1890s. That at St Matthias, Torquay (DMB SW/TQ/8) has a generous moulded cope of 'reefal' *Red Ogwell* (Fig. 5.8a) with a great display of the appropriate *Red Ogwell* colour, fossils and texture. It is by John Loughborough Pearson, not previously noted, but a well-respected Gothic Revival architect who trained under Philip Hardwick, designer of the richly marbled Goldsmiths' Hall in Central London (see above). The final screen is at St Peter's Church, Shaldon, near Teignmouth (Fig. 5.8d, DMB SW/TQ/15). It is capped by a similar moulded cope, here in typically veined and fractured *Grey Ipplepen*. There is a lot that looks reefal in this stone as well. The architect was the less-well-known Edmund Sedding, a north Devon man and one time church organist in Soho, London. He trained under George Edmund Street (architect of St John's, Torquay, and St James's, Sussex Gardens, see above) and so was well acquainted with marble. In his own turn, Street developed his skills during a five-year period working for George Gilbert Scott.

5.5.7 Marble ecclesiastical furnishings (Fig. 5.9)

Having said that this project did not specifically seek such items as pulpits and fonts there are some magnificent Devonshire marble examples and they emerge as works of art in their own right. We return to George Edmund Street's St James's Church, Sussex Gardens, London (Fig. 5.9b. DMB L/W/4. Chapter 11 Group 3 Fig. 11.8) for the best of these, where the elaborate carved pulpit is a Devonshire thoroughbred with eight varieties and only the small *Connemara* cabochons extraneous. It must be the ultimate piece of Devonshire marble artwork, themed effortlessly into the remainder of this great church. Manufacture is attributable to Blackler (St James, undated).

For a fabulously ornate pulpit, that of William Butterfield at All Saints Church, Babbacombe, also executed by Blackler (All Saints, 1992), is hard to beat (DMB SW/TQ/1. Chapter 11 Group 8 Fig. 11.21). His very similar font is illustrated (Fig. 5.9a) and only the white *Carrara* is not from the South West. The font has some intricate stone mosaic work that includes rare fossil coral from Bradley Woods, near Newton Abbott. Fonts and pulpits often show this style of stone decoration. The work is done as a veneer, using flat plaquettes of stone arranged next to one another, where the term mosaic is appropriate. If

---

Figure 5.9. (facing page) Devonshire marble ecclesiastical furnishings. a: All Saints Church, Babbacombe, Devon (DMB SW/TQ/1). b: St James's Church, Sussex Gardens, London (DMB L/W/4). c: St Matthias Church, Torquay, Devon (DMB SW/TQ/8). d: St Augustine's Church, Kensington, London (DMB L/W/3). e: Chapel of St Nicholas, HMS Drake, Plymouth, Devon (DMB SW/PL/5). f: St Matthias Church, Torquay, Devon (DMB SW/TQ/8). Key as follows: RO: *Red Ogwell*. PO: *Pink Ogwell*. PP: *Pink Petitor*. YP: *Yellow Petitor*. GP: *Grey Petitor*. CP: ?Crinoid *Petitor*. RI: *Red Ipplepen*. GI: *Grey Ipplepen*. AS: *Ashburton*. LU: *Lummaton*. AL: alabaster. C: White *Carrara*. S: serpentine.

a — Font, All Saints Babbacombe / Bradley Wood Corals

b — Pulpit, St James's, Kensington

c — Bishop's Chair, St Mary Magdalene's Torquay

d — Credence table, St Augustine's, Kensington

e — Font, St Nicholas, HMS Drake, Plymouth

f — Pulpit, St Matthias, Torquay

the work is inlaid into cut sockets rather than veneered, the term *pietra dura* is preferable. Stone mosaic work on floors is referred to as Cosmati. It turns out that the wide colour palette offered by Devonshire marbles placed them in demand for all three types of ornament. We met *pietra dura* at St James's, Westminster (DMB L/W/4) (Fig. 5.7a) and we shall encounter Cosmati soon.

A further way of achieving a Devonshire marble thoroughbred font is to make the whole thing from as few pieces as possible. This is done with elegant simplicity in the pristine-looking font (Fig. 5.9e) in the chapel of St Nicholas, HMS Drake, Plymouth (DMB SW/PL/5). The base is *Ashburton*, the plinth *Pink Petitor* and the top is a greyer variety of *Petitor*. This Edwardian style is in remarkable contrast to the high Gothic of Butterfield's font at All Saints (Fig. 5.9a) and if, for the sake of comparison, we momentarily overlook the carved panels and intended use of John Loughborough Parsons' pulpit of 20 years later (Fig. 5.9f) at St Matthias, Torquay (DMB SW/TQ/8), it is easy to see how the high Gothic Butterfield font morphs by simplification of form through the late Gothic Parsons pulpit (by Blackler again) to the early 20th century Edwardian 'Wilson' font at HMS Drake (Fig. 5.9e). The carved panels in white alabaster at St Matthias feature great preachers and the base is in four different Devonshire varieties (Fig. 5.9f), of which *Red Ogwell* is repeated further up in the more slender colonnettes next to the carved panels.

This leaves two other very different pieces of marble furniture to note. The earlier one of the mid 1870s is a Butterfield credence table in St Augustine's, Kensington (Fig. 5.9d. DMB L/W/3, Chapter 11 Group 2 Fig. 11.7). After what we have already seen of Butterfield's work, this stately and relatively simple piece of *Pink Ogwell* furniture, slightly owl-like, is an improbable attribution to him, but we know that he designed entire interior 'packages'. In this case the *Red Ogwell* cabochon decorations (the owl's pupils) are an exact match to the larger cabochons in the sanctuary walls (e.g. Fig 5.11b). This hardly used table, in a building that is now as much an education and community centre as a parish church, is a dangerously overlookable piece of history. The *Red Ogwell* Bishop's Chair at the Church of St Mary Magdalene, Torquay (Fig. 5.9c. DMB SW/TQ/5. Chapter 11 Group 7 Fig. 11.18) is sadly damaged by water penetration from the walls behind. The carved *Ashburton* above it is badly bleached, hardly recognisable and the damage seriously affects wall panelling. Colour can only be confirmed by dampening it with yet more water. At some stage someone thought it was a good idea to coat everything here with a varnish, which has simply made matters worse and is now flaking off messily. It is believed that the cause of the problem has been remedied and the church now serves, part time, as a popular and hard-working urban community centre.

5.5.8 Steps and pavements (Fig. 5.10)

It might seem a degrading use of Devonshire marble to place it beneath the feet, but embellishment of floors is an ancient art form, not far from Roman floor mosaics, and some famous exponents of the genre were the Cosmati family of 12th and 13th century Rome. Great cathedrals and basilicas abound in Cosmatesque or Cosmati work on the floors, ignored by most of us as we enter and immediately gaze upwards. In fact there may be more fine marble set in floors than there is anywhere else. Not all marble pavement is strictly Cosmati though. Much is simple rectangular marble pavement inside or out, as seen in the recycled Plymouth marble paving in the Civic Square at Plymouth (Figs 1.6; 11.26, 'DMB' SW/PL/3). Many church and cathedral interior pavements use Minton or similar encaustic ceramic tiles. These are unglazed, manufactured with deep-set clay patterns,

Figure 5.10. (facing page) Devonshire marble pavements. a: All Saints Church, Babbacombe, Devon (DMB SW/TQ/1). b: Sidney Sussex College, Cambridge (DMB E/CB/4). c: Hereford Cathedral (DMD MW/HR/1). d: Guildford Cathedral (DMB SE/GU/1). e: St. John's Church Torquay, Devon (DMB SW/TQ/4).

Nave pavement, Sidney Sussex College Chapel, Cambridge

Grey Ipplepen, Devon. *Green Connemara*, Ireland, brown flowstone, possibly Devon.

Red Ogwell and *Grey Petitor* within white *Carrara: Yellow Petitor* and green *Connemara* outside.

b

d

Ashburton marble with abundant fossil stony sponges.

Sanctuary pavement, St John's, Torquay

Grey Petitor right, *Pink Petitor*, left

Royal Surrey Regt. Chapel, Guildford Cathedral

c

e

Step edges are obscured by non-slip tape

Sanctuary pavement, All Saints, Babbacombe

Red Ogwell and grey *Ashburton*. Unknown Irish grey at margins.

a

Nave altar steps, Hereford Cathedral

119

mostly browns and yellows, that endure wear for centuries. Glazed tiles were also used where a wider range of colour was required but the thin glaze wears through to the plain brown ceramic much more quickly.

It is convenient to base this review of pavements on the three familiar designers GG Scott, W Butterfield and GE Street. George Gilbert Scott's cathedral restorations abound with marble-tiled floors, verging into Cosmati at Exeter Cathedral (Fig. 11.28. DMB SW/EX/1. Chapter 11 Group 10). Amongst his many other cathedral renovations is Hereford (Fig. 5.10c. DMB MW/HR/1), where there is a fine set of *Ogwell* steps at the transept, now the location of the new nave altar. The pavement in front of the steps is generously tiled in grey *Ashburton* and *Red Ogwell*. Scott's renovations at this cathedral had a controversial outcome because his huge, mainly wrought-iron choir screen, greatly celebrated when first installed at the north side of the transept in 1863, was removed in 1957. It was supposedly done away with for liturgucal reasons, but it is easy to regard its removal as part of a general reaction against Gothic designs, prevalent at the time when the new nave altar and suspended corona above were brought in. The splendid screen, since refurbished and reassembled, is now an important showpiece at the Victoria and Albert Museum in London. The cathedral's loss is the nation's gain.

In contrast to Scott's almost military orthogonal and diagonal pavement designs, Butterfield added circles, roundels and complex inlays at All Saints, Babbacombe (Fig. 5.10a), as well as elsewhere. These are much more Cosmatesque, especially in the use of white *Carrara* background, but the designs remain abstract. Marbles at All Saints, Babbacombe include *Red Ogwell*, *Grey Petitor* and an unusually rich *Yellow Petitor*.

The roundels at Sidney Sussex College Cambridge (Fig. 5.10b. DMB E/CB/4) include Irish *Connemara* and *Grey Ipplepen* from near Newton Abbott and there is probably a story behind the choice of *Ipplepen*. The designer, Thomas Henry Lyon, became the first Director of Design in Architecture at Cambridge in the 1920s and hailed from Devon. He was also a landscape designer and one of his gardens is actually at Ipplepen. It is replete with its own baroque bench in *Ipplepen* marble. Back in the chapel, the fine centrepiece of Lyon's roundel (Fig. 5.10b) is stalactitic limestone or flowstone, geologically much younger than Devonshire marble, but the abundance of red in this and its quirky textures are quite consistent with flowstone in cave and cavity systems in Devonshire limestones, such as at Kents Cavern near Torquay.

Far more recent (architecturally) than the rest of the examples are the *Ashburton* marble steps (Fig. 5.1) in the chapel of the Queen's Royal Surrey Regiment at Guildford Cathedral (Fig. 5.10d. DMB SE/GU/1). These date from the 1960s and the stone is technically still available in Linhay Hill Quarry at Ashburton. There are very few other Devonshire marbles that can still be found at outcrop. For the interest of any true marble seeker, we discovered a table in a doorway on the opposite side of Guildford Cathedral that is topped with *Ashburton*-faced Formica, the one-time famous durable melamine laminate product. Formica was originally manufactured in great brittle sheets using a photographic reproduction technique, and it dominated kitchen designs in the 1950s and 60s. This particular Formica featuring faultless *Ashburton* marble must have been intended for use in the *Ashburton*-floored chapel.

At St John's, Torquay, once again (see above) George Street's pavement design in front of the altar (Fig. 5.10e) is a mix of tiles and Devonshire marble. Its orthogonality and controlled magnificence is much more like the designs of Street's mentor, George Gilbert Scott. Characteristically, Street used the best pieces of marble he could find. The two piec-

Figure 5.11. (facing page) Sanctuary designs compared. a: Exeter College Chapel, Oxford (DMB SE/OX/1) by George Gilbert Scott. b: St Augustine's Church, Kensington, London (DMB L/W/3) by William Butterworth. c: St John's Church, Torquay, Devon (DMB SW/TQ/4) by George Edmund Street. d: St James's Church, Sussex Gardens, London (DMB L/W/4) by George Edmund Street.

a. Exeter College Chapel, Oxford, GG Scott, begun 1856

b. St Augustine's, West London, W Butterworth, begun 1870.

c. St John's, Torquay, GE Street, begun 1864

d. St James's, West London, GE Street, 1881

121

es figured here (Fig. 5.10e) are a specialist's dream for they display better sedimentology (cross-bedded *Grey Petitor* reef trash, see Chapter 7) and structural geology (en echelon shear zones in *Pink Petitor*, see Chapter 8) than can be found in the field!

5.6 Style and meaning in marble

Given that there are clear differences in the ways different architects have used marble, it is worth exploring style and meaning a little further. Illustrated in Fig. 5.11 are the north sides of marbled sanctuaries by the three architects already drawn together above, George Gilbert Scott (1811–1878), William Butterfield (1814–1900) and George Edmund Street (1824–1881). This is not a safe number of interiors from which to draw sweeping conclusions, but stylistic differences are certainly evident. Marble is an architectural medium just as are plain or sculptural stone, brick or even concrete. Its properties channel its use. Nonetheless we can argue the extent to which differences are inspired by the marbles themselves or merely reflect the distinct styles of the architects concerned.

Scott's style at Exeter College Chapel, Oxford (Fig. 5.11a. DMB SE/OX/1, Chapter 11 Group 5 Fig. 11.12) conforms to his normal rich, stately and lofty. Scott's polished marble always seems to be confined to shafts. They support the elegant Gothic blind arcade whilst stouter ones soar upwards past these to meet the vaulting. There are more marble shafts next to the windows. The stones are red *Lizard Serpentine* (the right vaulting shaft in Fig. 5.11a) and Devonshire *Red Ipplepen* (the rest). This is a very restricted palette for Scott, who loved his Irish green *Connemara* and *Red Cork*, as we have seen. These stones all abound in the spectacular display of coloured vaulting, window and arcade shafts at St John's College Cambridge, noted above, and they appear in other GGS churches. Here at Exeter he restricted himself, and we might ask why. The founding principles of Exeter College, written into the statutes and pursued by an influential Exeter bishop and his wealthy Devonian sponsor, were to train west-country clergymen so that they could return and preach. Scott always did his research and there can be little doubt that his choice of exclusively west-country stone was an acknowledgement of this original exclusive tradition.

Scott's use of red Devonshire stones in the shafts adds colour, texture and emphasis to his otherwise plain walls and piers. The streaks of colour add movement and reach. Only in the apsed sanctuary (Fig. 5.11a) did he add further wall ornament in the form of mosaic in the arch tympani and on the spandrels. This ornament comes to a climax in his mosaic reredos (Fig. 11.12) at the focal point of the building. The somewhat dense-coloured tapestries placed at the back of the apse arcade (Fig. 5.11a) add nothing. They cover Scott's plain ashlar and were never part of his original intentions. They are reproductions of a William Morris design, but Morris was only a student here when the building went up between 1856 and 1859.

If Scott's designs were stately, then Butterfield's were transcendental, and the contrasts abound. Butterfield's elaborate ornamentation (Fig. 5.11b) in the sanctuary at St Augustine's Church, Kensington, London, (begun 1870. DMB L/W/3. Chapter 11 Group 3 Fig. 11.7) is typical of his wall-to-wall polychromy and diapering (use of colour and intricate pattern). The central part of the design is the network of cinquefoil and quadrefoil tracery made entirely in Devonshire and Italian marbles. This is very similar to the extensive Devonshire-panelled carved stone tracery on the outside of his All Saints Church at Babbacombe in Devon (Fig. 11.21). This coloured wall-to-wall marble panelling was probably never meant to be spectacular, just glorious. Some might claim that he overdid it, but at St Augustine's the range is soothing (Fig. 5.11b) although the giant marble flush-work leaf motifs high in the arcade diminish the scale of the work, as do the big stone relief cabochons. George Gilbert Scott managed to make interiors look bigger using his marble shafts; here Butterfield made his giant blind arcade seem smaller. The dark pink is *Red*

Ogwell, the light pink is *Petitor*, the dark grey is *Ashburton* and the light grey and white are Italian *Tuscan*. There are bands of alabaster high in the east wall that disappear behind a fairly alien and much later gilt timber reredos that covers most of the east wall. No one seems to know what the rest of Butterfield's wall treatment looks like behind this and his original reredos is fully obscured (see Fig. 11.7).

George Edmund Street's sanctuary walls at St John's Church, Torquay (Fig. 5.11c, DMB SW/TQ/4) seem to bridge between Scott and Butterworth. The arcade and masonry above were installed in 1875 by Andrew Blackler (Boggis, 1930), just post-dating Butterworth's St Augustine's, but they probably relate to a much earlier design. The chancel was complete by 1864, including the reredos, so that the arcade was probably already on paper, perhaps even under manufacture at the time.

Using an arcade was how to ornament a chancel in the mid 1800s, so inevitably the styles of Street and Scott are convergent, even down to the toned and patterned tympani just inside the arches. Street's arcade is more squat, making space above for the plain masonry with inlaid quatrefoils and cinquefoils. The faced masonry itself is undecorated, like much of Scott's, with none of the structural polychromy or diapering associated with Butterworth. What Street brings are his individual flashes of intricate detail. The recessed panels are not just blocks of coloured marble like Butterworth's, intended to create and unify a greater picture, they are pictures in themselves, each an individually designed floral or cruciform specimen mosaic done in several colours of marble and semi-precious stone, including bright green malachite. Butterfield probably only used highlights like this in his pulpits and fonts and Scott seems to have been able to avoid them, perhaps because his showy style was everywhere, particularly his soaring marble shafts.

Street's early professional development, five years with George Gilbert Scott, must have strongly influenced him. He may well have wanted to emulate some of the Scott-type splendour, but without letting it get out of control, so perhaps he tried to encapsulate it in his flashes of detail. If so, it doesn't quite work in this corner of St John's (Fig. 5.11c), and the whole assembly fails to fit properly anyway. Some of the red panelling is painted faux marble and some *Red Ogwell*. The arcade shafts are all varieties of *Petitor* (mottled or light pink), *Ogwell* (dark pink), *Lummaton* (light grey) and *Ashburton* (black). *Ogwell* and *Ashburton* figure in the mosaic highlights as well.

The equivalent corner of George Edmund Street's much later designed church (1881) at St James's, Sussex Gardens (Fig. 5.11d. DMB L/W/4) is more successful and unique to him. Here he largely abandoned relief, verged on minimalist and allowed the flush-panelled Devonshire marble do the talking. He clad an entire full-height baptistery with Devonshire (noted above) and most of the nave and aisle walls as well (Fig. 11.8, Chapter 11 Group 3). In this sanctuary (Fig. 5.11d) he used some of the best *Pink Petitor*, with darker *Red Ogwell* in the flush skirting. The small green *Connemara* cabochons (the same as in the pulpit) are recessed, suggesting buttoned upholstery that transforms the entire cold marble surface into something warm and enveloping. At the centre he inserted his flash of detail, a small, simple, white, focal Celtic cross. Immediately to the right is his architectural culmination, a bright botanically explicit *pietra dura*, set in deeply toned panels, within an elaborate and fine tracery of *Red Ogwell* marble (Figs. 5.7a, 5.11d). Street died in the same year that St James's Church, his supreme marble masterpiece, was completed.

Saving the best till last, and stepping outside the confines of these three architects, the final word on messages in marble can rest inside the somewhat foreboding yet romantically intended Todmorden Castle in West Yorkshire (Fig. 5.12. DMB NY/OL/1. Chapter 11 Group 11 Fig. 11.34). It was designed by the highly respected and widely consulted, John Gibson, and the whole building is said to have been a wedding present from local mill-owner John Fielden Jnr to his one-time millworker bride Ruth. The story goes that she had made the building of a castle her condition of marriage. The interior is dotted with

Figure 5.12. Meaning of marble – the *Rose Red Radford* mantelpiece in the entrance hall, Dobroyd Castle, Todmorden, Yorkshire (DMB NY/OL/1). For detail see text.

allusions to Fielden's passion for the younger Ruth, but none more so than the fireplace (Fig. 5.12a) that takes centre stage in the two-storey marble colonnaded entrance hall, surrounded by carvings and panels that seem to tell of the convergence of the two lovers (Chapter 11). On either side of the mantel shelf are empty plinths of blushing marble carved with the entwined initials of Ruth and John Fielden, 'RJF' (Fig. 5.12b), loosely held by looped cord. A wedding cord signifies lifetime unity and marital protection whilst a loop signifies love. Now look at the clock. It is held in a marble case that is framed in a more robust braided cord seeming further to signify the unity of the couple, but note how it runs (5.12c). It appears to loop the clock, lassoing it, but in fact one strand is a ring, eternally circling the timepiece whilst the other reaches from the plinths at either end to pass through the ring, gently securing it. If you are in any doubt about the declaration of eternal love here, then just note which Devonshire stone it is all made from. This is *Rose Red Radford* and over the clock case is carved an open clam with rows of pearls, projecting purity, innocence and worth. We can be in no doubt about the intent of this mansion centrepiece, or indeed of the entire mansion.

5.7 Devonshire marble fireplaces

Devonshire marble (DM) fireplaces were not necessarily architect-designed as in the Todmorden example. Doubtless they were often themed as part of an interior scheme but details may have been left to a marble works where more of their creations were on sale in the showroom. Commonly DM fireplaces are an eclectic mix of stones along with the Devonshire types (e.g. Fig. 5.13c).

DM fireplaces have not formed part of the focused research for these volumes largely because their presence in a building is unpredictable and they are normal embellishments in many types of domestic interior—there must be thousands of them through the south-west and elsewhere. Nonetheless, good examples of DM fireplaces have been recorded when encountered and the genre deserves better attention, not least because where they are a surviving original feature of a building they can be accurately dated and can provide very early examples of the use of specific marble varieties.

A case in point are the fireplaces in Saltram House, Plympton, Plymouth (DMB SW/PL/10). These date from the Georgian makeover of the house attributed to Robert Adam (Fig. 5.13a,b). In the bedrooms an uncertain Plymouth stone is used in facings around fire openings and probable *West Hoe* slabs are used in the hearth. In one or more of the ground floor rooms a more richly coloured stone in the facings is *Radford* marble from Radford Quarry not far to the south of Saltram (Fig. 5.13a). These fireplaces, with their Adam-style painted surrounds are mid-to-late 18th century and some of the earliest uses of DM recorded.

DM fireplaces dating from the 19th century are more common, in particular from the middle part onwards. A good example is the *Petitor* marble fireplace in Petitor House, Petitor Road, St Marychurch, only 50 m from Petit Tor in the cliffs and not much further from the Petit Tor quarry that it came from (Fig. 5.13c). The Fireplace is thought to be mid-19th century and will have been carved and assembled at the Royal Marble works in the village not far away.

More anonymous are two further 19th century fireplaces from a modern showroom. One, in *Pink Petitor* is elaborately carved and very likely to be from the same St Mary-church works, but well before 1850, in which case John Woodley might have been responsible for the carving. The final example is in *Rose Red Radford*, from Oreston, Plymouth (Fig. 5.13f) and likely to be mid-to-late Victorian. The stone is the same as in the fireplace at Todmorden Castle (see above).

5.8 Some conclusions

Marble embellishment is an art form that dates back to classical times but it reached a renewed peak in Victorian Britain that reflected both the increased wealth of the time and a fashion for Gothic pastiche.

The installation of marble in prominent buildings is easily taken as a mere flight of fancy, proclaiming status or self esteem, but we have seen that there is something more. Architects used it in different ways, according to their own styles, but it also gave altruistic expression, with colour, texture, meaning, beauty, glorification, movement and perhaps even sound (p. 337). George Edmund Street did indeed find his own way to control splendour by punctuating expanses of elegant simplicity with sudden contrasts of bright magnificence, all done using Devonshire marble.

The number of noteworthy buildings embellished with ornamental stone is a small proportion of our high-end national heritage and those with Devonshire marble (DMBs) are a smaller number still. Despite its slide into anonymity, Devonshire marble was once the pre-eminent British ornamental stone. From the 75 or so known DMBs we can expect the roll call to grow, perhaps more than double, as we become better at recognising the marbles. A good half dozen DMBs can be selected as representing the finest, given four or five star status in the grading scheme adopted in Appendix 1. All of these are noted and figured in this chapter. Of the public and commercial buildings two stand out; Birmingham City Museum and Art Gallery (DMB ME/B/1. Figs 5.4a; 5.5c; 11.10) and Lloyd's Register, London (DMB L/C/3. Figs 5.5a; 11.3). Their Devonshire marble work is diverse, clever, and assertive. There are four top churches, three of which are in the vicinity of Torquay; St Mary Magdalene Church, Torquay (DMB SW/TQ/5. Figs 5.6e; 5.7b; 5.9c; 11.18), St John's Church, Torquay (DMB SW/TQ/4. Figs 5.3c; 5.7c; 5.10e; 5.11c; 11.23) and All

Figure 5.13. (facing page) Some Devonshire marble fireplaces. a: Saltram House, Plymouth (DMB SW/PL/10). Radford marble insert in a mid/late-18th century Adam-style fireplace. b: Saltram House, as above. Plymouth marbles, including *West Hoe* in hearth. c: Petit Tor House, St Mary-church. An early Victorian *Petitor* mantlepiece trimmed and embellished with green Onyx and *Connemara* marble. d, e: An intricately carved Baroque-style *Petitor* marble fireplace in an antiques showroom f: A late Victorian-style fireplace in *Rose Red Radford*. (*Photos d, e & f courtesy of Adrian Ager, Ashburton.*)

Saints Church, Babbacombe (DMB SW/TQ/1. Figs 5.9a; 5.10a; 11.21). The fourth is St James's Church, Sussex Gardens, London (DMB L/W/4. Figs 5.6b; 5.7a; 5.9b; 5.11d; 11.8). These have colonnades, panelling, flooring and fittings completed almost exclusively in Devonshire marble to the highest standards. Two are designed by GE Street and three are known to have had their marbles manufactured by the firm of south Devon master mason Andrew Blackler. These interiors proclaim passion, supplication and glorification.

Buildings such as these, and there are a good deal more with a lot of interior Devonshire and other British marbles, have an especial claim to status amongst the best in our national heritage. Devonshire marble buildings, and those with other British marbles, are a poorly researched category in their own right and deserve fuller recognition as such.

Figure 5.14. Devonshire marble shafts substituting for *Purbeck*. West Front, Salisbury Cathedral (left) and West Door, Ely Cathedral (right). Work specified by George Gilbert Scott in mid-19th century.

6. THE TREASURED LANDSCAPES

6.1 Uneasy neighbours

A large quarry seldom makes an attractive contribution to a landscape. Geologists are amongst the most tolerant of such intrusive elements, largely because quarried exposures can provide good rock outcrop where otherwise there is none. Abandoned quarries are scattered right across south Devon wherever limestone lies at the surface and was extractable (Fig. 1.2). Only a very small fraction of the total limestone output found its way into the ornamental stone industry and most went into lime burning, but several quarries did a good sideline in building stone or marble, with only the residue being burned to lime.

Many smaller rural quarries are now hidden or lost, making the rediscovery and verification of marble localities difficult, but some of the larger ones are still very obvious (e.g. Fig. 6.1a). These big quarries are good honest holes in the ground, but there is another type that cannot be seen any more, not because it has been reinstated to its original state but because it has permanently remodelled the landscape.These are where entire cliffs, farmland or downland have disappeared and we are hardly the wiser. There are several examples in this chapter, which is about quarried landscapes and their post-industrial recovery.

6.2 Permanent change and new directions

Photographs can recapture some of this lost heritage, but photography did not come into general use until the second part of the 19th century, by which time many quarries were well established, but paintings and engravings go back a lot further and can reveal some of the lost landscapes (e.g. Figs 6.1b, c; 6.2). Old maps are particularly useful in the quest, but large-scale ones usually do not go much further back than the mid 1800s. The body authorised to provide national map coverage was the Ordnance Survey, set up in the late 1700s by the Board of Ordnance, or Defence Ministry, in response to national security concerns over revolutionary unrest in France. They are still responsible for our official national mapping although aerial and satellite telemetry have largely replaced the original methods of ground surveying. It was only in the mid 1800s that mapping on the old '6-inch' scale became widespread, but a remarkably early example of the Plymouth area at this scale dated around 1784 still survives and will prove particularly useful (Fig. 6.3a).

Many of the larger quarries that have wrought major changes in the landscape are now industrial sites, business parks or housing estates, such as on either side of the Cattewater sound at Plymouth (Fig. 1.1a). Any remaining scientific value in the quarry faces is fast diminishing behind security netting, fences or commercial clutter, with brambles shrouding the remainder. On the coast around Torquay (e.g. Fig. 6.1a) and Berry Head (e.g. Fig. 6.10; also Fig. 9.18, Volume 2) many old quarries are more obvious, naked in their abandonment in the more exposed locations. Much of the geology is still clear and useable in these gaunt relics but even better are the three remaining working quarries, at inland sites

Figure 6.1. (facing page) Lost Devonshire landscapes—the quarrying heritage. a: Long Quarry Point and its abandoned quarry occupy the foreground, with Anstey's Cove to the left and Oddicombe (Babbacombe) Bay to the right. (*Aerial photograph by courtesy of English Riviera Tourism Company and Motion Graphix.*) b: Pomfleet (Pomflett) Creek in 1793 by Rev. John Swete (Swete 1789–1800, V2, p. 11). This former small gorge is now incomparably widened, with a dual carriageway, factories and silted-up mudflats. (*DRO 564M/F5/35 by kind permission of Devon Record Office.*) c: Oarstone (Oreston) in 1794 by Rev. John Swete (Swete 1789–1800, V2, p. 12). This view is over Oreston and across Mount Batten (with tower) and Cattedown on the right. It must be Mt Edgcumbe beyond this (centre, with mansion) on the opposite side of the sound but this view would have required a good telescope. (*DRO 564M/F5/39 by kind permission of Devon Record Office.*)

129

near Plymstock, Stoneycombe and Ashburton (Fig. 2.1). These have evolved into busy superquarries, their great annual tonnages mainly going straight into cement or aggregates.

Today we would vociferously resist the opening of a new quarry, and in the case of a coastal one we would almost certainly be successful. We like to think that ours is an enlightened age where a sensible balance can be struck between amenity and commercial need. That has not always been the case. We have already met the Rev. Thomas Moore who, observing the quarried coastlines around Babbacombe, Berry Head and Plymouth in 1829, complained that *"The artist and the man of taste may possibly turn from works of this kind with something like disgust, lamenting that the ruthless hand of commerce is permitted, with provoking unconcern, to demolish by piecemeal the grand and magnificent ornaments of the coast, and that the owners of these splendid scenes, with the sordid love of gain absorbing all other considerations, are literally retailing the picturesque and beautiful by weight and measure; whilst the friends of industry and productive labour will observe only in such operations a rich increase of agricultural produce, and consequently of general benefit."*

New quarrying operations today are subject to the strictest planning rigour, and conditions are normally imposed involving screening, dust and noise emission, water pollution, environmental protection, traffic movement and reinstatement works, so that in the long term they are viewed as ephemeral ventures that are expected to leave minimal environmental damage. We cannot impose such conditions retrospectively of course, requiring past generations to make good their depredations, and the quarries that Thomas Moore (1829) objected to were all opened when the only permission required was that of the land owner, and not even that if you were one and the same.

By a strange reversal, though, we can find ourselves today objecting to the removal of an artificial feature in the landscape where once we would have opposed its appearance in the first place. This is true of great railway viaducts, canals and 19th century industrial buildings, but might we really find ourselves trying to prevent the loss of an old quarry? Well, yes. Old quarries have sometimes become the last bastion of something animal, vegetable or mineral that is entirely unique (occasionally all three) and have been designated as Sites of Special Scientific Interest. A few of these are included in Chapter 9 where we look at limestone geology, but we also see how powerless the SSSI status actually is.

Only three years after Thomas Moore's (1829) rant against the loss of coastal scenery, Octavian Blewitt (1832) was praising an industrial scene with *"the scenery around Babbicombe is particularly fine. From the hills above we enjoy a prospect which is not surpassed in any part of this district. The ocean expands immediately below us, bounded on the north by the celebrated marble quarries of Petit Tor and the high land, including the rocky creeks of Watcombe and Maidencombe"*. This more tolerant account may have influenced subsequent writers of guides such as Pigot, Kelly and Billings whose words were much the same and all lauded the quarries at Petit Tor.

Evidently the beauty of the ornamental products from Petit Tor quarry, itself not at all pretty (Fig. 1.4c), were enough to mollify concerns over the degrading amenity. In fact there was one cleric who positively enjoyed a good quarry. This was the Rev. John Swete, the man who in 1793 observed Robert Fulton's pioneering efforts at Petit Tor quarry (Chapters 1 and 3). A good 40 years before Rev. Moore's (1829) outburst, Swete's *Picturesque Sketches of Devon* (1789–1800), unpublished at the time, is now probably the finest ever celebration of 'treasured landscapes' in Devon, his words and pictures comprising a diary of exploratory journeys across the county. He noted rocky valleys, gorges, cliff lines and quarries with equal relish, figuring and describing no less than 30 views of quarries or their associated lime kilns. Amongst them are glimpses of Cattedown headland and the narrow gorge at Pomphlett Creek east of Plymouth long before they were both obliterated by quarrying (Figs 6.1b, c).

Figure 6.2. Historical views of Cattedown, east of Plymouth. a: View, dated 1781, from Crabtree south-west (seawards) down the Laira and Plym Estuary to Cattedown (centre) and Cattewater (glimpsed between the headlands). Extract from a print by W. Hay. The Cattedown headland has since been quarried almost flat and the modern Laira road bridge and disused rail bridge cross in front of what remains. b: Prince Rock Quarry, Cattedown *c.* 1831 from an engraving by Henry Wallace, drawn by Harry Worsley. Quarrymen are handling large blocks. Prince Rock, a limestone quarry, became the dispatch point for Dartmoor granite blocks from the nearby granite works. The tramway is evident in the foreground and the prominent face of Pomphlett Quarry (also visible in Fig. 6.4b) is depicted behind the new Laira bridge.

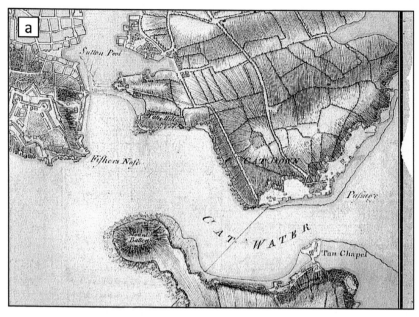

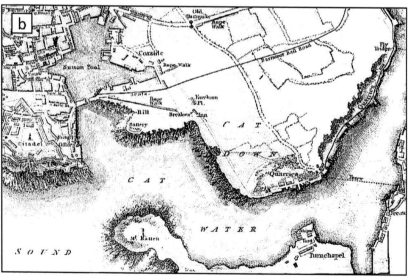

Figure 6.3. Early maps showing quarrying at Cattedown. a: Extract from six-inch scale Ordnance Survey map of 1784 by William Gardner *"An actual Survey and Measurement of Plymouth and Dock Towns with their Fortifications and the Adjacent Country, surveyed by order of His Grace the Duke of Richmond"*. (*Map extract by kind permission of the Public Record Office, National Archives Image Library.*) b: Extract from *"Borough of Plymouth"*, engraved by John Cooke, 1820. (*Map reproduced from Steve Johnson's Cyberheritage website, accessed April 2015.*)

Figure 6.4. Extracts from Ordnance Survey 1:2 500 (6-inch) scale maps of the late 1800s showing quarries on Cattewater, Plymouth Sound. a: Cattedown quarries have extended inland leaving very little of the original hillside apart from the elevated ridges that carry original lanes. Working by fingers of dragways shows clearly. The position of Prince Rock Quarry (seen in Fig. 6.2b) is shown (circled, 1, in red) and a rail line leads past it down to the main quarry where there are loading facilities near to lime kilns. Bunched contours nearby mark earlier surveyed positions of the quarry faces. b: Breakwater Quarry (circled, 2, in red) shows the remnants of William Stuart's tramway extraction system that converges upon two loading bays at a tidal wharf. A system of points provides infinite permutations of route (extract from 1:500 survey of 1857 inset). It is remarkable that this system survived for the most of the 19th century. A standard-gauge rail line crosses the worked-out floor of Pomphlett Quarry at top. (*Maps by kind permission of Old Maps.*)

6.3 Lost landscapes—the Plymouth Cattewater legacy

Much of Plymouth is underlain by limestone and former quarries are scattered around the city, but it is on the east side of the city that limestone quarrying has left its greatest mark, in the downland either side of the Plym estuary at Cattewater (Fig. 1.1a). Several of the Cattedown quarries on the north-west side of Cattewater are known to have produced stone for the Devon marble industry and there are named samples from Princerock Quarry (Fig. 6.4a) in the building stones collection of the British Geological Survey. In the Watson Collection at Cambridge there is a Prince Rock sample and one from Deadman's Bay Quarry (Fig. 6.4a, left). Today, Cattedown is a warren of industrial estates and the open downland is long gone. The only hints left are the elevated meandering ribs of rock that carry aloft the original public lanes separating quarry enterprises. The lost hillside is pictured in a few prints of the late 1700s (e.g. Figs 6.1c; 6.2a), and the near final configuration is shown in Ordnance Survey 6" to the mile (1:2500) maps of the late 1800s (Fig. 6.4a).

The far earlier 6-inch Ordnance Survey map (noted above), perhaps the first published at that scale, was completed for Plymouth in 1784 (Fig. 6.3a) and reveals quarrying at Catdown (later Cattedown) already nibbling into the southern cliffs, and there is clearly an engineered quayside from which stone could be shipped. A John Swete (1789–1800) watercolour of 1794 catches a bit of this quayside a decade later (Fig. 6.1c) and it is likely that there was both a fishing village here at the time as well as a ferry point taking traffic across the estuary. All of the Cattedown hinterland was intact in 1784 and even by 1820 (Fig. 6.3b), when quarries are actually marked, there was apparently only slight enlargement, but the ferry point is clearly marked, served both by road from the direction of Plymouth and a branch of the brand new "*Dartmoor Rail Road*" coming the other way. This was better known as the Plymouth and Dartmoor Tramway, a (slightly) narrow-gauge horse-drawn tramline that brought china clay and granite from inland pits and quarries mainly to the harbour at nearby Sutton Pool, just to the north-west of Cattedown (seen on Fig. 6.3). An engineer with the Plymouth and Dartmoor Tramway for a time was the talented scotsman William Stuart (Chapter 3), whom we shall shortly meet again.

A decade later, a print from around 1831 (Fig. 6.2b) shows stone being handled on the NE end of Cattedown at Prince Rock Quarry (location circled in Fig. 6.4a) and the tramway tracks are clearly shown. This Princerock branch of the mineral line appears again on the Ordnance Survey 1:500 Plymouth Town Plan for 1857 (not figured) but it no longer extended beyond Princerock to the ferry point. Limestone quarrying was well established and advancing inland in 1857 and perhaps the tramline helped to facilitate this, but the Prince Rock branch of the Plymouth and Dartmoor Tramway was also connected to a nearby "*Dartmoor Granite Works*" strategically positioned near the junction with the 'main' line from Dartmoor to Sutton Pool. It is likely, therefore, that the blocks shown in Fig. 6.2b are actually granite from the works waiting for outward shipment rather than limestone. The well-prepared rectangular blocks are in any case likely to have been destined for facing the Plymouth Breakwater.

Growth at Cattedown continued through the latter part of the 19th century, accelerated by the development of nearby Plymouth (Gill, 1997) and there is some dramatic change by 1895 (Fig. 6.4a). Faces are pushed back at the ends of lengthy horse-drawn drag-ways separated by long fingers of piled waste. The Breakwater Project was long finished in 1895, but output will still have been loaded directly into boats, although from 1888 a main-line rail service came right down the quayside in the form of the Cattedown branch of the London and South West Railway (Fig, 6.4a). This connected to a main line along the route of the original tramway through to Sutton Pool. An expensive additional branch line (Fig. 6.4b) even crossed the Laira eastwards to Pomphlett on a new rail bridge, but went little further.

6.4 Quarrying on the Oreston side at Plymouth

Landscape modification on the opposite side of the Cattewater is at least as dramatic. There are known marbles from this side as well, notably from Pomphlett Quarry (Fig. 6.4b) and particularly from Radford to the south-west (Fig.2.1). The biggest boost to excavation on this eastern side, though, was the opening of limestone quarries to supply stone blocks for the Plymouth Breakwater, constructed between 1812 and 1841. A visiting French survey-or (Dupin, 1820) described these quarries as lying "*under a surface of about twenty five acres...purchased from the Duke of Bedford for £10,000*". He claimed that "*they consist of one vast mass of compact close grained marble, many specimens of which are beautifully variegated.*" A Breakwater Project pioneer from 1811 and Superintendent from 1830 was William Stuart, noted above. His own more technical description was of a stone "*light blue or grey colour in general free from metallic veins but with some indications of manganese and iron stone*" (Stuart, 1838). It was from his own selected specimens of this stone that Stuart manufactured his marble exhibits for the Great Exhibition of 1851 (Chapter 3), comprising a marble table and a marble model of Plymouth Breakwater.

The Breakwater Project was designed to protect the Plymouth Sound anchorages and harbour inlets from storms and to enhance their security. It was precipitated by the Napoleonic wars in the early 1800s, when the French saw Plymouth as an important strategic objective, protected only by its single elevated central fort, the Citadel, offering poor defence at short range (Stuart, 1991). The English were well aware of this and knew from experience that the anchorages in Plymouth Sound provided insufficient storm protection for the Royal Naval channel fleet. Eventually consuming more than four million tons of rock, some of which was granite loaded from Princerock wharf noted above, the Breakwater Project became a nationally important undertaking.

The 'Breakwater Quarries' (circled, Fig. 6.4b) were operated on a level of efficiency that would seem progressive even today. Original Ordnance Survey maps reveal the same general method of face working by 'fingers' as at Cattedown, but the drag ways were equipped with narrow-gauge rail tracks that led down to a tidal wharf where there were two very precise loading points (Fig. 6.4b, inset). The layout reveals the revolutionary method of stone handling developed for the project by William Stuart and others that involved the first ever rail ferry. Narrow-gauge rail wagons loaded with stone were rolled straight from the quarry faces directly onto specially adapted barges (Fig. 6.5a). These were fitted with two pairs of track, one pair above the other, all accessed through two hatches at the stern either side of the rudder. The loaded wagons were rolled onto the lower tracks and conveyed directly out to sea where their contents were tipped one by one back through the hatches, directly onto the seabed. Empty wagons were successively taken out of the way by dropping a gangway and hauling each onto the respective upper length of track. (Fig, 6.5a). Later, as a structure appeared above the waves, the wagons were rolled off the barges and onto the growing artificial island, to be trolleyed to where they were required. This clever method of delivery direct from the faces avoided expensive multiple handling of stone and proved a great success. A few of the barges are captured on contemporary prints (Figs 6.5b, c), identifiable by their characteristic two-hatch stern.

To justify such a production line, Breakwater Quarry had to yield blocks big enough to stay put in storms, in huge numbers and at a sufficient rate. The enabler came in 1813 with one of the less well-known inventions of the steam entrepreneur Richard Trevithic (1771–1833). Trevithic's steam-powered drill for boring blast holes, completed in March that year, was evidently designed specifically for the Breakwater project (Trevithic, 1872). His method used the first-ever rotary drill bit, given a screw stem to clear the hole of accumulated dust. It considerably accelerated the formerly laborious method of percussive hand-tool drilling (Hodge, 1973) and was only significantly improved upon with the intro-

Section and Stern Views of Stone Vessels.

Scale

a

b

c

136

Figure 6.5. (facing page) The Plymouth Breakwater Project. a. A contemporary diagram of one of the sail barges (sheer vessels) that were used to ferry wagonloads of stone from the quarry face direct to the point of use. The twin hatches are shown open (left) and closed (right) and a scale-drawn cutaway (centre) shows two of the four onboard wagon lines, with loading ramps and methods of securing. There seems to be a technical error in the drawing, for the upper trackway must have been for the empty wagons or else each would have had to be removed from the track altogether to allow the next one through. b: The near completed Plymouth Breakwater *c.* 1832 with stone blocks being handled (similar in size to those in Fig. 6.2b). A sheer vessel with two open hatches is shown standing off on the left. Engraved by Henry Wallace from a drawing by Thomas Allom, figured in "*Devonshire & Cornwall*" illustrated by J. Britton & E.W. Brayley, 1829–32. c: Prince Rock Quarry near the Laira Bridge *c.* 1830. An anonymous sheer vessel with spanker sail set stands close to the quayside. Engraved by P. Heath from a drawing by Thomas Allom, source as in Fig. 6.5b.

duction of compressed air to clear the hole. There were several further Trevithic innovations, including drilling downwards from the top of a face instead of sideways into it, and the use of a plug-and-feather method in the hole for forcing stone out and so reducing the need for gunpowder and consequent wastage through shattering. He even showed how his steam-drilling equipment could be mounted on rails and converted to a loading machine, and then to traction power to take stone direct to the waiting barges. These transformations read like modern science fiction, but according to Trevithic (1872) his father's technology more than halved production costs, from around 2s 9d (almost 14p) per ton to 1s (5p) per ton.

6.5 From extraction to recovery—quarries on the Torquay peninsula

Seen from the sea off the Torquay peninsula it becomes clear how much of the cliff line and rocky headland between Petit Tor and Torquay Harbour has been modified by quarrying (e.g. Fig. 6.1a), but it is less clear the extent to which the natural recovery of parts of this is down to nature or the ambitions of the many clifftop residents. Stone was loaded directly into the holds of ships from these quarries and most of them had no other way out. It exploited the key feature of the peninsula, that it is mostly subtended by fairly deep water. Not all of this stretch of coast is limestone, though, so that the areas left alone were either another rock type or inaccessible even from the sea. Some of the quarries are anonymous today, and one or two of the more dangerous ones have collapsed. All the most prominent headlands on the Torquay peninsula have been reshaped by quarrying, the largest being Long Quarry Point (Figs 2.1; 6.1a) on the southern arm of Oddicombe Bay. This was already in place before the start of the 19th century and most of its present configuration was complete by the late 19th century (Figs 6.6a, b). Nonetheless it is easy to calculate that up to one million tons of limestone must have been removed from this one spot alone.

Quarrying at Petit Tor (Fig. 2.1) may date from even earlier, and the anecdotal reference to St Marychurch Rector Robert Ball being obliged to work there in the mid 1600s has been noted (Chapter 1). In fact there are three abandoned quarries in and around Petit Tor Hill (referred to as a 'Down' in some early accounts) all clearly shown on the Ordnance Survey map of 1887–9 (Fig. 6.7a). The first was on the seaward end of the headland and clearly loaded directly into moored sailing ships (Fig. 6.8b); the later and larger quarry worked by Fulton and then Hubbard was on Petit Tor beach and loaded from there, subsequently working up into the cliffs behind (Figs 6.7a; 1.4c, d). The smallest and most recent 'Blackler's Quarry' is behind the Tor (Figs 6.7a, b) and relied upon removal by road to the Blackler marble works at St Marychurch.

These two limestone headlands, together with Oddicombe Bay and the softer sandstones between them, are amongst the most photographed, sketched and painted parts of the south Devon coast. Images go back 200 years and give us direct evidence of the progress

Figure 6.6. Long Quarry Point from Anstey's Cove through the 19th century. a: Engraving by George Rowe *c.* 1835 with a quarry boat moored at Long Quarry Point being loaded. Only one pinnacle on the quarry floor is distinct. b: By the time of the Rock & Co print of November 1864 the south elevation of the quarry had evidently acquired its modern two-pinnacle profile.

of early quarrying and of the rate of post-industrial recovery and there is a case to be made that much has already returned to a pre-industrial state. In prints, postcards and photograph collections from the first half of the 19th century onwards, both arms of the bay, at Long Quarry Point and Petit Tor headland were rocky and bare reflecting a piecemeal quarried heritage. In the late 1800s the more accessible parts of the cliffs were substan-

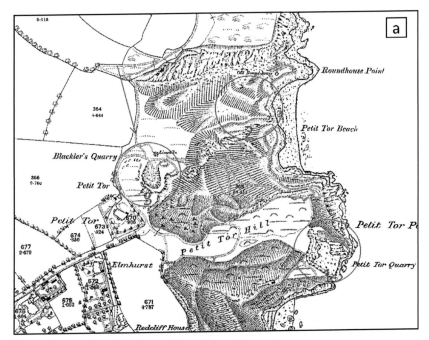

Figure 6.7. Quarries in and around Petit Tor, Babbacombe, St Marychurch. a: Quarries are numbered in probable order of appearance. 1. Petit Tor Quarry, also known as Osborne's quarry. 2. Petit Tor marble quarry. 3 Blackler's Quarry. The red arrow indicates the direction of view across which Fig. 6.7b was taken. (*Map by kind permission of Old Maps.*) b: Blackler's Quarry at Petit Tor *c.* 1890 (no. 3 above). The quarry is overgrown by trees at present (Fig. 6.9b) but in this view it is bare. Figures stroll along the recently upgraded paths. This picture was taken soon after the landscaping of the area by the local parish council (see text) and the limited size of the tip (centre) shows that it significantly predates a 1906 view in Pateman (1980). This postcard is the earliest-known view of Blackler's Quarry.

139

Figure 6.8. Oddicombe Bay and Petit Tor Down from the south; changes over 117 years. a: Oddi-combe Beach in 1896. Pathways are freshly laid out in the foreground and a recent cliff fall spreads blocks of limestone across the beach below. (*Photograph copyright: Francis Frith Collection with thanks.*) b: Enhanced enlargement of Fig. 6.8a showing the bare Petit Tor headland with the first quarry at the seaward end. Arrowed in 6.8b and 6.8c are: 1, the position of the Tor. 2, a surviving prominent rib of hardened Permian red sandstone. c: View taken Easter 2013 with the Petit Tor Headland well forested and a recent cliff fall from the red Permian sandstones. The quarry is un-changed, but a major fall from the Tor has since reduced its profile. The debris from the fall is found in the gully below at present.

Figure 6.9. Petit Tor Down, Oddicombe Bay and Long Quarry Point from the Tor at Petit Tor—changes over 100 years. a: Long Quarry Point from Petit Tor by Francis Frith, 1912. The gully (middle foreground) leading to Petit Tor Cove is mantled with low scrub but the downs are open, free of scrub and mature trees. A small oak (extreme left) has just been planted. The Tor on the left is an outcrop of *Petitor* marble. (*Photograph copyright: Francis Frith Collection, with thanks.*) b: The same view in 2012, taken from the remains of the Tor to the left of Fig. 6.9a. Abundant mature trees hide the gully and hill and they clothe the far headland. Housing has edged to the top of the cliff, but the cliff also edges towards the houses. The Oak is now a mature tree.

tially reinstated and landscaped by the Urban District Council in order to enhance visitor attractions. Using the local unemployed and calling it the 'relief works', wide paths and new planting were emplaced around 1888 (Figs 6.8a; 6.9a) and the area was subsequently given protection under local bye laws against damage and the removal of plants, which they enforced when necessary (Pateman, 1980).

The change since then is dramatically shown in photographs taken a century apart. An 1896 Francis Frith view looking north over Oddicombe Bay (Fig. 6.8b) shows the Petit Tor headland almost treeless with unstable-looking cliffs in red Permian sandstones above the bay. Its modern equivalent from Easter 2013 (Fig. 6.8c) shows that an almost complete cover of trees has sprung-up across the headland in the intervening century or less. There is also a substantial cliff fall in the adjacent red Permian sandstones that has (the night before) removed part of a house situated on what was open meadow in the earlier view. A second pair of photographs compares the same scene in the opposite direction, looking south. The Francis Frith image dated 1912 is taken from Petit Tor itself (Fig. 6.9a) and clearly shows the open downland, whilst the view taken in 2012 is almost unrecognisable as the same (Fig. 6.9b) owing to the growth of trees. In both modern views the Victorian landscaping is overwhelmed, and paths and railings have disappeared. An oak tree, freshly planted in 1912 (Fig. 6.9a), is in spreading middle age in 2012 (Fig. 6.9b). Despite the continued popularity of the area, brambles now constrain much of the formerly open downland, crowding in on what remains of the paths and poised to eliminate them altogether.

Conscious of the danger to the unwary of further movement in the red sandstones, and fearful of today's 'compensation culture', the Local Authority attempts closures and puts up disclaimers. In their defence, John Sweete's view of the offending sandstone cliffs from the late 1700s (Fig. 1.4b) shows an improbable-looking overhang, and the 2013 collapse (Fig. 6.8c) is just part of a long history of instability at that point. One factor that may be contributing to recent erosion is the state of the protective shingle beach in Oddicombe Bay. The abandonment of limestone quarrying in the headlands means that any accumulations of quarry waste under the bay are now running out so that there is no longer an onshore supply. Cliff fall debris in the centre of the bay (e.g. Fig. 6.8a) is also much reduced by an extensive modern protection scheme, and protection in one place can accelerate erosion in another.

The reasons for the vegetation changes are probably equally complex. The ancient coastline will have been richly clothed in trees but, due to human pressure on unprotected woodland as a fuel source for cooking, heating and lime production, tree cover did not survive the industrial revolution. Coastlines are never entirely static either, but there is a hint of just one more factor. The downs never maintained their own open state and the traditional control agent, deliberate or otherwise, was grazing animals. Pateman (1980) records that in 1902 *"the last of the goats that fed off the common and cliff"* at nearby Watcombe *"had gorged themselves to death"*. So if we want to redress the balance and improve access, perhaps grazing should be reintroduced.

The most prominent headland of all on the Torquay peninsula is Hope's Nose and at first glance it looks fairly undamaged. Nonetheless, the extensive flat platform just above high-tide level, so much loved by fishermen, is likely to have been quarried into its present layout and there is a larger and more concealed quarry just to the north.

Inland, there are numerous old limestone quarries in the Torquay/St Marychurch area These include Barton (originally Mincent Hill), Lummaton and Walls Hill in Babbacombe, St Marychurch and a series of unnamed quarries above Torquay, including former Sharland properties around the appropriately named Madrepore Road. Although disused, these inland quarries are no longer abandoned because they occupy locations where ground is a premium and they have been redeveloped either for industry or housing. The site of the former Sharland works itself (Chapter 3) is now a busy roundabout.

6.6 'Superquarry' to Nature Reserve—the Berry Head story

The big and obvious quarries on the south side of Torbay at Berry Head (e.g. Chapter 9, Fig. 9.18) were worked over a period of more than 200 years before finally being abandoned in the mid 20th century and they remain so. The stone was used for lime, aggregate and building, including the construction of the Napoleonic fort that tops the headland, but there is no known record of polished ornamental stone from here. Successive Ordnance Survey maps and aerial photographs record the progressive modification of this landscape (Fig. 6.10). More than four million tons of limestone have been taken from this headland, nearly all of which went out directly by ship. The quays on the north side are reasonably well protected by the peninsula itself and the seaward approach held minimal risk because the edge shelves quickly to 35 m or more. There could be as much of the headland below sea level as there is above because during the last few million years successive periods of sea level much lower than present have cut their own cliffs, milling the whole to a steep drop that is now half drowned by our most recent post-glacial rise in sea level.

Here there is a different post-industrial story because the peninsula is now a highly valued National Nature Reserve and contributes to the eastern limit of a nationally important designated 'Area of Outstanding Natural Beauty'. There is something magic about a large abandoned quarry. Lacking trees, large animals and people, it can be almost silent; even wind has little to play upon to create sound. A quarry floor can experience considerable diurnal and seasonal extremes of temperature and in the absence of soil it takes years for plants to colonise and rebuild anything like the original soil-based ecosystem. A used quarry floor can remain grassed but treeless for many decades following abandonment. Butterflies, dragon flies, rabbits, field mice and other small mammals, foxes, bats, nesting birds and raptors take over, whilst rare orchids and white rock rose can invade the floors. Berry Head demonstrates how old quarries can add value to a landscape by protecting the unusual and becoming a nationally important Nature Reserve.

6.7 The Italian (and French) connection

Despite the extensive and now abandoned limestone quarrying activity on the coast, lamented by the Rev. Ian Moore in 1829, but 'celebrated' at Petit Tor by Octavian Blewitt (1832), the combination of climate and scenery has led to some very romantic, even grandiloquent comparisons. Mediterranean references have survived, becoming popular in the 19th century This is the 'English Riviera', the term conjuring up visions of a coast with a subtropical climate and vegetation to match. In particular the Mediterranean Riviera is the stretch from Marseilles in France to La Spezia in Italy, the location of many luxury holiday resorts. The rocky Torquay peninsula was even better than that a very long time ago, when what is now rock was all coral sea, sparkling beneath a tropical sun. At best today we can only claim that the Torquay peninsula, along with the rest of this western flank of Lyme Bay, is climatically advantaged beneath otherwise indifferent English Channel skies as a result of a relatively protected exposure. The storms hold less fury on this east-facing coastline and clouds dissipate in the warming air when winds descend from Dartmoor.

Perhaps those continental allusions were inevitable once the great English Architect John Nash had introduced the 'Italian' style to the banks of the River Dart in 1805 (Russell, 1960), after which the Italianate villa became the 'must have' style for new mansions along the coast for the next 40 or 50 years, and many are still there. Victorian art critic and social commentator John Ruskin famously described this part of the Devon coastline as "*the Italy of England*" (Born, 1989), and a good bit earlier even Napoleon Bonaparte had declared that the scenery here resembled Porto Ferrajo in Elba (Russell, 1960). In summer 1815 Bonaparte had been sequestered by the Royal Navy in an attempt to prevent

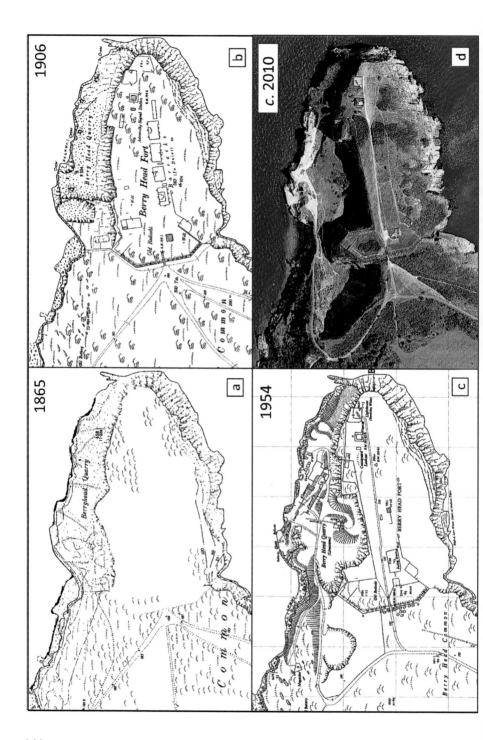

Figure 6.10. (facing page) Berry Head at *c.* 45-year intervals 1865 to around 2010. a: By 1865, quarrying is already well advanced, modifying the northern cliff line of the headland. Berry Head Fort was constructed 1794–1804, 60 years earlier than this map, but it was omitted in 1865 for security reasons. It appears in later editions of the map. b: By 1906 quarrying had encroached on the walls of the fort and the barracks are disused. There is still no landward removal and all stone was taken out by sea. c: By 1954 a landward road access had been established down into the quarry and a stone crushing and grading plant was in operation. The fort was becoming increasingly isolated by advancing quarry faces. A new extension has opened beside the access ramp. d: In the early 21st century (*c.* 2010) the quarries lie abandoned. Closed in the 1960s, the western extension was nearing its limit against the access ramp. Quarry plant was subsequently removed and natural recovery is well underway, the whole site now a nature reserve. (*Maps by kind permission Old Maps; aerial photo courtesy of the Southwest Regional Coastal Monitoring Programme.*)

him trying for political asylum in the newly independent and enthusiastically republican United States. Imprisoned on board the 74-gun Bellerophon, he was ferried from Torbay to Plymouth Sound and back again, and must have become reasonably acquainted with the passing coastline, but it is possible that his comment was less than innocent. Anchored once again beside Berry Head, just below the looming battery, his reference to Elba, his former island of exile from which he had relatively recently absconded, might have been a deliberately sardonic one. Alternatively, aware of his impending imprisonment on St Helena, perhaps he was just trying to be nice.

Napoleon Bonaparte's shadow fell across so much around the turn of the 18th–19th century and the Devonshire marble industry was no exception. The mysterious departure of *Petitor* marble pioneer John Fulton in 1797 to work on Napoleon's behalf during his ascendency is one example (Chapters 1 and 3) and the insecurity of coastal enterprises in the early 1800s is another. So was the post-Napoleonic depression which sucked wealth from where Devonshire marbles might most have been going (Chapter 5).

7. THE CORAL SEAS

7.1 Introduction

It is the corals, or 'madrepores' as all the textured, coral-like fossils were once known, that most readily enable us to recognise a Devonshire Marble. The South Devon tourist trade might rightly benefit from the notion of 'Coral Seas' along the south Devon 'Riviera', but the live corals and warm water are long gone. Even the fossils are now hard to come by. Back in the 1800s, though, tens of thousands of pebbles containing them must have been collected by 'madrepore workers' and fossil hunters from the beaches along the broad stretch of coastline between Teignmouth and Babbacombe (Chapter 3). The fossils actually mostly came from conglomerates and breccias of Permian age. The Devonian coral seas were long gone even by the Permian (Figs 1.3; 8.14) and the fossils were in limestone pebbles eroded from the mountainous landscape that had risen to replace them. Already having gone through a cycle of burial, uplift, erosion and re-deposition these pebbles commonly showed alteration colours of red and yellow, which made them highly sought after for ornamental work and in jewellery making (Chapters 4 and 5). The most iconic of the corals was '*Featherstone*', a delicate branching form, the finest of which was never found in beach pebbles but came from the Lemon Valley west of Newton Abbott. Correctly known as *Thamnopora cervicornis* (e.g. Fig. 7.11d) it may well be the most readily identified of all the corals from Devon's ancient coral seas and it found its way into jewellery, stone ornaments, tables and even church fittings. Indeed, so popular was it that its use spread as far as ornamental stone products made in Derbyshire (Chapter 5).

Several other types of Devonshire coral are illustrated in the fossils guide (Chapter 13) and corals are by no means the only fossil type to be encountered. More numerous, but coming close second in the ornamental stakes, were another type of 'madrepore' the stromatoporoids. These were round sponge-like organisms, often with a fine net-like internal texture, sometimes as big as one metre across. Stromatoporoids are also illustrated in the fossils guide (Chapter 12). The coral seas were also rich in crinoids, a form of sea lily, the disarticulated remains of which can make up substantial volumes of the Devonian limestones. The best places to see these fossils now are in one or two of the coastal sites that lie south-east of Torquay (Itineraries T1 and T2) and they are well displayed in the Plymouth Hoe foreshore (Itinerary P4). These are all protected sites where collecting is no longer permitted. There are good display collections in some museums, including Torquay Museum (Chapter 11, Group 8, SW/TQ/3), the Royal Albert Memorial Museum in Exeter (Chapter 11, Group 10, SW/EX/3) and the Oxford Museum of Natural History (Chapter 11, Group 5, SE/OX/2).

Geologists have long used fossil corals to characterise and recognise limestones of many ages, including those that belong to the 'Devonian' period (Chapter 1), and Alfred Slater's late 19th century shell and fossil dealership in Teignmouth (Chapter 3) supplied specimens to fossil experts and museums worldwide. It is 375 million years since the warm coral seas of Devon teemed with life but the fossils tell us the story of the reefs, lagoons and even the beaches that developed across the area. However the ancient organisms are not the same as modern ones, and the reefs and lagoons were unlike those of today as well.

7.2 How the coral seas formed

If we plot the former position of the Devonian coral seas across today's south Devon landscape they define a narrow and variable zone between Plymouth and Torquay (Fig. 7.1). They were once a lot wider than this and the bit of Earth's crust they once flooded has since been considerably foreshortened. The key to many changes in the past distribution of

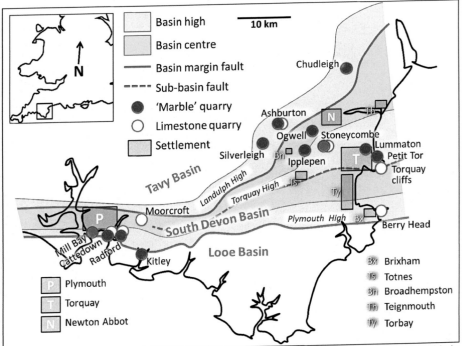

Figure 7.1. The extent of Devonian seaways across present day south Devon. Important marble locations and other quarries are shown. Only the quarries at Ashburton, Moorcroft and Stoneycombe are still working, and not for marble. Scale and key as shown.

land and sea on our planet is the jostling that takes place between the great crustal plates that form the planet's surface. The narrow linear zones where these great plates meet are points of incredibly slow geological turbulence, perhaps one plate being slowly consumed beneath another, subsiding into the mantle, or the opposite situation where the edges of plates are actually growing and moving apart with the addition of new crustal material from the mantle below. These interactions at plate boundaries set up disagreements between plates elsewhere and as they ship the changes they stretch, compress or slide sideways, but all very slowly and inexorably.

The point is that this jostling creates faulting, folding, subsidence and uplift, referred to as tectonic movements or tectonism. The subsiding areas can be many km across, usually flooded by sea, and they become the dumping grounds for muddy and sandy sediment, whilst the uplifted areas, sometimes mountains, are the ones that get eroded away and supply the sediment. These processes happened no faster in the past than they do today, and we notice little change in our own lifetimes. Earthquakes and volcanoes are our best direct evidence that such processes are at work.

In the Middle Devonian, around 380 million years ago, what became south-west Britain was undergoing its own crustal stretching, compression and sideways shifting, well summarised in Woodcock & Strachan (2012). Sedimentary basins had been developing from the Early Devonian, some 410 million years ago (Fig. 7.2) and these were the local response to the interplay of plate movements that were the final stages in the assembly of the piece of crust we now recognise as North West Europe. In fact the land we regard as the 'South West' wasn't even there the time—it was some 400 km east, under what is now France (Fig. 7.3) and had its own name—'Cornubia'.

147

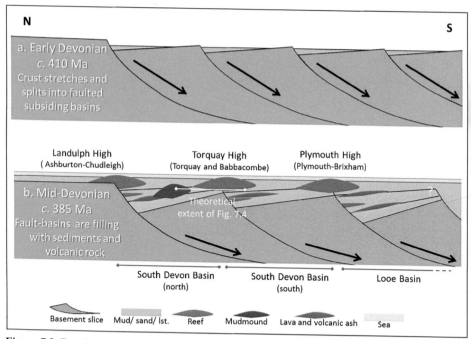

Figure 7.2. Development of the South Devon Basin during the Devonian. a. Early Devonian, showing how the stretching of the crust created faulted blocks. b. Mid-Devonian, showing how the subsidence accompanied continued stretching and further fault movement, creating linked sedimentary basins. The rough position of the block diagram in Fig. 7.4 is shown on 7.2b.

The earliest Devonian sediments that found their way into these subsiding basins were detrital mud and sand eroded from rising highlands to the north, but by the Middle Devonian a 'South Devon Basin' had differentiated itself from the rest (Figs 7.1–7.3) and it became dominated by mud and sand of a different sort, produced by lime-secreting organisms, the precursor of limestone. Soon these carbonate sediments blanketed whole sectors of the basin, organised into reefs and lagoons.

Just as 'Coral Seas' were encroaching into what was to become the South West, tectonic forces were also remodelling Wales and the Lake District, great compression creating mountainous areas and remodelling former muds into slates (Fig. 7.3). What we can say for certain is that there was land to the north and sea to the south. Just how exposed the South Devon Basin was to oceanic conditions from the south is less clear. There were further mud- and sand-filled sedimentary basins to the south-west (Fig.7.3) and these were already being affected by a northward-spreading wave of tectonism that was squeezing, pushing and uplifting them (Leveridge & Shail, 2011; Woodcock & Strachan, 2012).

7.3 Coral seas in a Devonian world

Remarkably, this trend toward Middle Devonian reefs and lagoons (the term 'lagoon' is used here instead of 'shelf' or 'platform') took place in sedimentary basins worldwide (e.g. Copper, 2002). This moment in geological time became one of the most important periods of reef formation that the planet has experienced. Some of the carbonate areas were very extensive, for example the Canning Basin in NW Australia which extended across more than 150,000 km². The South Devon Basin was a fraction of that, perhaps up

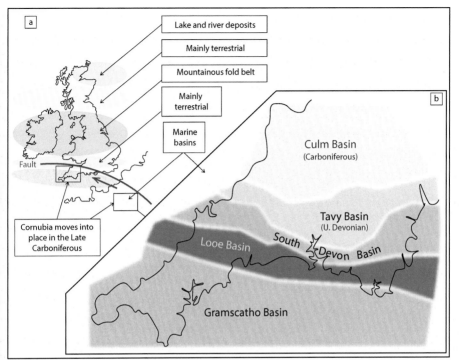

Figure 7.3. Mid-Devonian environments and palaeogeography. a: Distribution of depositional areas and upland across what is now UK and Ireland. b: Mid-Devonian and later sedimentary basins across south-west England. Note the original position of 'Cornubia' where northern France is now located, sliding into position to create the South West during the Carboniferous.

2,000 km² allowing for some later crustal compression. This worldwide expression of carbonate deposition was related to an ongoing global rise in sea level (e.g. Haq & Schutter, 2008), which progressively drowned low-lying plains and river estuaries, ponding up the incoming muds and sands.

Once this 'detrital' sediment input was reduced, carbonate-secreting organisms were no longer so regularly swamped by incoming plumes of detrital mud or sand from land areas and they reached their fullest rate of production. Carbonate sediment came from the accumulation of the remains of these myriads of marine organisms and it became the dominant sediment type in parts of the basins. The type and distribution of the organisms and consequent sediment type came under the influence both of minor worldwide blips in the rate or direction of sea-level change and of tectonically generated local highs and lows of the sea floor. These processes vied with one another to raise or drop relative sea level locally, sometimes combining to achieve moments of significantly deeper water or of shallowing and even emergence. This sort of constant change, large and small, meant periodic survival challenges for any burgeoning communities of marine organisms. Nonetheless the fact that they were still there at all means that they are were already well designed to meet such challenges, for example, their larval stages washing far and wide after reproduction, guaranteed to chance upon some new sweet spot to colonise and carry on.

Evidence for changing sea level on a worldwide scale is certainly not new. Only the widespread awareness of the links between oceans, atmosphere, climate and sea level is new. The Devonian world and its climates would seem very strange to us today, for example the amount of CO_2 in the atmosphere was a lot greater in the Devonian than it is today (but was already less than the steadily increasing O_2 content) and it dropped significantly around the middle of the Period when the first-ever terrestrial forests started to tuck away CO_2 in soils and swamps. The coral seas did not do a lot to help the balance, though, because for every molecule of CO_2 they took out of the oceans to make their calcium carbonate, $CaCO_3$, they also took an additional O, pushing the balance in favour of CO_2. Insects and allied arthropods were also quite new, and in the later part of the Devonian a few groups of fish started to experiment with the terrestrial environment, soon to become the first land-living vertebrate organisms. By contrast, the coral sea 'ecosystem' had been going for a good 100 million years, so it was a lot more sophisticated than any of the brand new terrestrial ones.

7.4 'Where corals lie'

The Devonshire marble men did not know that the best corals and best marbles would lie within and around what were once tropical reefs. It is the reefs that provide the most interesting textures, the best colour contrasts and the most diverse 'madrepores'. It was these reefs, in the vicinities of Plymouth, Torquay, Ashburton, Ipplepen and Ogwell (e.g. Fig. 7.1) that became the prime sites for marble. The reefs matter; they are the prime reason for the patchy distribution of the Devonshire marble industry but these Devonian reefs were not by any means conventional, or full of corals.

Modern reefs mostly do contain a lot of coral. They are mainly confined to shallow tropical waters where warmth makes lime precipitation easier and allows faster growth. Shallow water increases the warmth, entrains more oxygen and increases light, critical for some of the organisms in the food chain, though these alone are not enough. An elevated position above the surrounding seabed is a great help. It increases water movement by waves and tides, maximises available light and makes it easier to expel internally generated mud and sand. It also reduces the threat of sediment influx from outside that might stifle or overwhelm. All these factors optimise metabolism and growth. Many modern reefs are situated next to deep water where upwelling currents bring clear, cooler water with its own dissolved nutrients to be processed across the reef. Once established, reefs can promote their own success through upward growth. The reef is one of the most complex, beautiful and clever ecosystems that we have, and it is also one of the oldest.

Suitable sites today are on drowned topographic highs created by erosion during the last glaciation when sea level was much lower than today. Glacial cycles may also have operated in the Devonian but in the South Devon Basin there was a more reliable process that created neat seabed highs with a slope in front, and it did it in several places at once. The stretching of the crust, noted above, caused deep fracturing in its upper levels which converted directly into sliding rotational faults (Fig. 7.2). These slowly carried the seabed with them, and great chunks of it, kilometres across, majestically subsided and rotated out of the horizontal. This compartmentalised the sedimentary basin into shallow and deep areas, with the shallow areas located on the faulted crests. Not only do the reefs occupy these persistent fault-controlled highs (Fig. 7.2), but the faults went on moving, leading to fracturing and breaking up of the reefs as they formed, continually providing pathways for fluids that would indurate them and create further texture in the form of fissures and calcite veins (Chapter 8).

7.5. Where corals die

Fossil reefs can be found in rocks going back as far as 500 million years ago. As ecosystems they depend not just on the mere presence of diverse and vigorously growing organisms, but also upon the interactions and interdependence between the organisms. For example, modern corals depend upon algae, but they do not always eat them. They live with them and for both parties there are metabolic and growth advantages derived from the relationship. There is no evidence that there was this relationship in the Devonian. In fact the Devonian corals themselves are not even directly related to modern ones.

The plants and animals that build reefs have seen many changes through geological time and some of these have been brought about by ancient extinction events that decimated reef and other marine populations, forcing whole groups of organisms into extinction. However, reefs proved to be such a successful ecosystem that they became re-established after the extinctions, perhaps populated by freshly adapted forms of animals. The result is that the actual organisms that occupied reefs at different times in geological history and that became fossilised as part of them, have changed substantially. We associate reefs today with corals, but in the past corals have not always been there; at certain times the dominant reef organisms have been algae, sponges or even coral-like oysters. In the Devonian, it was mainly about stromatoporoids, but it is the corals that we seem to look for.

The corals did well in the Devonian and flourished through the subsequent Carboniferous and Permian, but came to their own end in the greatest extinction of all time at the end of the Permian when more than 90% of marine species of all types were wiped out. For a while there were no reefs at all, and no corals, but then a completely new group of corals appeared, of uncertain origin. These soon became well established, evolving to populate the seas and especially reefs even to the present day. A good review of ancient reefs, reef organisms and their evolution is in Wood (1999).

7.6 Where corals become stone

Corals are great candidates for becoming fossils. Their cups and branches (but not their bodies) are already made of calcium carbonate, which is the basis of any limestone, so once buried in a carbonate sediment they are readily preserved along with the rest. This preservation always involves water. It is water that brings in the necessary dissolved calcium carbonate, precipitating it in the pores and empty spaces, turning spacious coral into solid rock and so creating the fossil. This water can come from the sea, either pumped in by waves and tides, or expelled from below as the sediments pile up, compact, and squeeze out water. Dissolved calcite is also easily carried by freshwater, removed from an exposed surface after the reefs and the surrounding lime banks have been uplifted by one of the minor seabed tectonic movements or sea-level changes noted above. Such uplift is surprisingly common on the timescale of tens of thousands of years and is a normal part of the evolution of a reef and its surroundings (see Chapter 8). Inside many modern reefs, such brief periods of uplift in the past have allowed freshwater to slowly recrystallise the calcium carbonate in the coral skeletons, turning it from a variety known as aragonite into the much more stable variety calcite. However, Devonian corals (and stromatoporoids) were already built of calcite so this additional fossilisation pathway was closed to them. They simply became locked into the rock and their internal structures were protected and beautifully preserved, sometimes to jewellery quality.

This fossilisation process, achieved by addition of calcite into pores, is just one of several ways that a fossil can be formed but it is the important one that also turns a soft carbonate sediment into a hard rock. It can happen, as we have seen, whilst the sediment is still at or near the surface and it is a crucial stage in the conversion of a carbonate sediment into an ornamental stone, but there is a lot more to come, dealt with in the next chapter. Any organism that has a resistant bio-mineralised shell of some sort can be fossilised in this way, so it holds true for many reef organisms, but not all. The actual soft tissues of corals, the polyps with the ring of tentacles, are never preserved. In fact there are all sorts of organisms in modern reefs that consist only of soft tissue and likewise cannot be fossilised. Sea anemones, common in modern Devon shoreline rock pools, are a familiar example of a soft-bodied animal with little to no fossil record. Seaweeds, which are actually algae rather than more advanced plants, similarly lack any fossil record. We can only guess at what the ancestors of most modern soft-bodied organisms must have looked like.

7.7 Reconstructing environments

The Devonshire marbles, now distributed far and wide, often provide us with better outcrops of the reefs and associated sediments than the beaches or quarries today. Polished to perfection and selected for their colours and textures, the 'marbles' remind us that there is a lot more to the original carbonate sediments than just the corals and stromatoporoids. By combining study of the marbles in buildings with their equivalent outcrops today we can go beyond the idea of 'Coral Seas' into the diversity and dynamics of Devonian seabeds. The sediments, best seen at outcrop, usually have an 'architecture' that reveals the way they accumulated; stormy, current-swept or still, shallow or deep, fast or slow. They can tell us of beaches, shell banks, mudflats, reefs, lagoons and deeper seabeds. The fossils, well seen in the marbles but also at outcrop, tell us of the organisms that inhabited these areas, for example what they were, how they lived, how they interacted and how they passed from living state to dead. This sort of study becomes a little like forensic science—focused on the dead, how they came to be that way and what they were doing just before. In the following sections we look for the clues that enable us to unlock the probable stories of the fossil organisms and of the sedimentary environments in which they once lived.

A combined study of fossils and sediment leads us to the notion of the sedimentary 'facies', a distinct type of sedimentary environment. Across a sedimentary basin of Devonshire type (Fig. 7.1) we ought to be able to recognise a good number of sedimentary facies, each with a definable range of organisms (a fauna) and a distinct set of sedimentary characteristics. Two modern examples, easy to visualise, are a beach shingle and a lagoon mudbank. The first is deposited on an exposed shoreline and is a 'high-energy' deposit; the second is in a sheltered marshy area and is a 'low-energy' deposit. The sediments and organisms in the two sedimentary environments are very different despite both being deposited at the same time, in roughly the same place and within the same tidal range. Deeper water in both settings would also have their own distinct facies types.

Reference to high, medium and low energy as broad non-committal expressions of turbulence caused by storms, everyday waves, tidal currents or none at all, is useful and is adopted from here on. Devonshire marbles reveal some very clear facies types, simply because they are finely polished and thus reveal much detail of their fossil and sedimentary characteristics. Part of this project has been to find the equivalents of these marbles at outcrop and to find out what their spatial relationships are like. The term 'facies' is a technical one, used in the most specialist research literature, but some of the facies recognised here are great generalisations.

In part this comes from the need for obvious distinctions but, in the tectonically jumbled South Devon rock outcrops, seeing what was originally deposited near to what is no easy matter. Numerous well-known and not so well-known localities have been visited, the best of which are included in the Field Guides (Chapter 9). Hundreds of samples of rock have been collected and hand-polished to reveal what the typical Devonian limestones taken from beaches and outcrop look like when given a fine finish. Out of this 'ground-truthing' exercise has emerged a facies diagram (Fig. 7.4) that attempts to show the distribution of depositional environments through a slice of the South Devon Basin. This is a generalised picture of the distribution of some clear sediment/fossil associations that can be found in marbles, in old collections or collected from beaches and outcrop today.

7.8 A 'facies' diagram for Devonshire marbles

The facies diagram (Fig. 7.4) runs across a typical fault-controlled basin margin (theoretical position shown in Fig. 7.2b). It centres upon the sediments that accumulated above the rising crest of an active basin-margin fault (called a foot wall) where persistently shallow water conditions led to a concentration of high-energy deposits subject to the action of waves and tides. The fault itself (e.g. Fig. 7.2b) is not seen because it may seldom have formed an actual fault-scarp feature on the seabed, instead being constantly mantled by accumulating sediment. Most of the time there was probably just a seabed high, but reefs were able to develop there, seen for example in the vicinity of Torquay (e.g. Fig. 7.1). Right at the front of the reef where the downward movement of the fault progressively stretched the seabed away there are deeper water and lower energy deposits. The block itself was slowly tilting backwards (Fig. 7.2b), so that towards the rear, subsidence was a little faster and a similar deeper-water setting may have developed. It is unlikely that the full facies diversity shown in Fig. 7.4 was ever present across the South Devon Basin at any one time and the diagram is idealised. The successions are too faulted and tectonically disrupted to find any one continuous profile. For example, basin-margin reefs are only well developed during the later part of the Middle Devonian (Givetian, see Fig. 9.1). These distinctions still require more work to be fully understood.

This diagram leans heavily on previous work of others who have recognised and mapped the extending faults and understood the relationship between these and the sediments that must have accumulated across them (e.g. Scrutton, 1978; Leveridge & Shail, 2011). The diagram also recognises what we already know about Devonian limestone accumulation in basins elsewhere in the world and around Devonian reefs in general (e.g. Copper, 2002; Wood, 1999). There are summaries of the south Devon limestone successions and their distribution in Chapter 9, Fig. 9.1.

There are many facies types that can be distinguished in the limestones of south Devon, and they need to be brought down to just a few easily recognised and easily distinguished types. A comprehensive scheme has not been attempted before and the following is chosen based upon a spectrum of depositional environments from high-energy turbulent ones to low-energy stagnant ones (Fig. 7.4, illustrated in Figs 7.5 to 7.13). In the following account the terms 'shelf', 'platform' and 'ramp' are avoided. There is no compelling evidence for a persistent, self-regulating and widespread carbonate buildup as seen in other Devonian basins. Perhaps the active tectonic and volcanic interventions across the South Devon Basin inhibited the development of large-scale platforms such as those seen, for example, in the later British Lower Carboniferous. Instead, the weaker term 'lagoon' is used here and it substitutes for the concept of a 'platform floor'.

7.8.1 *The turbulent basin margin*

Facies types 1–4 are draped over the basin-margin faults. It will be remembered that the faults create high points in the basin floor (Figs 7.1; 7.2). Organic growth and calcite precipitation are at a maximum in these high-energy locations and accumulations readily build upwards to maintain shallow water. On the landward side behind the build-ups there is generally a more protected lagoon whilst at the front they are exposed to more open water with the full force of whatever storms and tides were operating and coming their way.

These high-energy sediments usually show few to indistinct bedding planes because of their coarse texture or regular reworking by storms and tides. They are light coloured as a result of the absence of fine organic carbon, lost through winnowing or selection and ingestion by reef organisms. Facies 1 and 2 are right over any break in slope between the reef front and the faster subsiding lagoon beyond and are two distinct but probably related variants.

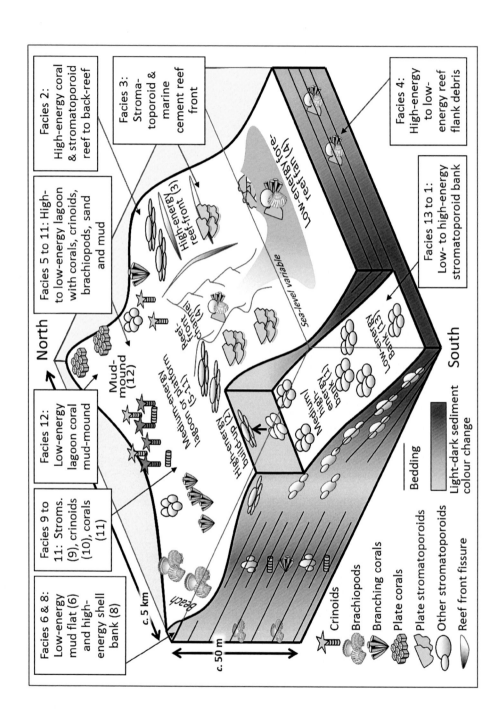

Facies 2:
High-energy coral & stromatoporoid reef to back-reef

Facies 3:
Stromatoporoid & marine cement reef front

Facies 4:
High-energy to low-energy reef flank debris

Facies 5 to 11: High- to low-energy lagoon with corals, crinoids, brachiopods, sand and mud

Facies 13 to 1:
Low- to high-energy stromatoporoid bank

North

High-energy (3) reef-front

Low-energy fore-reef fan (4)

Facies 12:
Low-energy lagoon coral mud-mound

Mud-mound (12)

Sea-level variable

Medium-energy lagoon or platform (5-11)

Reef-front channel (4)

Facies 9 to 11: Stroms. (9), crinoids (10), corals (11)

High-energy build-up (2)

Low-energy bank (13)

Medium/high-energy bank (1)

South

Facies 6 & 8:
Low-energy mud flat (6) and high-energy shell bank (8)

c. 5 km

beach

c. 50 m

Crinoids

Brachiopods

Branching corals

Plate corals

Plate stromatoporoids

Other stromatoporoids

Reef front fissure

Bedding

Light-dark sediment colour change

154

Figure 7.4. (facing page) Block diagram showing idealised distribution of sedimentary environments and the typical positions of 13 sedimentary facies types across the South Devon Basin. The position of this diagram is indicated on Fig. 7.2. The 13 facies are listed and described in the text.

Facies 1. This is the stromatoporoid bank, made of mainly domal stromatoporoids that were loose in the sediment (Fig. 7.5a). The facies is well seen in the foreshore at Hope's Nose (Chapter 9, Loc. T1.3) where there are stromatoporoids up to 0.5 m, with smaller ones and various types of coral wedged between. This is a classic stromatoporoid bank, at the top of which the stromatoporoids and corals have been thrown at angles in a storm deposit. It is possible that this facies was the precursor of Facies 2 and this is suggested in the cutaway in Fig. 7.4.

Facies 2. This is the stromatoporoid reef where the stromatoporoids are much flatter and interleaved with the sediment to provide stability (Figs 7.5b; 7.6a). The energy from waves and tides was more persistent and a coarse sediment made up of crinoid debris washed to and fro, filling crevices and burying the flanks of the repeatedly spreading stromatoporoids (Figs 7.6a; 7.6b). There is much fossil and sedimentary diversity here and the facies extends laterally to include the similar and contiguous back-reef area where stromatoporoids grew more upright. Corals are present here but are not abundant, perhaps because they found it hard to secure themselves. They adopted extended or branching growth forms that would support them amongst the more firmly rooted stromatoporoids (e.g. Fig. 7.6c).

Other organisms occur in single-species or restricted-species 'nests' which occupied protected cavities, perhaps sheltered by a flat stromatoporoid. The 'nests' include small brachiopods (Figs 7.5c; 7.5d) and, less commonly, orthocone cephalopods (Fig. 7.5.d). These quieter spaces also contain mud, commonly laminated, that had the chance to settle (e.g. 7.5d). Modern reefs have similar mud-filled cavities.

Spaces not completely filled by mud commonly show a form of calcite at the top that was precipitated into the remaining empty space directly from the seawater (Figs 7.5b; 7.5c). This marine precipitate has unique characteristics, very uncommon today, lining the sides of a cavity with palisades of elongated crystals that grew into the empty spaces. Called 'cements' these precipitates are often concentrically growth banded, showing how they slowly filled the empty space growing from the edges to the centre. There can be a core of mud filling the last remaining space at the centre. Technically, such calcite is known as radiaxial fibrous calcite. The marine cement pockets gave strength and resistance to the reef crests, even cementing the sediment itself (Fig. 7.6b). More of this marine cement will be seen in Facies 3. In fact marine calcite provides a good way of spotting the more exposed reef-type deposits especially in well-fractured marbles such as Ipplepen (Fig. 7.5c). The absence or presence of marine cement is the key difference between Facies 1 (the stromatoporoid bank), which lacks it, and Facies 2 (the stromatoporoid reef) that has lots of it. The storm-jumbled stromatoporoids of Facies 1 (Fig. 7.5a) reveal that they were loose on the sediment rather than locked in as in Facies 2 (Fig. 7.5b).

Reefs are found south-east of Plymouth (Fig. 7.1, e.g. Chapter 9, Loc. P3.3), at Berry Head (Fig. 7.1, e.g. Chapter 9, Loc. T2.1) and they occupy a stretch across the Torquay area (e.g. Chapter 9, itinerary T2). Much less well known are the reefs at Stoneycombe (Fig. 7.1), seen in the quarry today (figured with itinerary S1 but not normally accessible). The ones at nearby Ipplepen (Fig.7.1) do not seem to be recorded at all, but the marbles

Figure 7.5. (following page) Examples of high-energy reef environments in Devonian limestones (Facies 1 and 2). Locality numbers refer to the field guide (Chapter 9). a: Facies 1, Hope's Nose, Torquay, Loc. T1.3. b: Facies 2, reef core, Long Quarry Point, Loc. S2. c: Facies 2, *Ipplepen* marble shaft, St Mary's Church, Sunbury, DMB SE/TW/1. d: Facies 2, *Red Petitor* marble, Torquay. Watson Coll. # 28, Sedgwick Museum. DMB numbers relate to Appendix 1 which gives building locations. Captions, key and scales as shown.

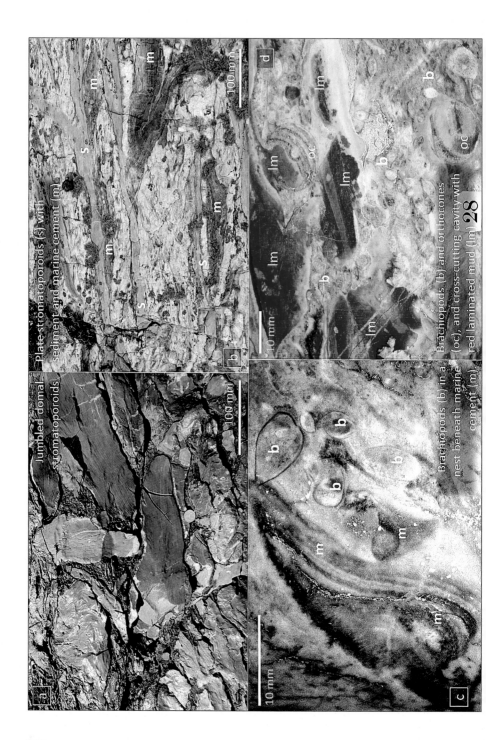

a. Jumbled domal stromatoporoids

b. Plate stromatoporoids (s) with sediment and marine cement (m)

c. Brachiopods (b) in a nest beneath marine cement (m)

d. Brachiopods (b) and orthocones (oc), and cross-cutting cavity with red laminated mud (lm) 28

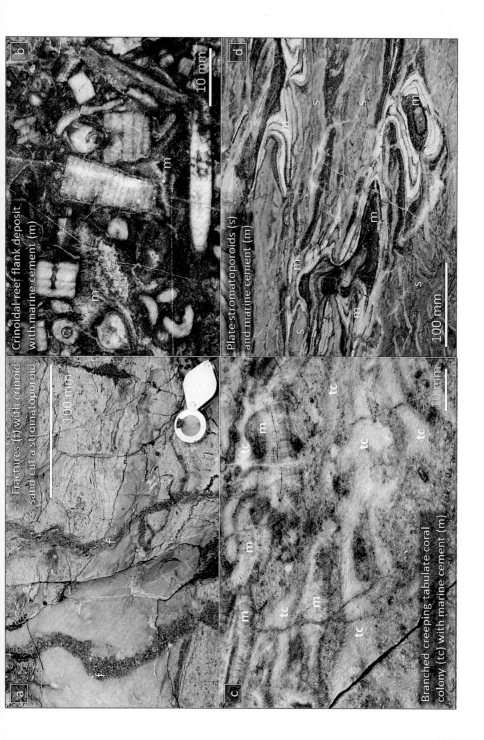

b Crinoidal reef flank deposit with marine cement (m)

10 mm

d Plate-stromatoporoids (s) and marine cement (m)

100 mm

a Fractures (f) with crinoid sand cut a stromatoporoid

100 mm

c Branched creeping tabulate-coral colony (tc) with marine cement (m)

10 mm

157

Figure 7.6. (previous page) Examples of reef cores and reef-flank deposits in Devonian limestones (Facies 2, 3 and 4). a: Facies 2, reef core, Long Quarry Point, Torquay, Loc. S2. b: Facies 4, pulpit, St James's, London. DMB L/W/4. c: Facies 2, reef core, Long Quarry Point, Loc. S2. d: Facies 3, *Petitor* marble tile, St Augustine's, London, DMB L/W/3. Locality numbers refer to the field guide (Chapter 9). DMB numbers relate to Appendix 1 which gives building locations. Captions, key and scales as shown.

from there, in buildings up and down the country, commonly show marine cements as well as brachiopod nests (Fig. 7.5c) and associated pockets of fine, laminated sediment.

Facies 3. This is the *Grey Petitor* marble facies, the most characteristic and abundant texture of all the Devonshire marbles. The seaward reef face was evidently characterised by an abundance of marine cement. It is typically grey and growth banded, filling the seaward-facing open spaces between flat stromatoporoid plates (Figs 7.6d; 7.7a)—the sorts of places where sediment is found instead in Facies 2. This cement fills some big cavities (Fig. 7.7c) and must have completely plugged and hardened the reef fronts. Sometimes the volume of cement seems to exceed the likely original space available, where early fracturing established new cross-cutting surfaces on which further cement could grow (e.g. Fig. 7.7d). Fracturing was commonplace on ancient reef fronts and given the instability of this setting over a tectonically active margin it comes as no surprise. This is further examined on the beach at Petit Tor in Chapter 9, Loc. T2.3e.

Marine cements have also been found forming small spheres, usually a few mm across (Fig. 7.7b). There are several ways that spheres of calcite can grow in sedimentary environments, but these ones, consisting of radiaxial fibrous marine calcite, may be unique. They grew a little like the well-known ooids, tiny spheres of calcite that form oolite shoals as they sweep to-and-fro in tidal settings, but they are much bigger. Movement was critical for these rounded marine 'pisoids' to form, for when jostling stopped they continued to grow, locking themselves together. This suggests that they may have occupied a tight space, perhaps a current-swept crack in the reef front.

Corals seem to have been excluded from this reef-front setting (i.e. they are seldom seen complete and flourishing in cement-rich *Petitor*), probably because they had no means of cementing themselves down. In contrast, stromatoporoids were adept at extending outwards in sheets that invited entombment by cement. In modern reefs, where corals can cement themselves down, they commonly grow as laterally extending fans at the reef front. The growth habit is very similar to what is envisaged for the plate stromatoporoids. There is one exception to the absence of corals amongst the fans of stromatoporoids in the Devonian reefs. The tabulate coral *Syringopora*, normally found in quiet environments growing in clumps, was able to entrain itself with the stromatoporoid fans and appears within them as tiny tubes (see fossils guide Chapter 12, Fig. 12.10b).

Facies 4. In all shallow-water reefs, storms and tidal energy break up the remains of dead organisms and churn them about, abrading and rounding jagged edges. Two Devonian examples are shown in Fig. 7.8, demonstrating how early cement has fully preserved the original depositional texture of the sediment and prevented subsequent compaction during burial. One of the most sought-after marble textures seen in panelling and ornamental objects is what is termed '*Petitor* shadow rock' (Fig. 7.8a). This consists of wave-washed

Figure 7.7. (facing page) Examples of fractures, cavities and calcite cements in high-energy reef environments in Devonian limestones (Facies 2 and 3). a: Facies 2/3, reef core, Cattedown, Plymouth (Loc. P3.3). b: Facies 3, reef fracture or pocket, Permian breccia, Babbacombe, Loc. T2.3c. c: Facies 3, *Petitor* marble pillar, HMS Drake, DMB SW/PL/5. d: Facies 2/3, *Petitor* marble pillar, HMS Drake, DMB SW/PL/5. Locality numbers refer to the field guide (Volume 2, Guide 1). DMB numbers relate to Appendix 1 which gives building locations. Captions, key and scales as shown.

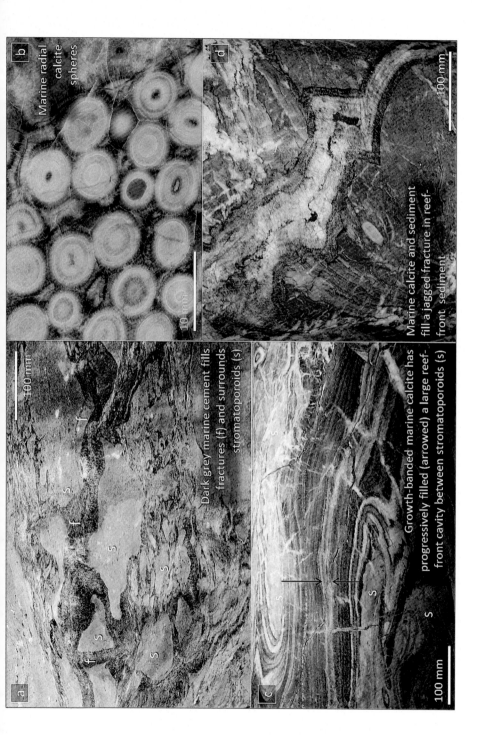

b Marine radial calcite spheres

10 mm

a Dark grey marine cement fills fractures (f) and surrounds stromatoporoids (s)

100 mm

d Marine calcite and sediment fill a jagged fracture in reef-front sediment

100 mm

c Growth-banded marine calcite has progressively filled (arrowed) a large reef-front cavity between stromatoporoids (s)

100 mm

pebbles of coral and stromatoporoid displaying a dark underlying fringe. This is the pendent bacterium *Renalcis* that grew into empty spaces. The growths give us the correct way up of the sample and indicate that soon after accumulation the inter-granular spaces were empty and still open to water movements. These first encouraged the growth of the bacteria and then enabled the precipitation of marine calcite that prevented later compaction.

The 'shadow' is not always there and a second example of this high-energy, reef-flank deposit (Fig. 7.8b) shows a sharp junction between a light, well-cemented layer and a darker one, presumed to be above. Grains at the contact are planed off. This is not an obvious post-depositional effect such as pressure dissolution (a stylolite) and is likely to be an original marine-cement-hardened surface that was polished flat before the deposition of the overlying layer. Modern examples are known in the bottoms of surge channels in reefs.

These coarse reef-derived sediments accumulated in hollows, pockets and fractures and they spread out on the flanks on either side. The Devonian reefs may seldom have had particularly sharp-defined relief—they didn't need it to operate properly—but the fault-enhanced subsidence at the front enabled fans of debris to develop in that direction. This is particularly well seen at Mount Batten near Plymouth (Fig. 7.8c and Chapter 9, Loc. P1.5). Thick units of light-coloured limestone in Castle Quarry contain broken stromatoporoids and chunks of reef rock that slid or tumbled down into place. Layers of coarse reef-derived debris are common in parts of the Plymouth limestone successions and there are some spectacular examples in local buildings (e.g. Fig. 7.8d).

The distinction between compacted and uncompacted sediment is worth emphasising. Wherever the early marine cements are abundant they provided sufficient strength to the sediment to prevent compaction by the weight of sediment building on top, but where only mud got into the spaces it squeezed flat and the fossil components became locked together. This was emphasised by later pressure dissolution, as shown in an example of a reef-flank deposit (Fig. 7.8d). As a rough indication, it requires some 100,000 pore volumes of calcite-charged water to pass through a pore space before it can finally fill with crystalline calcite. The high-energy reef environment is one of very few places where there is sufficient pumping action from waves and tides to achieve this. What actually triggers precipitation is less easy to account for and likely to be one or more of temperature, pressure change, in-sediment bacterial action and seawater evaporation.

7.8.2 *The quieter lagoon floor: sediment-dominated facies*

Facies 5 to 11 are lagoon-floor sediment types, deposited where depth or shelter generally reduced the effects of storms and tides. These are generally located on the protected side of the reefs (Fig. 7.4) but conditions were by no means permanently quiet. This was a carbonate factory in its own right where animals, plants and bacteria competed or collaborated to generate large volumes of 'bioprecipitated' sediment ranging from mud through sand to coarse shell debris, depending upon energy conditions. Most common in marbles and especially in building stones is the coarser fossil-rich debris, where the more obvious fragments are crinoids, corals, gastropods and brachiopods, examples of which are figured and described in the fossils guide (Chapter 12).

Lagoonal sediments are normally well bedded. Fine-grained ones such as muds usually being the thinnest bedded (say, 100 mm) or even finely laminated (say, 1 mm). A bedding

Figure 7.8. (facing page) Examples of high- and low-energy reef flank sediments in Devonian limestones (Facies 4 and 5). a: Facies 4, *Fossil Petitor* marble, Ugbrook House chapel, DMB SW/TQ/10. b: Facies 4, reef-flank deposit, *Fossil Petitor* marble floor slab, St John's Church, Torquay. DMB SW/TQ/4. c: Facies 4, Castle Quarry, Mount Batten, Plymouth (Loc. P1.5). d: Facies 4/5, exterior building stone, HMS Drake, Plymouth. DMB SW/PL/5. Locality numbers refer to the field guide (Chapter 9). DMB numbers relate to Appendix 1 which gives building locations. Captions and scales as shown.

a. Coarse, rounded, non-compacted coral/strom. reef-flank. Pendent bacterium *Renalcis* beneath grains.

10 mm

b. Non-compacted, rounded coral and stromatoporoid debris

Possible erosion surface

c. Probable broken and stylolitised stromatoporoid-s

Fore-reef debris

100 mm

d. Coarse, stylolite-compacted coral/stromatoporoid reef-flank.

100 mm

161

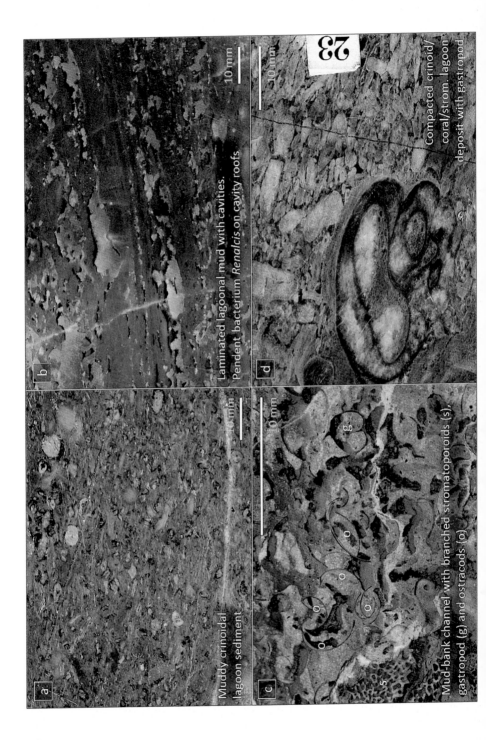

a Muddy crinoidal lagoon sediment

b Laminated lagoonal mud with cavities. Pendent bacterium *Renalcis* on cavity roofs

c Mud-bank channel with branched stromatoporoids (s), gastropod (g) and ostracods (o)

d Compacted crinoid/coral/strom. lagoon deposit with gastropod

23

Figure 7.9. (facing page) Examples of high- to low-energy shallow lagoon deposits in Devonian limestones (Facies 5, 6, and 10). a: Facies 10, Prince Rock Quarry, Cattedown, Plymouth (Fig. 8.7 inset). Watson Coll. # 35, Sedgwick Museum. b: Facies 6, in specimen table, Sedgwick Museum, OMB E/CB/1. c: Facies 6, Broadridge Wood Quarry, Lemon Valley, Loc. T3.1. d: Facies 5, Kingsteignton, nr Torquay. Watson Coll. # 23, Sedgwick Museum. Locality numbers refer to the field guide (Chapter 9). Captions, key and scales as shown.

plane usually marks a pause in sedimentation, a new sediment type or just a response to current activity or erosion. It takes burial to enhance bedding, usually through pressure dissolution. Lagoonal sediments can be dark, especially low-energy muds, owing to the retention of fine particulate organic material. Black carbonate muds made prized marbles (Facies 7, Fig. 7.10a).

Facies 5. The highest-energy lagoon sediments are a lot like those on the flanks of the reefs. In fact they can be one and the same thing, perhaps driven off the back of the reefs by storms (e.g. Figs 7.8d; 7.9d). Pretty much by definition the lagoons experienced only intermittent storm turbulence rather than the more persistent pumping by waves and tides experienced across the reefs. As a useful generalisation coarse sediments on the lagoon floor can be recognised through their matrix of in-filtered mud (e.g. Figs 7.9a; 7.10b) in contrast with the marine cement seen in the equivalent sediment near reefs, but the rule becomes gloriously unreliable in some muddy and cementy reef-like build-ups which require a separate explanation (Facies 12).

Coming down a bit in grain size, most of us can readily visualise a sandy seabed. There are ripples and dappled sunlight with occasional fish and bits of seaweed. In the geological record only the sand survives. Scavengers and bacteria degrade dead fish and seaweed and waves and tides sweep on the finer mud. Given a bigger storm, the sand itself gets carried on and dumped. That is just what happened in Fig. 7.10c. The sand is made of fine pieces of broken calcite-secreting organisms and it smothered the branched coral (probably *Remesia*) beneath. The coral formed part of a living seabed ecosystem (Facies 9) seen at Triangle Point, Torquay (Chapter 9, Loc. T1.1).

Facies 6. On the more protected margins of lagoons mud can dominate and in the intertidal zone there is growth of mudflats. If not too much disturbed by grazing and burrowing organisms a laminated texture can be detected. The example in Fig. 7.9b is particularly notable for the cavity systems that extend along the laminae. These are generally explained as the result of intertidal drying and wetting cycles that resulted in de-lamination, with the added ballooning effect caused by gasses from decomposition of organic material. It is technically termed a 'fenestral mudstone'—one with open spaces. But look inside these spaces (Fig. 7.9b) at the black rims on their roofs. These are the pendent bacterium *Renalcis* again, now hanging down inside the fenestrae. These *Renalcis* textures have not been noted in the Devonshire successions before.

Tidal flats are seldom actually flat. The water movement in and out maintains branching channel systems, on the bottoms of which coarser materials can accumulate (e.g. Fig. 7.9c). Here are small gastropods, bits of the branched stromatoporoid *Amphipora* and masses of tiny two-shelled (bivalved) crustaceans known as ostracods.

Facies 7. Black or dark grey lime muds such as Fig. 7.10a are quite common across the lagoons, especially in the Plymouth area. They make very smart marbles when veined by white calcite. As noted above, the dark colour is caused by abundant organic particles. These rocks will once have made good sources of oil or gas, but the organic compounds are well beyond this now, having been converted to microscopic coal-like particles. These organic-rich muddy seabeds were probably fairly stagnant with few organisms willing to

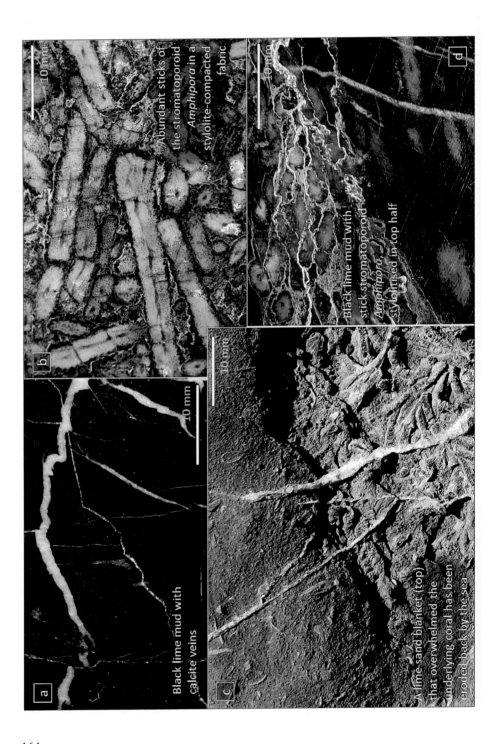

Black lime mud with
calcite veins

Abundant sticks of
the stromatoporoid
Amphipora in a
stylolite-compacted
fabric

Black lime mud with
stick stromatoporoid
Amphipora,
stylolitised in top half

A lime-sand blanket (top)
that overwhelmed the
underlying coral has been
eroded back by the sea

live there, but *Amphipora* seems to have got everywhere. It was a bush-like branching stromatoporoid, but brittle and easily reduced to layers of debris (e.g. Fig. 7.10b). The in-filtered black mud in this example has been much reduced by compaction and pressure dissolution and the sticks now embay one another along stylolite seams. In Fig. 7.10d we can see this mud-elimination process in a half-way state. Here the broken *Amphipora* are supported by black organic-carbon-rich mud in the lower right, but the mud is gone in the upper left where it has been removed by a network of pressure-dissolution seams. This is a muddy example of *Ashburton* marble, normally more abundantly fossiliferous, referable to Facies 13, yet to be examined.

7.8.3 *The generally quieter lagoon floor: fossil-dominated facies*

A distinction between sediment-dominated facies and fossil-dominated ones looks a bit artificial. After all it takes just a storm to turn one into the other. Nonetheless the following facies mostly represent the remains of distinct stable living seabed ecosystems with their own characteristic faunas, analogues of meadow, scrub and forest in the plant world. Only some of the most obvious examples are listed here.

Facies 8. In storm-swept, shallow-water settings, shelled organisms, especially brachio-pods, are easily disarticulated and the shells become stacked into one another (Fig. 7.11a). All graduations are found between this storm-packed state and the original articulated brachiopods (Chapter 12, Fig. 12.15a), still in their original life position in the mud. The individual shells (valves) of *Stringocephalus* are thick and robust, designed to survive the occasional storm and Facies 8 represents a shallow-water, high- to medium-energy near-beach environment.

Facies 9. Thinner-shelled brachiopods are associated with corals and stromatoporoids in the bedded assemblages at Triangle Point (Figs 7.10c; 7.11b). This is as close as we shall get to a fully preserved ecosystem and it rivals the mud mounds (Facies 12) for relative completeness. The assemblage is described in Itinerary T1.1 (Chapter 9) which need not be repeated in detail. The little brachiopods are thin shelled (Fig. 7.11b) and attached themselves to other objects. We can visualise them hanging onto the small branched cor-als that were themselves positioned between the more stable, mounded stromatoporoids. They lived in harmony in the sub-tidal region until a storm came along of sufficient in-tensity to disturb the seabed, break a few corals and knock off lots of brachiopods. At its worst, turbulence brought in sand from an up-slope sandbank that overwhelmed them all (Fig. 7.10c).

Facies 10. Crinoids were designed to sway with the storms and it can be seen from their accumulated remains that they could survive in high-energy, near-reef environments (Fig. 7.6b). They are explained in the fossils guide (Chapter 12, Figs 12.5a; 12.18). Made of many articulated calcite building blocks, their calyx (head) was surrounded by multi branched 'arms', all held aloft on a stem attached to the seabed. Entire forests of these animals occupied parts of the lagoon and they readily disintegrated on death, contributing vast quantities of sand to the sediments. The result is the ubiquitous crinoidal limestone (e.g. Figs 7.9a; 7.11c). Lagoon-floor sediments such as this often display coarse and fine materials mixed together, but complete crinoid 'heads' (e.g. Fig. 7.11c) are quite unusual.

a

b

Close-packed disarticulated brachiopod valves

Small brachiopods (white) amongst broken, compacted fine coral branches

c

co

co

co

co

co

ch

ch

ch

ch

Crinoid ossicles (co) and crinoid head plates (ch)

d

Branching tabulate coral *Thamnopora cervicornis*

166

It is unlikely that storms were responsible for this disturbance, for they tend to wash out finer materials, and evidence from modern carbonate environments suggests that burrowing organisms searching for food are responsible for the mixing of the sediment where coarse and very fine debris are enclosed together.

Facies 11. This facies is the coral thicket. The branching corals created the most prized of the marbles, the finest which was the so-called '*Featherstone*' of the Lemon Valley (Fig. 7.11d). There are some good colonnettes of this in the parish church at East Ogwell (Chapter 9, Loc. T3.2) and there are pieces of it in nearly every inlaid artefact (Chapter 4). A fine example of one of these reef patches made of branching coral can still be seen in Dyer's Quarry (Chapter 9, Loc. T1.4 Fig. 9.17) where the loosely branching habit may have provided mutual support enabling the growth of a 'coral thicket' on the seabed. Coral patches were seldom single species assemblages and there are smaller solitary forms here as well. Specialist stromatoporoids and algae encrusted the branches of corals in the Lemon Valley (e.g. Fig. 7.11d) and brachiopods clung onto them as well. Domal stromatoporoids seem to be missing, though. There are no stromatoporoids at all in the coral thicket at Dyer's Quarry.

There could be many reasons why corals and stromatoporoids might become ecologically separated, and we have seen that turbulence around the reefs favours stromatoporoids over corals. The opposite is not the case, however. Stromatoporoids could certainly survive in quiet conditions; see Facies 13.

Facies 12. This facies corresponds to the suite of textures found in the generally muddy *Ogwell* marbles that all come from one place, Ransley Quarry, at East Ogwell (Chapter 9, Locs T3.2, T3.3). The original quarry is in poor condition and it is difficult to see much, but its products are widespread, in panels and carved tracery as far afield as Australia. Here is where the ground-truthing exercise has not turned up photogenic examples of the rock and the following account mostly relies upon panels in buildings. We are fortunate that the finest examples are already in a museum, on the walls of the Fitzwilliam Museum, Cambridge (Fig. 7.12; Chapter 11, Group 6), but they have hung there unrecognised for a long time!

The facies corresponds to what has been termed a mud mound. This can be reef-like in some of its characteristics but is generally regarded as a deeper-water deposit. Much has been written about mud mounds worldwide and through time (e.g. Monty *et al.*, 1995; Wood, 1999). They are isolated and elevated masses of muddy sediment, often with no animal fossils but common bacterial ones. The mounds developed in relatively deep parts of a basin and can be a kilometre or so across with a depositional relief off the basin floor of 100 m or more.

The *Ogwell* facies is not strictly typical of mud mounds because it tends to be rich in fossils and, in terms of its overall size, the *Ogwell* mound is unlikely to have been in the international league. The *Ogwell* sediment is mainly buff, pink or red mud, often patchily coloured and patchily distributed. Stromatoporoids are absent, in complete contrast to the marginal reefs. The fossils are mainly flat or plate-type corals such as the densely set colonial rugose form *Frechastraea* (Fig. 7.12b; Chapter 12, Fig. 12.14b) and the much finer

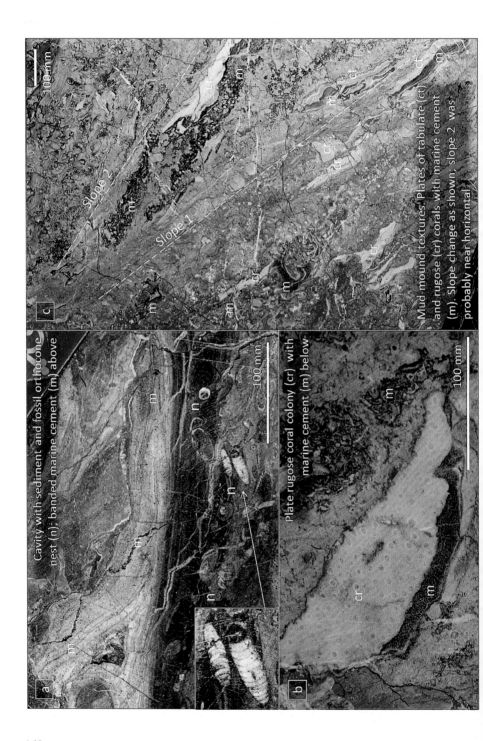

a. Cavity with sediment and fossil orthocone nest (n); banded marine cement (m) above

b. Plate rugose coral colony (cr) with marine cement (m) below

c. Mud-mound textures. Plates of tabulate (ct) and rugose (cr) corals with marine cement (m). Slope change as shown; slope 2 was probably near horizontal.

Figure 7.12. (facing page) Examples of mud-mound textures and fossils in Devonian limestones (Facies 12). a: Facies 12, Black/grey *Ogwell* pavement, St Augustine's Church, Kensington, DMB L/W/3. b: Facies 12, *Red Ogwell*, newel, Fitzwilliam Museum, Cambridge, DMB E/CB/3. c: Facies 12, *Red Ogwell* stair panel, Fitzwilliam Museum, Cambridge, DMB E/CB/3. DMB numbers relate to Appendix 1 which gives building locations. Captions, key and scales as shown.

tabulate form *Alveolites* (Chapter 12, Fig. 12.9d). Orthocones, nautiloids and goniatites are common and in Fig. 7.12a there is a mud-filled cavity with orthocone cephalopods. The laminated texture indicates lengthy accumulation and the distribution of the orthocones throughout this indicates that they lived and died there over a protracted period, perhaps 10s to 100s of years.

Where cavity-filling mud fails, the remaining space in Facies 12 cavities is taken by a lot of grey to white, banded cement (Fig. 7.13) identical to the marine cement found in the basin-margin reefs. Just as seen in the marginal reefs this cement is commonly located beneath the plate-shaped fossils; in this case it underlies the flat corals (Figs 7.13b; 7.13c). There are other much less easily explained cavities, branching or randomly shaped, but usually given away by their final fill of grey to white, banded marine cement. There may be many further cavities that are entirely filled with mud and so much less easily detected.

The partially filled cavities provide us with 'fossil spirit levels', known as geopetal infills. The key to these is that fine-grained muds deposited in protected cavities always tend to build to a flat horizontal surface. When mud can no longer filter in, the remaining space is then filled by cement from the water alone, preserving a reliably horizontal interface. This can be compared with surrounding bedding relationships and any discrepancy will indicate that the sediments themselves were deposited at an angle. The analysis in Fig. 7.13 shows a discrepancy of around 25°, suggesting that the flanks of the *Ogwell* mud mound were, indeed deposited at a substantial angle. The larger-scale stair panels at the Fitzwilliam Museum (Fig. 7.12c) even show that this angle may have changed locally during deposition, becoming less steep.

The presence of marine cement in Facies 12 is consistent with mud mounds elsewhere but its abundance strongly suggests that the growing tops were not far away from surface-generated turbulence, but if so, turbulence was clearly insufficient to remove or prevent the deposition of a lot of organically generated mud. The *Ogwell* colour variants grey and black are cement dominated, in other words they had a lot of unfilled space within them, and these may be winnowed examples, as in the top right corner of Fig. 7.12c. All this mud is unlikely to have been mechanically generated and most authorities believe it was precipitated through the action of microbes. It might even have been sticky or hard. It is quite possible that the unusual radial fibrous marine cements are also microbe mediated.

The origin of the cavities, so often found beneath a flat coral, requires some further discussion. Shelter spaces are suggested above, but this seems not to explain them all. In modern carbonate environments organisms commonly maintain shelters beneath corals and other seabed objects and burrow systems are also common. Animal shelters may be the case here, especially since active animals like cephalopods are found within some of them (Fig. 7.12a), but the explanation seems not to fit them all. Mud- and cement-filled cavity systems of the *Ogwell* type are characteristic of mud mounds in general and have been placed in a mysterious category termed 'stromatactis'. There has been much debate over the origin of stromatactis cavities and they have been attributed to physical changes in the mud or to the aftermath of soft-bodied organisms that have failed to become fossilised; something like a soft sponge. Some *Ogwell* cavities are quite big (e.g. Figs 7.12a; 8.28), extending up to 1-m wide or more. This is bit big for a burrow and these look more like small dissolution caves, fractures or both. This opens up questions about the physical stability of the *Ogwell* mud mound and about its closeness to sea level and the possibility of emergence taking place.

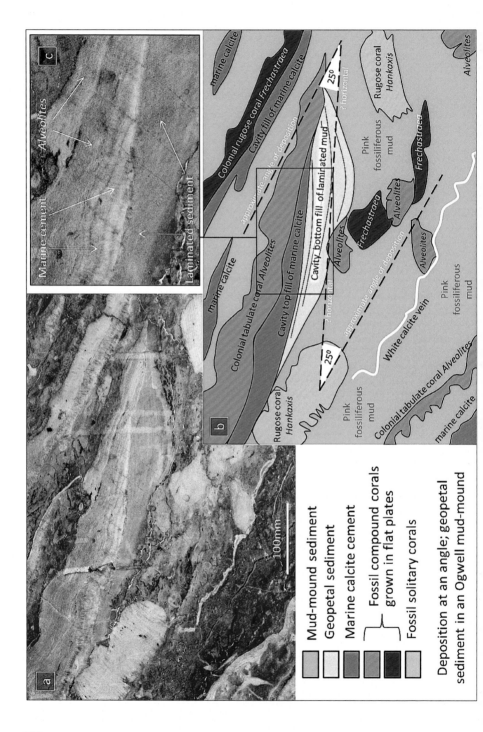

c

Alveolites

Marine cement

Laminated sediment

a

100mm

b

Marine calcite

Colonial rugose coral *Frechastraea*

Cavity fill of marine calcite

25º

? horizontal

Rugose coral *Hankaxis*

Alveolites

Pink fossiliferous mud

Frechastraea

Alveolites

approximate angle of deposition

Cavity bottom fill · of laminated mud

Frechastraea

Alveolites

Marine calcite

Colonial tabulate coral *Alveolites*

Cavity top fill of marine calcite

? horizontal

Alveolites

approximate angle of deposition

White calcite vein

Pink fossiliferous mud

Rugose coral *Hankaxis*

25º

? horizontal

Pink fossiliferous mud

Colonial tabulate coral *Alveolites*

marine calcite

Mud-mound sediment

Geopetal sediment

Marine calcite cement

Fossil compound corals grown in flat plates

Fossil solitary corals

Deposition at an angle; geopetal sediment in an Ogwell mud-mound

170

Figure 7.13. (facing page) A stair panel at the Fitzwilliam Museum, Cambridge shows fossiliferous *Red Ogwell* marble from the mud mound exposed at Ransley Quarry, East Ogwell, near Newton Abbott (Loc. T3.3). Fossils, sediments and diagenetic features are identified in Fig. 7.13b. A cavity beneath an inclined coral, *Alveolites*, has a geopetal infill consisting of horizontally bedded internal sediment overlain by cavity-filling marine cement (Figs 7.13a and c). The 'marble map' analysis of this (Fig. 7.13b) shows a 25° discrepancy between laminae within the cavity and the inclined bedding outside it. Corals are evidently aligned parallel to inclined bedding, some at a higher angle and some at a lesser one. Key as shown.

Of all the Devonshire marble varieties, *Red Ogwell* and *Pink Ogwell* are physically most like the brown, red and pink Devonian marbles that come from Belgium and France. There can be no surprise at all, therefore, that they are all derived from Devonian mud mounds.

Facies 13. This is the obviously bedded dark, stromatoporoid-rich facies that includes *Ashburton* marble (Fig. 7.14). The quarries from which the marble comes (Fig. 7.1) are located not far beyond the northern bounding fault of the South Devon Basin, on the Landulph High (Fig. 7.2). The schematic diagram (Fig. 7.4) is designed to show generalised facies variations either side of a fault-controlled high rather than a representative section through the complete basin, so the equivalent position of the *Ashburton* facies in this diagram is somewhere at the front, positioned near the fault-controlled high, but this position raises a number of questions discussed below.

Ashburton fossils include abundant growth-banded stromatoporoids 10–500 mm. Smaller fossils of all sizes are also abundant, mainly corals and small stromatoporoids, set in a matrix of muddy sand that gives the sediment its dark colour and bedded texture. These smaller fossils are commonly broken and disarticulated, but that is not unusual in a vertically compacted mud. So how much wave or storm disturbance is represented here?

Looking for signs of overturning of stromatoporoids, it is often difficult to determine the correct way up of *Ashburton* marble in the first place. Half-filled cavities (geopetal infills) are uncommon, but from stromatoporoid growth features it is possible to see that they are not all the same way up. In Fig. 7.14b, for example, a group of three stromatoporoids (bottom right) seem to be stacked together, but whichever way up the panel is orientated, there is always one fossil that seems to be the wrong way up. Stromatoporoids have apparently been toppled and rolled. The fragile branching stromatoporoid *Amphipora*, can help us a bit here as it is occasionally seen in branching form as well as in broken and abraded fragments. Brachiopod shells and gastropods have been noted in single species groups suggesting very little disturbance. Clearly, *Ashburton* marble had its moments of turbulence and yet the dark, muddy sediment tells us of prolonged periods without disturbance in the sort of muddy oxygen-poor environment that corals and stromatoporoids ought to have disliked.

There is a paradox here, especially since as far as we can tell, the *Ashburton* sediments were laid down at about the same time as the turbulence-dominated reefs were growing around Torquay. One way to resolve this is to avoid the assumption that depositional conditions across the faulted basin margins were all the same. Conditions just across the Torquay margin itself varied through time but were persistently turbulent. Situated on the more protected 'inner' north-western margin of the South Devon Basin (Fig. 7.1), the *Ashburton* basin margin was probably altogether quieter than Torquay, protected behind all the mud mounds, mudflats and crinoid groves of the central part of the lagoon (Fig. 7.4). Instead of being a high-energy reef with all the plate stromatoporoids and marine cements like the Torquay high, the *Ashburton* margin was probably just a gently sloping carbonate bank. Certainly there is no evidence in the Ashburton area of any conventional reefs. The dark colour of the sediment represents the local burial of organic carbon instead of its degradation or removal in turbulent and well-oxygenated conditions, as happened at Torquay.

Domal stromatoporoids (s), smaller corals and stroms. (cs). Growth directions arrowed in b.

172

Figure 7.14. (facing page) Examples of mixed-energy sediments and fossils in Devonian limestones (Facies 13). a: Facies 13, loose block, Linhay Quarry, Ashburton, Loc. S1. b: Facies 13, *Ashburton* marble stair panel, Civic Centre, Plymouth, DMB SW/PL/4. c: Facies 13, masonry block, Meadfoot sea wall, from nearby Triangle Point, Loc. S1. Locality numbers refer to the field guide (Chapter 9). DMB numbers relate to Appendix 1 which gives building locations. Captions, key and scales as shown.

We can visualise the stromatoporoid-rich *Ashburton* facies (Facies 13) accumulating on an extended sloping bank, perhaps a kilometre across and extending down to several tens of metres deep. Extreme turbulence, capable of rolling stromatoporoids, breaking branching coral and disarticulating brachiopods, was a rare event, happening only when the region was swept by extreme storms. At other times, only the living surface of the stromatoporoids and branching organisms needed to be kept clear. This was achieved by tidal movement and gentle oscillation caused by everyday sea conditions. The carbonate mud with its organic carbon generally filtered into the surrounding debris. The serious clean-up and washing on of the mud came only with the bigger storms.

If there was an up-slope, shallow-water equivalent of the *Ashburton* facies in the Ashburton area we know nothing of it—the outcrop there is a large and isolated faulted lens, but we can get a clue about what it might have been like in the Torquay area. It is the Hope's Nose mid- to high-energy stromatoporoid bank (Facies 1). This is a mound of stromatoporoids with a wave-washed top that could easily represent the wave-cleaned upper, shallow-water edge of an *Ashburton*-type stromatoporoid spread. We do not know what lay in front of the Hope's Nose stromatoporoid bank because it is submerged, but a little further west, in rocks of similar age, there is a convincing *Ashburton*-type facies exposed in the vicinity of Triangle Point. The best pieces are in the Meadfoot sea wall (Fig. 7.13c).

The Hope's Nose bank and the *Ashburton*-type facies in the Meadfoot sea wall all lie stratigraphically beneath the reef developments a bit further north. No transition is exposed, but in Fig. 7.4 it is suggested that the low-energy stromatoporoid bank (Facies 13) formed the springboard for the later development of the high-energy stromatoporoid banks (Facies 1) and finally reefs (Facies 2) of the Torquay area.

7.9 And then...

Towards the end of the Devonian, a wave of tectonism began to reverse the extensional faults that created the South Devon and other adjacent sedimentary basins across the South West. The contents of the basins became uplifted, folded, faulted and eroded and the tectonic processes turned the sedimentary rocks into what sometimes became very complex low-grade marbles. The events are followed in the next chapter.

8. THE MAKING OF MARBLE:
THE POST-DEPOSITIONAL TEXTURES

8.1 From limestone to 'marble'

The sedimentary and fossil textures that developed on the Devonian sea floor and gave the marbles their unique 'Devonshire' signature (Chapter 7) was only the start of their textural evolution. These original depositional textures became modified over the next 50 million years or more as the area became buried, faulted, folded, sheared, uplifted and eroded during a succession of dramatic changes driven by crustal movements beneath what became South West England. This chapter examines these post-depositional changes and shows what can be recognized in the marbles.

The crustal upheaval that caused the re-texturing was part a major tectonic disturbance known as the Variscan orogenesis. The Greek word '*oros*' means 'mountain', but it is not clear just how much elevation there was across South Devon. The creation of an elevated landscape is just one manifestation of the orogenic process and there is always a lot more going on underneath to cause the uplift. There is no evidence in Devon for the scale of uplift as seen, for example, in the modern Alps—a much more recent orogenic zone. In fact the relatively limited rock pile up and consequent restricted depth of burial of the Devonshire limestones is a key factor in the survival of their original depositional textures. Some Alpine limestones are completely recrystallised to a coarse white calcite; the best example being *Carrara* marble. Its precursor limestone was driven kilometres deep into a substantially hot pile of sliding and contorting sedimentary rock before being returned to the surface as pure marble by the erosional removal of everything that had buried it. Such recrystallisation does not affect Devonshire marbles and its absence introduces a tension between the popular term 'marble', used throughout this book, and the true state of the rocks, which in geological terms is certainly not a true marble.

This orogenic phase in the story of the South Devon Basin is the point in geological history when stretching of the crust and the associated formation and fill of sedimentary basins came to an end and horizontal crustal compression took over (Fig. 8.1). The result was that the extensional faults that defined the basins reversed their movement and drove the other way, compressing, folding, slicing and dislocating the contained sediments and ejecting them over the next basin to the north. One by one, basins from the south-western tip of Cornwall to South Devon ground shut, adding their ejected sediments to the burden of the next basin. Nonetheless, the consequent tectonic burial of the South Devon Basin was never very great. In the Torquay area it was perhaps just a few kilometres, little more than might be achieved by simple subsidence and sediment accumulation alone. Moving back down the line to the south-west, past Brixham and towards the south coast of Devon, then further south-west into Cornwall, recrystallisation of the rocks increases suggesting greater tectonic burial and more extreme burial conditions (Leveridge *et al.*, 2003).

This was all part of a more widespread and persistent phase of crustal instability at the time when the major elements of the crust in North West Europe were finally being assembled. It is difficult to pin down the moment it all started, perhaps the Early Devonian, and it continued through the Carboniferous and into the Permian. The story of this more widespread jostling of crustal plates is highly complex and some parts of it are still problematic (summarized in Woodcock & Strachan, 2012) but the local story in south-west England is increasingly well understood (e.g. Leveridge, 2011; Leveridge & Shail, 2011). Now much clearer, for example, is the connection between the suite of ornamental stones that is Devonshire marble and the suite that is Cornish serpentine, the two often used together in British buildings. Serpentine comes from the Lizard Peninsula, the southern tip of Cornwall and was once a basic igneous rock rather than a limestone. It was part of a series of

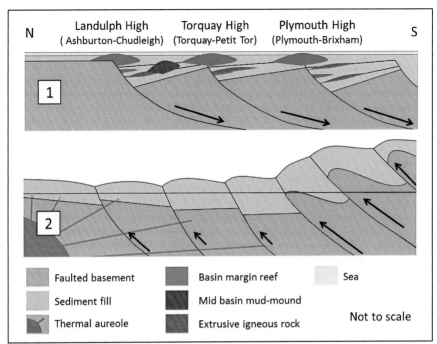

Figure 8.1. The transition between crustal extension and crustal compression in the South Devon Basin. 1. Mid Devonian. Crustal extension continues to slide basins apart and carbonate sediments and reefs build on basinal highs. Igneous rocks (lava and volcanic ashes) are extruded nearby, having risen to the surface along the faults. (As shown in Fig. 7.2.) 2. Composite late Carboniferous to early Permian. Extension is reversed and tectonic compression refits the crustal blocks. Sediments are thrust out of the basins, being eroded away as they rise. Basin closure took place from S to N in stages. Finally, the Dartmoor granite was intruded nearby and heat effects and mineralisation extend into the area. Diagram modified after Leveridge *et al.* (2002) and Leveridge (2011).

igneous rocks known as ophiolite that started life on the floor of an open Devonian ocean. Crustal extension at this far south-westerly location had parted the continents so effectively that there was an open stretch of ocean floor with its typical oceanic igneous geology. As compression took over, a slice of this became scooped up by a major thrust, altered to serpentine and then shoved north-westwards beneath an advancing thrust sheet (Leveridge & Hartley, 2006). This thrusting encountered the Gramscatho Basin, the more distant of two basins that lay south-west of the South Devon Basin (Fig. 7.3). It was a lengthy process, the first compression taking place whilst limestones were still forming in the South Devon Basin, but by the end of the Devonian the sedimentary contents of the Gramscatho Basin had themselves been shoved north-west to encounter the Looe Basin (Fig. 7.3), just south of the South Devon Basin. This overwhelming of the Looe Basin was probably the event that one way or another terminated sedimentation in the neighbouring South Devon Basin (e.g. Fig. 8.1). Soon it would be the turn of the South Devon Basin itself to feel the full effects of this wave of compression that was slowly creeping northwards.

These are epic events and ones that geologists are happy to model, yet they are hardly believable in the context of the rate of change we see in our own lifetimes or even through human history. Much of the detail of what happened across the South Devon Basin and in the wider region has only been decoded from the rocks in recent years (e.g. Selwood *et al.*, 1984; Leveridge *et al.*, 2002, 2003; Leveridge, 2011; Leveridge & Shail, 2011). This field-scale analysis has revealed at least three separate phases of tectonic deformation during the Variscan storm, each marked by cleavage (a metamorphic re-texturing) folding, faulting and thrusting. As for the marbles, none of them tells us anything like the whole story, and some of them tell us none of it.

The following account is intended to help the recognition and understanding of the fracturing, shearing, veining and pressure dissolution seen in the marbles that resulted from tectonic re-texturing. What remains unclear is how these relate to the three mapped Variscan deformation events seen on the ground and the connections are not attempted here.

8.2 The transition from deposition to uplift

The 'Coral Seas' of Devon were eliminated before the end of the Devonian period, ushered away by falling worldwide sea levels and hastened out by the local tectonic storm that was gathering beneath the basins. Perhaps it was tectonic compression and uplift that delivered the final *coup de grace* for the seaways, or perhaps it was the blanketing of the South Devon Basin by muddy and sandy detrital sediment shed from tectonically driven rising ground to the south. Either way, blame it on the Cornish Serpentine ejection event. This was the moment of geological transition between rolling sea and active tectonism, and evidence for the actual transition has been inherited by some of the limestones, which became fractured and invaded by mud.

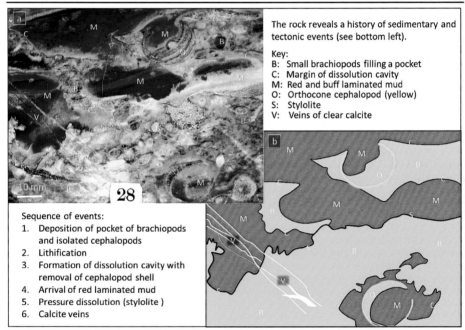

The rock reveals a history of sedimentary and tectonic events (see bottom left).

Key:
B: Small brachiopods filling a pocket
C: Margin of dissolution cavity
M: Red and buff laminated mud
O: Orthocone cephalopod (yellow)
S: Stylolite
V: Veins of clear calcite

Sequence of events:
1. Deposition of pocket of brachiopods and isolated cephalopods
2. Lithification
3. Formation of dissolution cavity with removal of cephalopod shell
4. Arrival of red laminated mud
5. Pressure dissolution (stylolite)
6. Calcite veins

Figure 8.2. Sedimentary textures in a block of *Red Petitor* marble, Petit Tor Quarry, St Marychurch, Devon. Specimen 28, Watson Collection, Sedgwick Museum, Cambridge (Chapter 11, Group 6, E/ CB/1). a: The marble – a 115-mm-wide block. Contrast is digitally enhanced to aid interpretation. b: Marble map at 1:1 scale showing the distribution of the main sedimentary features. Key and captions as shown. The marble shows evidence of early uplift and exposure to erosion by rainwater, with the formation of small dissolution cavities and the removal of marine shell material. Marine mud then filled the vacated spaces. For further explanation see text.

Extensive fissures containing red mud are seen at outcrop in the limestones at both ends of South Devon, at Petit Tor (Chapter 9, Loc. T2.3b), Western King (Loc. P2.3), Plymouth Hoe (Loc. P4.2) and Cattedown (Loc. P3.3). The mud can be squeezed along bedding, looking like tectonic injection effects, and it can be seen within irregular cavities that appear to be fractures, fissures and/or dissolution effects. The widespread invasion of the limestones by mud in the Plymouth area was noted by Leveridge *et al.* (2002) who regard it as surface-derived Late Devonian sediment that found its way into the raised, exposed and fissured surface in the Late Devonian or early Carboniferous (Fig. 1.3).

Sea-floor instability was not new in this crustally active setting (Fig. 8.1) and at Petit Tor there is also earlier invasive mud that needs to be distinguished. The mud fills small irregular cavities and extends into empty spaces vacated by the dissolution of shells of marine organisms (Fig. 8.2). Not only that, but in order for the texturally cross-cutting cavities to form and maintain their shape, the sediments containing the shells must already have been lithified to rock, perhaps by cementation following uplift whilst dissolution took

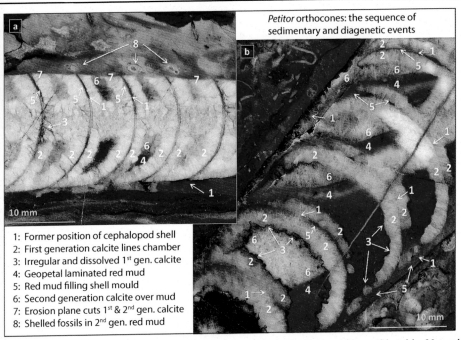

Petitor orthocones: the sequence of sedimentary and diagenetic events

1: Former position of cephalopod shell
2: First generation calcite lines chamber
3: Irregular and dissolved 1st gen. calcite
4: Geopetal laminated red mud
5: Red mud filling shell mould
6: Second generation calcite over mud
7: Erosion plane cuts 1st & 2nd gen. calcite
8: Shelled fossils in 2nd gen. red mud

Figure 8.3. Sedimentary textures in two fossil orthocones in the Devonshire marble table, Natural History Museum, South Kensington, London (Chapter 11, Group 2, L/W/2). The key to the numbers is included with the figure. The succession of events starts with deposition of calcite (2) on the internal walls of the orthocone (1). The shell, made of aragonite and soluble in fresh water over many years, was weathered away leaving empty spaces throughout. This erosion also etched the more stable calcite that lined the internal walls, leaving the surface irregular and stained (3). Red mud then incompletely filled the calcite-lined orthocone chambers, laminated in places (4), and the mud also squeezed into the spaces formerly occupied by shell (5). The mud fill of the chambers was incomplete and the remaining space was sealed by a further generation of calcite (6) creating a geopetal fill that reveals the angle at which the orthocone rested. Renewed erosion, this time probably mechanical, planed off the top of the horizontal-lying orthocone seen in (7). The calcite fills of the chambers (6) are clearly intersected by this erosion. A second generation of marine mud, with small marine shells (8) was then deposited across the eroded surface.

Figure 8.4. Early invasive mud in the headland quarry, Petit Tor, St Marychurch, Devon (Chapter 9, Loc. T2.3b). a: Red mud (M) in vertical and horizontal fissures and cavities. Grey limestone between. Note the apparently loose-draped bedding in a cavity at M1. b: Red mud (e.g. M) smeared along shear planes on the NE seaward side of the quarry.

place. Better detail of the actual dissolution of shell material comes from specimen pieces of *Petitor* marble set into some ornamental marble tables (e.g. Fig. 8.3). Spaces around orthocones created by the dissolution of shell have been filled and covered up by lime mud with its own separate population of small marine organisms.

Such intricacies of textural development are not unique and are known in shallow-water carbonate sediments elsewhere in the world where exposure of the seabed led to the dissolution of mollusc shells by rainwater, known to attack their special mineralogy, followed by invasion of the vacated spaces by soft mud. The shell dissolution at Petit Tor took place during uplift between phases of normal marine deposition. Micro-events such as this are not quick. Dissolution alone could take a hundreds of years, so these exposure events are well within the likely time frame of fault adjustments within the tectonically active basin.

The early fossiliferous carbonate mud at Petit Tor is thus distinguishable from the more obvious and abundant silty mud of the sort noted by Leveridge *et al.* (2002), but it is part of the same story of tectonic instability. Large volumes of the mud fill some extensive fracture systems both parallel to and cross-cutting bedding and it seems to be bedded in its own right (Fig. 8.4a). This mud is also squeezed along lenticular tectonic shears, evidently remobilized (Fig 8.4b), so its arrival pre-dated tectonism. This suggests first uplift and disruption of the limestones with enhancement of fissures by substantial and prolonged karst-type erosion and then (or simultaneously) invasion of the cavities by detrital mud. Where later tectonic shear zones intersected karst cavity fills the mud contents became squeezed and remobilized along the shear planes.

Figure 8.5. (facing page) Ductile deformation in limestones at Plymouth and Berry Head. Localities identified below. a: Deformed bedded limestone, Plymouth Hoe (Chapter 9, Loc. P4.6). The sediment contains lenticular (compacted) stromatoporoids and is cut by a calcite-filled fissure. The crack indicates that the limestone was lithified when it was formed, but its convoluted, meandering edges and the flattened fossils demonstrate later tectonic deformation. The crystalline structure of the fissure fill survives this deformation. b: Deformed reef, Berry Head, Brixham (Chapter 9, Loc. T2.1). The reef contains grey cement-filled cavities (C) and red mud. Crinoid stem sections are respectively compressed (A) and spread (B). Compression and stretching were concurrent and substantial. Short pieces of crinoid stem like these are common as resistant objects on the sea floor. The stretching at B demonstrates that ductile deformation overcame the cemented attachment of ossicles to one another and acted uniformly, but did not deform the individual ossicles themselves, which were made of rigid calcite. c: 'Spread' crinoid stems, nave shaft, Plymouth Cathedral (Chapter 11, Group 9). The host rock is compressed and nearby shafts show deformed veins, as in 8.5a. Internal shear has dislocated the individual ossicles (D) but they have not become deformed themselves, as shown by the nearby circular cross section (E). A swarm of reddened stylolites (S) eats into the base of the ossicle at (E).

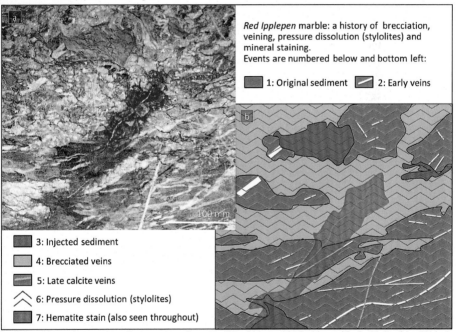

Figure 8.6. Mapping complex textures in a *Red Ipplepen* marble, nave shaft, Unitarian Church, Todmorden, West Yorkshire (Chapter 11, Group 11, YH/OL/2). The quarries were at Ipplepen, near Newton Abbot, Devon and this is likely to be from Barton Quarry, Ipplepen. a: The original *Ipplepen* marble in a nave shaft. Scale as indicated. b: Marble map, 1:1 scale, of the textures in 8.6a. These are numbered in probable order of development in the adjacent key. A similar specimen to this with the same sequence of events is Watson Collection specimen 18, Sedgwick Museum, Cambridge.

8.5 Sediment Injection

There are actually three ways extraneous sediment can get into a hardened limestone. It can wash in (as in Fig. 8.3), it can get squeezed in (there are some Plymouth examples in Itinerary P2, Chapter 9) and it can get smeared in along shears (Fig. 8.4b). As already noted, it is common to see red/brown sediment within veins and fractures in Devonshire

181

marbles but, even in an ideal polished marble specimen, proving that the mud is injected or sheared is not always straightforward. Examples of injection are found in *Ipplepen* marble, which commonly shows fields of brown and largely structureless carbonate mud (Fig. 8.6, event 3). Sample 18 in the Watson collection at Cambridge, the type specimen of *Red Ipplepen* (Chapter 10, Fig. 10.5a), shows more of this evidently remobilized brown mud. A necessary distinction here is that the mud behaved in a liquid manner and was originally structureless when emplaced. In these examples we cannot be certain that this was the case because of subsequent shearing and pressure dissolution, yet to be discussed.

8.6 Veins and fissures

Veins are perhaps the most abundant and obvious post-depositional feature in Devonshire marble. They are normally recognised by their white or clear calcite, but dolomite (where magnesium replaces calcium) also occurs, usually more yellow because of small quantities of iron. There are two types of vein that are empirically distinguished. One is irregular and parallel sided, sometimes branching and often elongated. The other consists of discontinuous essentially lensoid structures, usually small, parallel and often numerous. These are fractures of some sort, the first perhaps shallow, even surface connected, termed a 'fissure vein'; the second a deep burial and tectonic-related phenomenon, termed a 'shear vein'. The two types of vein are illustrated in a single shaft of *Petitor* marble in Fig. 8.7.

Fissure veins. Fissure veins are distinguished here as rents that have obviously lain open for a while as they filled passively with mineral material or surface-derived sediment. A mineral-filled one is characterised in Fig. 8.7b and has matching jagged margins that could theoretically be re-fitted and a lining of crystals that grew off the walls into a water-filled space. This sort of crystal lining is commonly growth banded with parallel layers mirrored on both sides of the fissure, reflecting changing conditions of precipitation. Fissure veins can also be sediment filled indicating that they have been surface connected but they can also be much deeper effects, perhaps with a range of mineral types lining the sides, but no examples of such 'mineral veins' have been noted in Devonshire marbles. Only very early fissure types (seabed and early uplift, Fig 8.7b) and very late ones (linked to the Permo-Trias surface, e.g. Fig. 8.19c and Chapter 9, Fig. 9.20) have been recognized.

Shear veins. Shear veins are here distinguished as formed under compressional forces and are more complex, more abundant and more paradoxical. Individual veins are short, lens-shaped, irregular and the mineral fill is uniform, without evidence of parallel growth zones. There are examples in Fig. 8.7a, enlarged in Figs 8.7c, d.

How can compression lead to the opening of a vein? The answer familiar to geologists is that they form at times of faulting and folding when the rock pile is being compressed and sheared but still in a semi-brittle state. Shearing becomes concentrated along planes

---

Figure 8.7. (facing page) Distinguishing characteristics of an early fracture vein and late shear veins, *Red Petitor* marble, Cambridge Room, HMS Drake, Plymouth (DMB SW/PL/5). a: The base of a *Red Petitor* marble shaft shows fissure veins and shear veins (terms defined in the text). The shaft rests on a base of *Grey Fossil Petitor*. b: An early calcite-filled fissure (termed here a fissure vein) cuts sediment and original cement. Note that shear veins cross this earlier fracture at the left and rear of the marble shaft, but generally the vein is free of later shear effects. This indicates that whilst the rock acted coherently, the vein deformed along its many crystal boundaries. Further notes are inset. c: A zone of white calcite-filled shear veins form an 'en echelon' set. Further notes are inset. d: A zone of white patchy calcite marks a more mature shear zone where movement has been more persistent and vein-filling calcite has grown, fractured and dissolved, finally becoming pressure-dissolved to form stylolites.

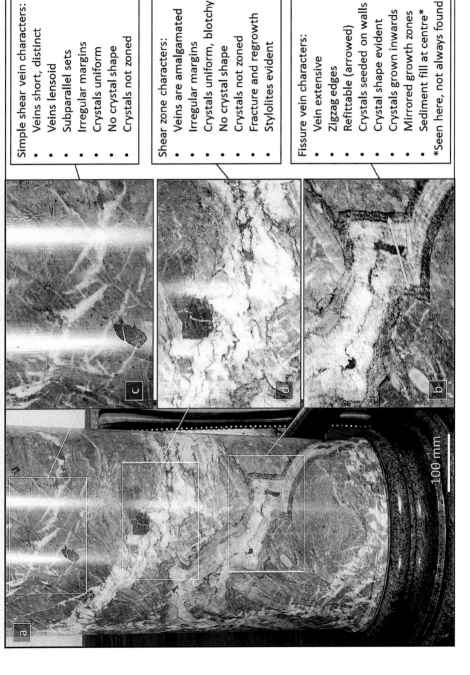

Simple shear vein characters:
- Veins short, distinct
- Veins lensoid
- Subparallel sets
- Irregular margins
- Crystals uniform
- No crystal shape
- Crystals not zoned

Shear zone characters:
- Veins are amalgamated
- Irregular margins
- Crystals uniform, blotchy
- No crystal shape
- Crystals not zoned
- Fracture and regrowth evident
- Stylolites evident

Fissure vein characters:
- Vein extensive
- Zigzag edges
- Refittable (arrowed)
- Crystals seeded on walls
- Crystal shape evident
- Crystals grown inwards
- Mirrored growth zones
- Sediment fill at centre*
- *Seen here, not always found

100 mm

Within the figure:

Petitor sometimes shows a history of shearing, veining and faulting.

Key to letters and symbols below

→ Fault movement

— Fault zone

— Shear direction

∿ Shape of vein

- - - Margin of shear zone

A Rock stratigraphy

-·-·- Bedding boundary

S Leading edge of a shear lens

100 mm

Figure 8.8. Shearing, faulting and bedding deformation in *Red Petitor* marble, sanctuary pavement St John's Church, Torquay (Chapter 11, Group 8, SW/TQ/1). The key to symbols and letters used is included in the figure. The original bedded sediment (A-D) has experienced both plastic deformation (folding) and brittle deformation (veining). The pattern of deformation with two sets of veins that converge on one another (yellow symbols) is typical of compression in the direction top right and bottom left, indicated by the triangle marked 'S'. A repeated matching set of veins is usually termed 'en echelon' whilst a pattern such as this is a 'convergent conjugate set'. The fault (white symbols) was probably a final phase.

analogous to forcing the palms of the hands hard together and trying to slide them. Luckily skin is not brittle, otherwise it would drag and crack, but that is exactly what happens to rock along a shear plane. Individual vein lenses can be referred to as 'tension gashes'. In Fig. 8.7c the characteristics of simple shear veins are noted and they commonly occur in sub-parallel or 'en echelon' sets. Continued shearing opens further veins that may start to overlap and interfere. Crystals will grow, break, dissolve and regrow. With continued deformation this can end up in a confused jumble of crystals with ragged margins, of which Figs 8.6a and 8.7d show good examples.

The geometry of shear veins is illustrated in a piece of *Red Petitor* (Fig. 8.8) where movement (yellow arrows) either side of shear planes (within the areas defined by black dotted lines) has opened sub-parallel or 'en echelon' vein sets. Two of these sets seem to have moved in opposite directions, but shear zones are three-dimensional and swarms of them undulate and interfere. Point S (Fig. 8.8) is a bit like the prow of a ship, where movement has slid either side of a lenticular wedge, movement directions reflected by the s-shape or z-shape of the individual tension gashes. The centre of a tension gash actually rotates as the gash enlarges, becoming increasingly s- or z-shaped. One of the shears in Fig. 8.8 has evolved into a fault (white line and arrows) which is further discussed below. There are abundant shear veins in some marbles (e.g. Figs 8.9a, c), but not all surfaces

184

are cut in a plane that shows this geometry clearly. For example the veins in Fig. 8.11 are mostly parallel to the plane of the cut and so appear as random patches of calcite.

8.7 Folding and Faulting

Many of the limestones and other rocks in the cliffs around Plymouth and Torquay show evidence of folding and faulting on a large scale. Only what can be seen in Devonshire marbles is noted here. Shear zones inevitably produce folding effects, although whether the folds are caused by plastic flexure (i.e. 'bending') of the rock rather than by multiple small displacements on fractures is sometimes difficult to distinguish. In the *Red Petitor* paving slab (Fig. 8.8) the shear zone with s-shaped tension gashes is associated with a flexure in bedding (red dashed line), but individual elongated sediment components such as stromatoporoids and marine cement, originally hard and brittle, are also bent and there are no tension gashes to help. Plastic flexure, or true folding, seems to have been involved. In Fig. 8.9c the panel shows a similar bedding flexure (red) just where the rock is crossed by dense swarms of tension gashes. Here it would be easy to conclude that all of the apparent flexure could be accounted for by small displacements amongst the swarms of veins.

In rare instances we can see that early marine cements have responded to stress not by bending, but by multiple small movements along crystal boundaries. A clear example is shown from a slab of *Grey Petitor* in Fig. 8.9b. This is an enlargement of a long palisade of calcite crystals arranged side by side, growing from right to left under changing conditions that produced white to dark grey growth zones, but the growth zones are stepped. The crystals could never have grown that way and the steps are actually micro-faults along the crystal boundaries. There is an overall displacement of 15–20 mm over 30 mm. The nearby stromatoporoid surface on which the crystals grew (not shown) has no faulting and became flexed to accommodate the changes.

Obvious faults are unusual in marbles, probably because blocks usually separated along the lines of weakness caused by faults, but in Fig. 8.8 a small fault on the right side has survived cutting and polishing (white line and arrows) and displaces bedding by >100 mm. Towards the top this fault swings into line with the adjacent shear plane. The absence of a flaw along the fault demonstrates how subsequent annealing of the fractures has given the rock uniform strength. It is as if the fault had never happened. A structural geologist would probably refer to 'diffusional mass transfer' here, vital in the creation of a dense, uniform texture. One or two specimen marble types come from right within fault or shear zones where there are wide fills of exploitable vein calcite. The alliterative and romantically named *Rose Red Radford* is one of these (Fig. 8.10b) with almost jewel-like properties. Repeated shear movement has led to numerous events of crystal growth and brecciation.

Fractures, veins and faults enable us to distinguish several phases of textural development in the marbles and allow us to distinguish pre-tectonic, tectonic and post-tectonic effects. One example already noted (Fig. 8.7) has a pre-tectonic fracture over-stamped by shear veins. In Fig. 8.10a there is a further example where a pre-tectonic fracture is both over-stamped and deformed by later shear veins, but in Fig. 8.10.c it is the other way round. Here, the tectonic shear veins are cut by post-tectonic fractures showing parallel crystal linings. This series of fissures and veins in Fig. 8.10 covers a time-span of 60 million years or more between the initial uplift of the Devonian basins to the fracturing of the eroded stumps of the tectonised highlands in the Permian or later.

8.8 Pressure dissolution

Pressure dissolution is very common in limestones, most easily recognized in cross section by linear stylolites. Stylolites are irregular planes of dissolution that form at right

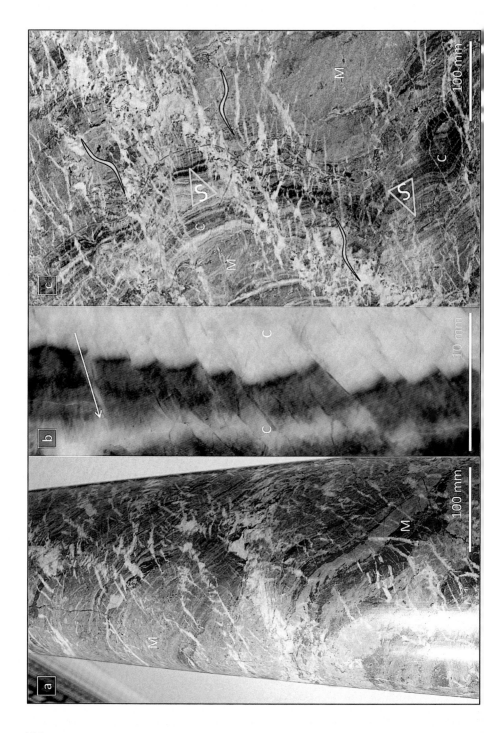

Figure 8.9. (facing page) Shear in *Petitor* marble. a: *Petitor* marble shaft with en echelon shears, Pembroke Room, HMS Drake, Plymouth (DMB SW/PL/5). b: Growth-zoned fibrous marine calcite cement with numerous progressive stepped micro-faults along intercrystalline boundaries. These show how this crystalline cement responded to stress by slippage along crystal boundaries. Arrow marks direction of crystal growth off a nearby fossil substrate. *Grey Petitor* marble, Walkden coll. # 6023. c: *Petitor* panel with shear-controlled folds, St Mary Magdalene Church, Torquay (Chapter 11, Group 7, SW/TQ/5). Key to all three figures: M - grey and pink reef sediment and stromatoporoids. C - growth-zoned marine cement. Red dashed line – deformed bedding and growth-zoned cement layers. Yellow symbols indicate vein shape and shear lens movement as in Fig. 8.8.

---

angles to directed pressure, a common cause of which is just the weight of a substantial overburden of sedimentary rock. Dissolution of calcite along these planes leads irregular interpenetration of the two sides, and the progressive accumulation and build-up of insoluble residue on the stylolite surface in-between emphasizes its location. Since stylolites can form just as a result of sedimentary burial they do not necessarily require tectonic forces to create them, but they are much more abundant in some Devonshire marbles (e.g. Fig. 8.11) than they are in equivalent non-tectonised limestones.

Stylolites are best spotted where they intersect objects with known geometry, such as fossils. In Fig. 8.12a a stylolite cuts some spectacular orthocone fossils in a piece of *Black Ogwell* marble cut for a church paving slab. In Fig. 8.12b a piece of *Ashburton* marble shows masses of anastomosing fine stylolites that have removed much sediment matrix and modify the boundaries of broken pieces of fossil coral and stromatoporoid. These two examples illustrate two different types of stylolite texture, of which the first could be found in a non-tectonised limestone succession resulting from sedimentary burial alone, whilst the second is more likely to be attributable to tectonic effects. Rocks that show abundant stylolites with significant reduction in thickness are referred to as 'stylo-compacted'.

Stylolite formation is poorly understood. Pressure dissolution can occur at the points of contact between individual grains of carbonate in soft sediments after only a few tens of metres of burial but the formation of stylolite planes in lithified rocks requires a lot more pressure. Moving groundwater accelerates the process because carbonate must first pass into solution before it can be removed, but a lot may happen by diffusion. Water movement is a lot more difficult at depth where rocks are fully cemented and impermeable and where stylolite seams have already accumulated much insoluble clay. Fluids can also be trapped in high-pressure zones, unable to migrate, and some oil reservoirs are like that, with lots of trapped fluid and nowhere for it to go. It is at this stage that mineral diffusion and more complex mineral reactions are required that can be accelerated in the heat and pressure of a tectonic environment. Even granite can dissolve away in extreme conditions.

The *Pink Petitor* marble in Fig. 8.11 has an abundance of stylolites with distinguishable generations. The first shows many grey close-spaced seams that cut the sediment and predate the veins (event 2). These may be a dissolution-generated form of cleavage where the rock has become re-textured with many tightly spaced planes of weakness along which it could be split, just like slate. A later, stronger generation of stylolites is more widely spaced, with brown to orange residues along it, and intersects the first generation and also the veins (event 5).

Perhaps this abundance of stylolites, all roughly parallel to bedding, results from the progressive thickening of the rock overburden through large-scale tectonic thrusting as the contents of adjacent basins were piled on top of one another. If so, not all *Petitor* marble shows this extent of styloilitisation. It is the same with *Ipplepen* marble, some of which shows abundant pressure dissolution (e.g. Fig. 8.6) and some very much less. The likely resolution is that, like veins, stylolites come in concentrated zones and the two may be intimately linked, the dissolution along stylolites supplying calcite for the growth of the veins. The key to switching on and off the process may well be to do with the ease with

Figure 8.10. (facing page) Pre-tectonic, tectonic and post-tectonic veins in *Radford* marble and at Berry Head, Brixham. a: An early fracture in *Radford Red* marble, nave shaft, Brompton Oratory, West London (Chapter 11, Group 2, L/W/1). Quarried from Radford Quarry, Oreston, Plymouth (Chapter 9, Loc. P1.6). The early veins are lined with growth-banded calcite. These are cut by later tectonic veins and have been tectonically modified. b: A colonnette of *Rose Red Radford* in the reredos at St John's Church, Plymstock (DMB SW/ PL/ 7), the local parish church for Radford Quarry (see a). The rock comes from a brecciated and multi-veined shear zone and consists of large shapeless crystals with irregular boundaries, later reddened by hematite. Cracks demonstrate its present day fragility. The rock can still be found in the quarry. c: Post-tectonic fractures with calcite-lined walls (left to right) cut across shear-zone calcite veins (top to bottom). Loose block, Berry Head, Brixham (Chapter 9, Locs T2.1, T2.2). These veins accompany Permian-age sediment-filled fissures and are generally vertical. No Devonshire marble varieties are known from Berry Head and these late veins, that create planes of weakness, may be a reason. V - Shear veins; F – Fissure veins (use of terms discussed in text).

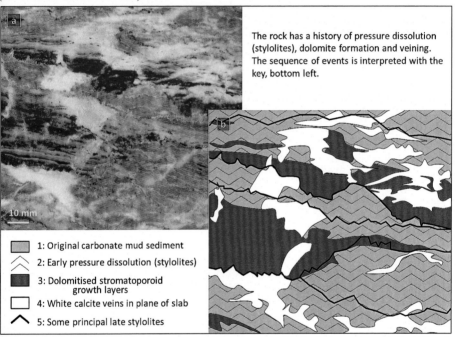

The rock has a history of pressure dissolution (stylolites), dolomite formation and veining. The sequence of events is interpreted with the key, bottom left.

10 mm

1: Original carbonate mud sediment
2: Early pressure dissolution (stylolites)
3: Dolomitised stromatoporoid growth layers
4: White calcite veins in plane of slab
5: Some principal late stylolites

Figure 8.11. Mapping complex textures in *Pink Petitor*, Blackler's Quarry waste tip, Petit Tor, St Marychurch (Volume 2, Guide 1, T2.3a). a: The original *Pink Petitor* marble specimen, a sawn and repolished specimen slab, # 6501, Walkden coll. b: Marble map, 1:1 scale, of the marble textures in a. These are placed in probable order of appearance in the key, bottom left.

which water is able to move through the rock body. It can act as an agent for dissolution and precipitation, as a medium for transporting dissolved minerals and even as a lubricating agent permitting shear movement.

8.9 Mineral alteration and mineral staining

The most common mineralizing and pigmentation minerals in Devonshire marbles are hematite (a simple iron oxide), limonite (a complex and variable iron oxide locked with water) and dolomite (a magnesium carbonate) (Fig. 8.13). These are well known for their

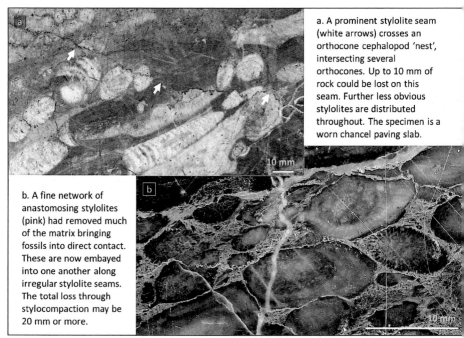

a. A prominent stylolite seam (white arrows) crosses an orthocone cephalopod 'nest', intersecting several orthocones. Up to 10 mm of rock could be lost on this seam. Further less obvious stylolites are distributed throughout. The specimen is a worn chancel paving slab.

b. A fine network of anastomosing stylolites (pink) had removed much of the matrix bringing fossils into direct contact. These are now embayed into one another along irregular stylolite seams. The total loss through stylocompaction may be 20 mm or more.

Figure 8.12. Stylolites in *Black Ogwell* and *Ashburton* marbles. Locality details are included below a. Stylolite intersecting fossil orthocones. *Black Ogwell* marble from near Newton Abbot. Sanctuary pavement, St Augustine's Church, South Kensington, London (Chapter 11, Group 2, L/W/3). The interpretation is inset. b. Fine stylolite networks in *Ashburton marble*. Watson Collection Specimen 15, Sedgwick Museum, Cambridge (Chapter 11, Group 6, E/CB/1). The interpretation is inset.

effects on limestones in general and their influence in the marbles is readily demonstrated. Nonetheless, the mineralization history of the South West is complex and this account is largely based upon observation of marbles at hand-lens scale and above rather than through detailed mineralogical or geochemical study. There may be some less obvious mineral types in the marbles, but the removal of representative samples from ornamental objects, even for research purposes, is generally frowned upon.

Pure limestone is made of calcium carbonate, usually calcite, which is normally white or clear. Calcite, together with the closely related aragonite, formed the great bulk of the bio-mineralised organisms on the Devonian sea floor. Once made into a limestone any aragonite has usually recrystallised to calcite anyway, aiding lithification, and the colour has usually become grey. Where other colours appear something has obviously happened. We have already noted that there was not sufficient burial for the calcite to become significantly recrystallised and the mineral texture and composition of the limestones remained fairly stable throughout the entire Variscan tectonic episode.

One new mineral that does appear, however, is dolomite. It is a common replacement of limestones generally where magnesium-rich solutions have soaked the rock and driven out calcium. In Devonshire marbles it appears as tiny crystals along stylolite seams or along layering in sediments and fossil stromatoporoids. The red colouration in specimens of *Red Petitor* and *Pink Petitor* (e.g. Fig. 8.11) is usually found to be altered dolomite, as is the pink colouration along stylolites in *Ashburton* marble (Fig. 8.12b). The reddening is apparently through alteration of an iron-rich variety of dolomite and it may well be that some, or even most of the red and pink colouration across the full range of Devonshire marbles has been produced in this way, by alteration of tiny dolomite crystals. The association of the dolomite with stylolites suggests that dolomitisation is a burial effect (it is placed at event 3 in Fig. 8.11) but the actual reddening of the dolomite may be a later effect of circulating groundwater (further discussed below).

Fig. 8.13c shows a rock made of abundant broken and formerly rounded fossils, between which are masses of sugary dolomite crystals that replace the original pore-filling calcite. This is a pebble taken from Permian breccias and is an example of one of the most striking of the ornamental inserts in specimen marble tables seen, for example, in the table at the Natural History Museum in London (Chapter 11, Group 2). The pores were originally top-lined by black microbial *Renalcis* (see Chapter 7) and the dolomitisation eats past this and into the margins of surrounding fossil fragments, turning them from rounded to fretted and irregular (Fig. 8.13c). The replacement texture is sometimes cleanly cut by white calcite shear veins, so it is either pre-tectonic or else it accompanied tectonism.

The principal changes that created colour in the marbles, though, seem to be those that followed tectonism and accompanied the return of the limestones to the surface in the late Carboniferous. By then the limestones were structurally complex and separated into tectonised chunks scattered through an eroding landscape of diverse Devonian and Carboniferous rock types (Fig. 1.2). These all became progressively reburied by erosion debris that consisted of red terrestrial breccias, sands and muds through the Permian and Triassic creating a widespread unconformable contact with the eroded stumps of the former highlands.

It is notable how some of the more intricately coloured marbles come from locations just beneath this unconformity. The implication is that the colouration was produced in the near-surface zone where iron-rich groundwater brought from depth was able to meet surface-derived oxygen-rich groundwater, where it precipitated a form of rust. It is common for ancient rocks below an unconformity to become red stained in this way, especially below deserts and similar arid environments.

Accompanying the final tectonic relaxation of the Variscan compressional episode substantial masses of magma were injected into the upper crust which crystallised into the Cornubian granites of Cornwall and Devon (e.g. Scrivener, 2006; Woodcock & Strachan, 2012). The Dartmoor granite is the most extensive of these, only about 20 km away from Torquay. Furthermore the granites are all linked at depth and their combined heat and relative buoyancy had a significant effect on the tectonic pile. Amongst these was mineralisation and alteration both within the granites and in an aureole surrounding them. Mineralisation was aided by water penetration which scavenged well-distributed metallic elements and redeposited them where water converged into fracture veins, forming concentrations of metallic ores around the granites. It is likely that this buried heat source remained influential for some time, driving groundwater circulation which leached rocks and precipitated minerals well into the Permian.

This heat-driven type of mineralisation is typical of some of the tin, copper and zinc mineralisation for which the south-west, especially Cornwall, is famous (Leveridge *et al.*, 2002; Scrivener, 2006) but certain mineralisation was evidently later than this, perhaps even of Triassic age. It seems to be the product of the circulation of salt-rich groundwaters, ultimately derived from the sea (e.g. Leveridge *et al.*, 2002, 2003). This is when much of the hematite and limonite mineralisation of the limestone seems to have taken place, becoming a significant 19th century source of iron ore and also of a powerful red iron oxide pigment used in paint and dyes.

The mineralisation was well capable of turning the surrounding limestone both red (hematite, Fig. 8.13a) and yellow (limonite and ochre, Figs 8.13b, d) and at Sharkham Point, south of Berry Head, limestones close to the unconformity became extensively altered and all stages between red-stained limestone and pure hematite can be seen in cliff exposures.

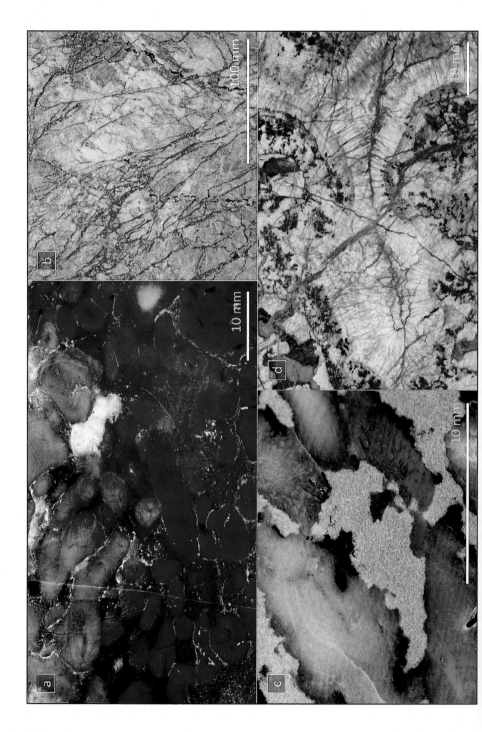

192

Figure 8.13. (facing page) Mineral alteration and colouration effects in Devonshire marbles. a: Hematite alteration in a piece of *Amphipora* (stromatoporoid) rock. There is progressive increase in hematite from top left to bottom. Devonshire marble table, Natural History Museum, London (Chapter 11, Group 2, L/W/2). Other samples in this table show more pervasive hematisation. The source of the stone was probably a pebble in the Permian Oddicombe Breccia near Petit Tor. b: Brown veins probably consisting of dolomite. *Yellow Petitor*, sanctuary pavement, All Saints Church, Babbacombe, Torquay (Chapter 11, Group 8, SW/TQ/1). c: Patches of tiny orange dolomite crystals occupy spaces between fossil fragments, mainly coral. The dolomite replaces early pore-filling calcite and has eaten into the margins of the fossil fragments as well, leaving irregular boundaries. Cavity linings of black *Renalcis* have survived this alteration in places. Cobble, Oddicombe Breccias, Permian, Babbacombe Beach. Walkden coll. # 6072. d: Growth-zoned marine calcite (banded white and grey) is invaded by yellow limonite, an iron-bearing oxide. Veins of limonite run throughout and pass along the radially arranged crystal boundaries in the calcite cement. Alteration follows this, turning radial fibrous calcite crystals to blocky white calcite. Complex red dendritic (branching) hematite replaces some of the mud matrix. Other matrix is also recrystallised to white calcite. Specimen marble table, Fitzwilliam Museum, Cambridge (Chapter11, Group 6, E/CB/3).

Comparable but smaller examples of hematite mineralisation are recorded from a number of locations around Torquay (Ussher, 1903) and hematised pebbles occur on the beaches in the vicinity of Babbacome, mostly derived from the Permian breccias.

Hematised fossiliferous Devonian limestone is commonly used in specimen marble tables (e.g. Fig. 8.13a) and the textures in transitional samples between limestone and hematite or limonite include recrystallised calcite. This far exceeds what was ever achieved during the Variscan orogenesis and once again the key to alteration was an abundance of water. In Fig. 8.13d, a central zone of banded former radiaxial fibrous calcite (marine cement, Chapter 7) is converted to white blocky calcite and it is further invaded along the formerly extensive inter-crystalline boundaries by yellow limonitic veins. The surrounding former pink matrix, with fossils, is similarly altered and invaded by limonite.

Processes that created the full range of colour and texture in Devonshire marbles evidently continued until well after the orogenic phase was over.

8.10 The burial framework

The work of Brian Leveridge and co-workers (cited above) has unlocked much information on the evolution of the original Devonian basins, their subsequent burial, tectonism, uplift, erosion and reburial. The foregoing review of the texturing and colouring of Devonshire marble brings out a few glimpses of this burial and reburial history and provides the opportunity for a first stab at a diagram that shows the full story (Fig. 8.14). This summarises what we can glean from the marbles about their passage deep into the crust, their eventual expulsion and their subsequent geological history. It is informed by previous work and provides a chronological framework for the final story told in this chapter that summarises the textural evolution of the marbles (Fig. 8.15).

It is important to emphasise for specialists what is missing here. This study of the limestones and ornamental marbles has not distinguished the three largely separate phases of tectonic deformation decoded from study of outcrop by Leveridge and co-workers (D1, D2, D3, e.g. Leveridge & Shail, 2011) and there is also no laboratory-based mineralogical and geochemical study tracing details of the textural changes at microscopic and finer scales. In fact Fig. 8.14 is unconventional for a geological burial history diagram, for it traces the story of a known specimen—a fossil coral from the *Petitor* reef. The coral is real and is contained in a specimen lodged with Torquay Museum. The diagram is self-explanatory and the timing and burial details are generalisations.

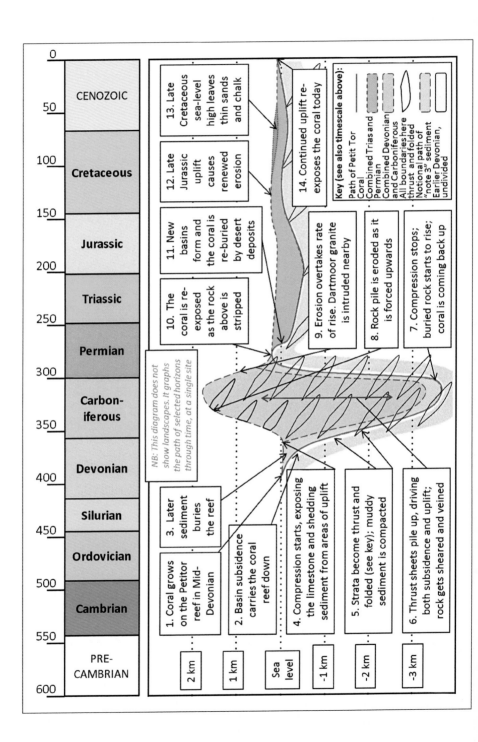

Figure 8.14. (facing page) Diagrammatic burial curve for Petit Tor, estimated from data in Selwood *et al.* (1984), Scrivener (2006), Leveridge *et al.* (2002, 2003), Leveridge (2011), Leveridge & Shail 2011). The curve is modelled upon the likely path of a known specimen of Devonian coral, buried in the mid Devonian, re-exposed at the surface in the Permian, soon buried again and exhumed in the recent past. Amounts of burial and uplift are approximate and key stages in the processes are captioned. The coral specimen is lodged with the Torquay Museum. NB: Numbers used in boxes here represent successive stages and do not equate to numbering used in other figures.

From seabed to highland. The coral, together with its surrounding reefs, sediment and marine cements starts its descent into a submarine world in the mid Givetian, at around 390 Ma, and a thickening pile of sediment starts to cover it (1–3). Soon a brief pause in subsidence terminates deposition (4), with resultant erosion and fissuring of the limestones, and then externally forced and tectonically driven subsidence takes over, forcing everything downwards. The sediments became compacted but remain identifiable through the diagram, although in reality they got convolved with folding, thrusting and shearing as compression took over (5). Tectonic burial is unlikely to have described a smooth continuous curve and included numerous shearing, veining and pressure dissolution events, but these are not distinguished in this diagram. Peak burial comes at around 310 Ma in the late Carboniferous, by which time a thickening root of tectonised sediment had forced an orogenic landscape to rise above it. The extent of topographic uplift and total consequent burial of the unfortunate *Petitor* coral are speculative. The burial curve here is informed by burial estimates in Leveridge *et al.* (2002) but reduced to reflect the lower metamorphic state of the Torquay area (Leveridge *et al.*, 2003).

The highlands are decimated. Uplift following the end of tectonic compression was accompanied by major igneous intrusion nearby and took place remarkably rapidly (7, 8). The uplift was facilitated by erosion as this started to exceed the rate of uplift (9) and eventually the coral, chastened by the heat, stress and pressure at depth, returned to the surface (10). A huge volume of sediment was shed in this erosive process, mostly dispersed, but some of it was caught in the new set of basins that formed across the area in the Permian and Triassic (11). This was mostly red terrestrial sand and mud but substantial thicknesses of breccia composed of bits of the eroded landscape are also held in these basins. Even the Dartmoor granite itself (9), only 20 km away, was probably unroofed by erosion by the late Permian (Scrivener, 2006).

The post orogenic phase takes over. All is now complete apart from colouration. This took place late, well after tectonism ceased, beneath the new cover of red terrestrial sediment shed and reworked from the eroding Permo-Trias post-orogenic landscape, but the timing is uncertain. This was the phase of hematite alteration that may have extended into the Triassic. Our *Petitor* coral was reddened. This renewed basin extension was accompanied by some spectacular cracking of the landscape that created surface fissures that immediately filled with groundwater, sediment and crystals.

The textural evolution story fades away at some time in the Triassic except for one thing, as a result of which the diagram needs to extend to the recent past. The intervening long period is dominated by terrestrial conditions locally (12), although the seas returned nearby at least twice, once in the Jurassic, leaving no accessible record locally, and once in the mid Cretaceous (13), the result of a remarkable worldwide rise in sea level. The Cretaceous event left a mark still visible as Cretaceous deposits on hilltops around Newton Abbot and Chudleigh. This extension of the geological history of Devonshire marble is because, technically, there is one more Devonshire marble to go, not so far described.

In a number of specimen marble tables and possibly also the chapel pavement at Sidney Sussex College, Cambridge, is a cave deposit, formed in the last few tens to hundreds of thousands of years. This is a stalactitic limestone, or flowstone, precipitated on the floor and walls of Pleistocene to Recent caves from calcite-saturated groundwater. Many of the specimens used ornamentally could have come from Kents Cavern, east of Torquay, but Pleistocene cave deposits are widespread in the Torquay, Brixham and Plymouth areas (e.g. Leveridge *et al.*, 2002, 2003). There are also candidates for earlier cave deposits that are reddened and crossed by veins (Walkden collection) that might extend as far back as the Permian. Meanwhile the fossil coral had been returned to the surface for a second time (14), and is now in Torquay Museum.

8.11 A brief synthesis of textural evolution in Devonshire marbles

The burial curve (Fig. 8.14) provides a framework into which we can now place the texturing events that created Devonshire marbles in general (Fig. 8.15). These are the events discussed above that include deposition, fracturing, compaction, sediment injection, vein emplacement, brittle shear, ductile shear, pressure dissolution and mineral alteration. They affected the whole of the South Devon Basin and beyond, but were not evenly distributed. The time frame of Fig. 8.15 is much narrower than that of Fig. 8.14 and some of the events extend beyond the limits shown. The numbers in the following text refer to numbered points on Fig. 8.15 and do not relate to Fig. 8.14.

Sediments, cements, erosion and sedimentary burial. There is a complex series of early pre-tectonic events that accompanied sedimentation of the carbonates (1). These include the precipitation of marine cements (2) that hardened the reefs, the fissuring (3) of these and the local uplift of the reefs with exposure to rainwater and dissolution (4). Cavities developed that received sediment fills (5) but extensive fracturing of the reefs is also revealed by cross-cutting marine cements (6) that produced the earliest calcite veins in fissures (7). Most carbonate sediment in the vicinity of the reefs became cemented, but much carbonate and non-carbonate mud on the floor of the basin probably remained soft and underwent compaction (8) as sediment piled on top. There may even have been limited formation of stylolites (9) at this sedimentary burial stage.

Early uplift and fracturing, then deep burial and tectonism. The point in time between the end of carbonate accumulation and the start of local tectonism was marked by a significant phase of emergence right across the South Devon Basin that is likely to have created a low-lying landscape. Limestones started to fracture (10) followed by weathering with karstic dissolution (11) that created enlarged cavities. These spaces soon received sediment fills (12) consisting of mud derived from sediment shed by the erosion of nearby uplifting areas. This mud blanket was the final phase in the story of sedimentation (13) in the South Devon Basin.

The separation between sedimentary burial of the limestones and their ensuing tectonic burial is blurred by the tectonic effects themselves, but when extension switched to compression the reversal of fault movement caused much local faulting and folding, perhaps marked by early shear (14) with shear veins (15) and perhaps early tectonic stylolites (16). The limited mineral alteration (17), for example the formation of dolomite, might have occurred at any stage through sedimentary burial into tectonic burial, depending upon

Figure 8.15. (facing page) The textural evolution of Devonshire marble. Events/processes are informed by Fig. 8.14 and based upon direct observation of polished samples, stone in buildings and rock at outcrop. The term 'fissure' relates to the opening of near-surface cracks and cavities soon filled either by sediment or calcite. The term 'vein' covers both fracture veins and shear veins as defined in the text. NB: Numbers relate to events noted in the text but do not equate to numbering used in other figures.

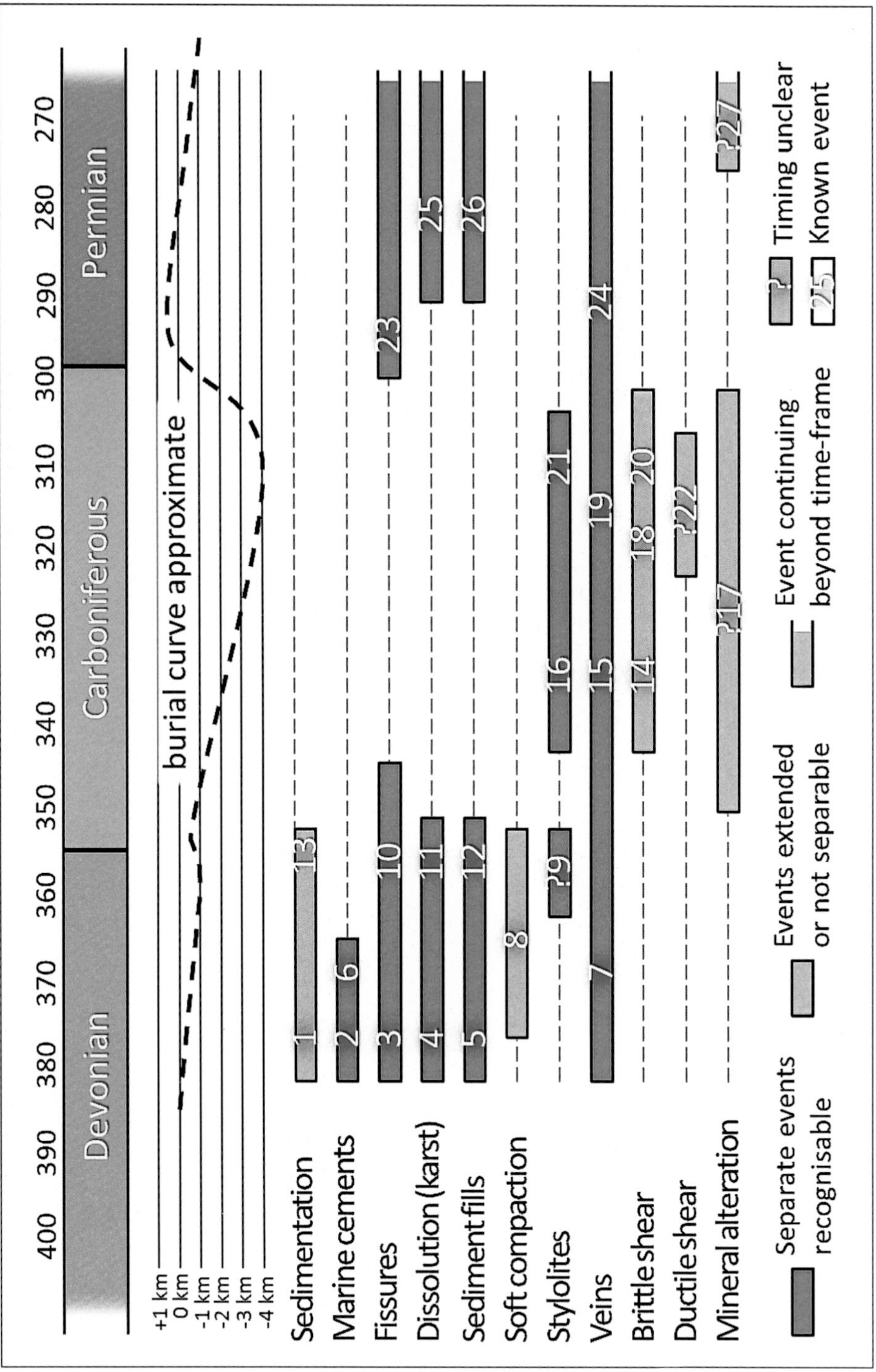

	400	390	380	370	360	350	340	330	320	310	300	290	280	270
	Devonian					Carboniferous						Permian		

burial curve approximate

+1 km
0 km
-1 km
-2 km
-3 km
-4 km

Sedimentation — 1 — 13
Marine cements — 2 — 6
Fissures — 3 — 10 — 23
Dissolution (karst) — 4 — 11 — 25
Sediment fills — 5 — 12 — 26
Soft compaction — 8
Stylolites — ?9 — 16 — 21
Veins — 7 — 15 — 19 — 24
Brittle shear — 14 — 18 — 20
Ductile shear — ?22 — ?17
Mineral alteration — ?27

Separate events
recognisable

Events extended
or not separable

Event continuing
beyond time-frame

? Timing unclear
25 Known event

197

when the reactive fluids were able to migrate into the rock body. Regional thrusting and slicing thickened the tectonic pile, with accompanying zones of shear (18) marked by the development of 'en echelon' calcite shear veins (19). These became progressively more abundant as shear zones grew and new veins started to cross-cut older ones. In extreme cases shear breccias and faults took over along shear planes (20). This most extreme tectonic phase was marked by further pressure dissolution that created the emphatic stylolites (21). The pressure dissolution of calcite is likely to have provided a local source of calcite in the developing veins.

Peak burial may be marked by some mineralogical changes but these are not obvious. Brittle shear gave way to ductile shear (22) probably long before this, evidenced by some whole-rock ductile distortion, but the timing of this is unclear. Most deformation seems poised on the boundary between brittle and ductile behaviour and different materials (e.g. crystalline calcite, fossils and carbonate mud) behaved in different ways.

Tectonic relaxation, uplift, fracturing and a return to surface influences. With the end of tectonic compression the rock pile was quickly reduced by erosion and uplift but no obvious textural mark of this has been recognised in the marbles. Even nearby large-scale igneous intrusions and mineralisation at this time had little obvious effect. Fracturing (23) resumed once the rocks were on their way up or near the surface and these are marked by post-tectonic calcite fissure veining (24). Some fractures were enlarged by karstic dissolution (25) and have sediment fills (26) that consist of surface-derived red terrestrial sand and mud. The most pervasive and important post-tectonic effect was the reddening and alteration (27) of the marbles either by near-surface oxidation of iron-bearing fresh groundwater or by iron mineralisation associated with migrating brines, or perhaps both. These processes may have occupied an extended time frame from Permian into Triassic.

The speleogenic afterthought. A long period of near-surface conditions ensued and the marbles could have been exposed to karstic dissolution, calcite veining and sediment fill, at any stage. There is no recognised direct evidence of this until the deposition of flowstone (speleothem deposits) in cave systems in the Pleistocene. Evidence of this is not seen in Devonian ornamental marbles but veins of it certainly cut them at outcrop. As already noted, Pleistocene flowstone has been used as a Devonshire marble in its own right.

Useful website:
http://www.see.leeds.ac.uk/structure/faults/stress/index.htm

REFERENCES

Andrew, K.J. 1994. John Watson and the Cambridge Building Stone Collection. *Geological Curator*, **5** (No.8), 303–310.

Anon, 1817. *A Guide to the Watering Places on the Coast between the Exe and the Dart: including Teignmouth, Dawlish and Torquay*. E. Croydon, Public Library, Teignmouth 1817. 72pp with a Conchology appendix. Online version available: http://books.google.co.uk/books?id=TtE HAAAAQAAJ&printsec=frontcover&source=gbs_ge_summary_r&cad=0#v=onepage&q=hub bard&f=false

Ayers, T. 2000. *Salisbury Cathedral The West Front*. Phillimore & Co, Chichester. 264pp.

Bannergee, V. 2008. *The Great Housing Boom: Housing in Victorian England*. Victorian Web: http://www.victorianweb.org/art/architecture/homes/housing1.html

Billings, M. 1857. *Billings Directory and Gazeteer of Devon 1857 (Torquay and surrounding areas)*. Online version: http://genuki.cs.ncl.ac.uk/DEV/TorquayStMarychurch/Billings1857.html (Accessed March 2015).

Blewitt, O. 1832. *The Panorama of Torquay, Descriptive and Historical Sketch of the District comprised between the Dart and Teign*. Simpkin and Marshall, Torquay. 288pp. Online version available at: http://books.google.co.uk/books?id=I3wfAQAAMAAJ&printsec=frontcover&source= gbs_ge_summary_r&cad=0#v=onepage&q&f=false The Trade Directory alone is accessible at: http://myweb.tiscali.co.uk/terryleaman/Tiscali/Blewitts%20Directory%20only.htm

Boggis, Rev. R.J.E. 1930. *The History of St John's Torquay*. Devonshire Press, Torquay. 301pp.

Born, A. 1989. *The Torbay Towns*. Phillimore, Chichester. 160pp.

Britton, J. & Brayley, E.W. 1832. *Devonshire & Cornwall Illustrated from original drawings by Thomas Allom, W.H.Bartett etc*. Fisher, Fisher & Jackson, London. 106 abd 199pp. Online at https://books.google.co.uk/books?id=gZEIAAAAQAAJ&pg=PA109&source=gbs_selected_ pages&cad=2#v=onepage&q&f=false

Copper, P. 2002. Silurian and Devonian reefs: 80 million years of global greenhouse between two ice ages. In: Kiessling, W., Flugel, E. & Golonka, J. (eds), *Phanerozoic Reef Patterns*. Society of Economic Paleontologists and Mineralogists, Special Publication, **72**, 181–238.

Cyberheritage, http://www.cyber-heritage.co.uk/

De La Beche, H.T. 1839. *Report on the geology of Cornwall, Devon and west Somerset*. HMSO and Longmans, London. http://archive.org/stream/reportongeology00bechgoog#page/n534/ mode/2up/search/Petit+Tor

Dickinson, H.W. 1913. *Robert Fulton Engineer and Artist: his Life and Works*. John Lane, London and New York. 447pp. Online version available: https://archive.org/stream/robertfultoneng01dick goog#page/n52/mode/2up/search/Torquay

Essexcc, 1887. *Draft and fair copy of licence D/DGs E85* (in respect of East Hill Quarry, East Ogwell) https://secureweb1.essexcc.gov.uk/seaxpam2012/ViewCatalogue.aspx?ID=837918

Foot, M.D.R. (ed.) 1968. *The Gladstone Diaries. Volume 1: 1825-1832*. Clarendon Press, Oxford. 6 Vols. 567–575.

Geoscenic. British Geological Survey British Building stones collection website. http://geoscenic. bgs.ac.uk/asset-bank/action/viewHome

Gill, C. 1993. *Plymouth. A New History*. Devon Books. 302pp.

Gill, C. 1997. *Plymouth River - a History of the Laira and Cattewater*. Halsgrove Press, Tiverton. 216 pp.

Gilpin, W. 1798. *Observations on the western parts of England relating chiefly to picturesque beauty, to which are added a few remarks on the picturesque beauties of the Isle of Wight*. pp. 203–5. T. Cadell & W. Davies, London. 359pp.

Grant, W. H. 1922. *Recollections by the Grand Old Man of St Marychurch 1836–1924*. Reproduced in Pateman 1980. 134-146.

Hardwicke, J. 1865–93. *Hardwicke's Science-gossip: an illustrated medium of interchange and gossip for students and lovers of nature 1865–1893*. Cooke, M.C. (ed.) Robert Hardwicke, London. All volumes in the above available online: http://www.biodiversitylibrary.org/title/1953#page/11/ mode/1up

Hardwicke, J. Editions for 1877: http://www.archive.org/stream/hardwickesscienc13cook/hardwickesscienc13cook_djvu.txt

Haq, B.U. & Schutter, S.R. 2008. A chronology of paleozoic sea-level changes. *Science*, **322**, 64–68.

Hardy, T. 1914. '*Marble-Streeted Town*' a poem noting Plymouth marble available online at: http://www.readbookonline.net/readOnLine/2856/

Hendersyde, 1859. *A catalogue of pictures, statues, busts, antique columns, bronzes, fragments of antique buildings, tables of Florentine and Roman mosaic, scagliola and inlaid wood, Indian, Neapolitan and other china ... at Hendersyde Park, Kelso.* Compiled by John Waldie. Printed for private circulation by Robert Stewart. 212pp. Online version available http://books.google.co.uk/books?id=9J0HAAAAQAAJ&printsec=frontcover&source=gbs_ge_summary_r&cad=0#v=onepage&q&f=false

Hennah, R. 1830. On the animal remains found in the Transition Limestone of Plymouth. *Proceedings of the Geological Society of London*, **14**, 169–70.

Hodge, J. 1973. *Richard Trevithick: an Illustrated Life of Richard Trevithick, 1771–1833.* Reprinted 2003 by Shire Publications, Buckinghamshire. 50pp.

Hopkins, I. 1855. *A short memoir of William Stuart, superintendent engineer on the Plymouth breakwater and the first president of the Devon and Cornwall Society of Architects and Engineers by his son-in-law Ian, honorary member of the Society.* Read at a meeting of the Society at the Plymouth Athenaeum 15th January 1855. Plymouth. 30pp. Online version: http://books.google.co.uk/books?id=VUQBAAAAQAAJ&printsec=frontcover&source=gbs_ge_summary_r&cad=0#v=onepage&q&f=false accessed April 2015.

Jenkins, A.C. 1973. (Unpublished). *Jenkins Family.* Jenkins Family Archives.

Jenkins, M.C. 2010. Expanded Horizons: an account of the interrelated achievements in the fields of architecture, sculpture and decorative arts of members of the family of the Torquay marble mason Henry Tozer Jenkins. *Torquay Museum Society Transactions and Procedings*, **36** (1).

Jenkins, M.C. 2011. *Frank Lynn Jenkins, Mapping the Practice and Profession of Sculpture in Britain and Ireland 1851–1951*, University of Glasgow History of Art and HATII, online database 2011. Online version: http://sculpture.gla.ac.uk/view/person.php?id=msib2_1203116159 (Accessed 02 Feb 2014).

Jenkins, M C. 2013. *Frank Lynn Jenkins (1870-1927): A concise life history.* Victorian Web: http://www.victorianweb.org/sculpture/jenkins/biography.html Accessed March 2015

Kelly, 1856. *Kelly's Post Office Directory of Devonshire, 1856 (Torquay).* Online version: http://myweb.tiscali.co.uk/terryleaman/Tiscali/1856-Kellys-tradesman.html (Accessed March 2015).

Kelly, 1880. *Kelly's Directory of the Watch & Clock Trades 1880.* Online version: http://books.google.co.uk/books?id=JOkNAAAAQAAJ&pg=PA236&lpg=PA236&dq=Jenkins+Marble+Torquay+1880&source=bl&ots=-fYf3T2xy0&sig=MN3bMlfRhEy2cmY82WVt4VJb3-8&hl=en&sa=X&ei=M-a9UPWjMcXa0QWA8IGYAg&sqi=2&ved=0CCwQ6AEwAA#v=onepage&q=Jenkins%20Marble%20Torquay%201880&f=false (Accessed April 2015).

Kelly's *Directory of Devonshire. Kelly and Co, London*.1044pp. http://specialcollections.le.ac.uk/cdm/ref/collection/p16445coll4/id/112362

Leveridge, B.E. 2011. The Looe, South Devon and Tavy basins: the Devonian rifted passive margin successions. *Proceedings of the Geologists' Association*, **122**, 616–717.

Leveridge, B.E. & Hartley, A. 2006. The Variscan Orogeny: the development and deformation of Devonian/Carboniferous basins in SW England and South Wales. In: Brenchley, P.A. & Rawson, P. (eds), *The Geology of England and Wales.* Geological Society of London, 225–255.

Leveridge, B.E. & Shail, R.K. 2011. Marine Devonian Stratigraphy of Great Britain. *Proceedings of the Geologists' Association*, **122**, 540–567.

Leveridge, B.E., Holder, M.T., Goode, A.J.J., Scrivener, R.C., Jones, N.S. & Merriman, R.J. 2002. *Geology of the Plymouth and south-east Cornwall area.* Memoir of the British Geological Survey, sheet 348 (England and Wales).

Leveridge, B.E., Scrivener, R.C., Goode, A.J.J. & Merriman, R.J. 2003. *Geology of the Torquay district.* Sheet Description of the British Geological Survey, 1:50 000 series Sheet 350 (England and Wales).

McKenzie, W.J. 1911. *Torbay Household & Business Directory 1911–12.* Published by W. J. McKenzie at the Torquay Times Office 64, Fleet Street Torquay. Online version: http://myweb.tiscali.co.uk/terryleaman/Tiscali/1911_business_directory.html

Monty, C.L.V., Bosence, D.J.W., Bridges, P.H. & Pratt, B.R. 1995. *Carbonate mud mounds: their origin and evolution.* Special Publication 23 of the International Association of Sedimentologists. Blackwell Science, Oxford. 537pp.

Moore, Rev. T. 1829–33. *The History of Devonshire: from the Earliest Period to the Present.* Robert Jennings, 62 Cheapside, London. 3 vols. Online surname index: http://genuki.cs.ncl.ac.uk/DEV/DevonIndexes/Moore1833.html (Accessed March 2015). There is a very good chapter on mining and minerals

National Trust Collections website. Slab tables: objects 871271, 871272. Specimen marble table: object 871375. http://www.nationaltrustcollections.org.uk/object/(place object # here)

Pateman, L.L. 1980. *Pictorial and historical survey of Babbacombe and St. Marychurch to commemorate its golden jubilee 1930–1980.* Traders & Hoteliers Soc, Babbacombe. 216pp. Online index to this volume: http://genuki.cs.ncl.ac.uk/DEV/TorquayStMarychurch/BabbacombeStMarychurch1.html (Accessed September 2015).

Pateman, L.L. 1991. *Pictorial and historical survey of Babbacombe and St. Marychurch Torquay.* Vol. 2. Babbacombe & St. Marychurch Traders Assn 435p: Online indexes to this volume: (A–J) http://genuki.cs.ncl.ac.uk/DEV/TorquayStMarychurch/BabbacombeStMarychurch2A.html. (K–Z) http://genuki.cs.ncl.ac.uk/DEV/TorquayStMarychurch/BabbacombeStMarychurch2K.html (Both accessed September 2015).

Pevsner, N. 1951–2014. *The Buildings of England.* 53 Vols. Yale University Press, London (listed online at: http://en.wikipedia.org/wiki/Pevsner_Architectural_Guides)

Pigot, 1844. *Pigot's 1844 Directory of Devonshire (Torquay and surrounding areas).* Online version: http://myweb.tiscali.co.uk/terryleaman/Tiscali/Pigots%201844.htm (Accessed March 2015)

Pocius, G.L. 1981. Eighteenth- and nineteenth-century Newfoundland gravestones: self-sufficiency, economic specialization, and the creation of artefacts. *Material History Bulletin,* **12**, 1–16.

Polwhele, Rev. R. 1797. *The History of Devonshire.* Cadell, Johnson and Dilly, London. 3 Vols., vol. 1,1797; vol. 2, 1793; vol. 3, 1806.

Price, M.T. 2007. *The sourcebook of decorative stone – an illustrated identification guide.* Firefly Books, 288pp.

Pubhistory.com, http://pubshistory.com/Devon/Plymouth/MillbayRoad1902.shtml

Renwick, W. G. 1909. *Marble and marble working: a handbook for architects, sculptors, marble quarry owners and workers, and all engaged in the building and decorative industries.* D. Van Nostrand Company, New York; C. Lockwood and Son, London. 226pp. http://archive.org/details/marbleandmarble00renwgoog

Rodwell, W. & Mortimer, R. 2010. *Westminster Abbey Chapter House.* Society of Antiquaries of London. 302pp.

Roscoe, I., Hardy, E. & Sullivan, M.G. 2009. *RA Biographical Dictionary of Sculptors in Britain, 1660-1851.* The Henry Moore Foundation. http://217.204.55.158/henrymoore/sculptor/browse record.php?-action=browse&-recid=3018&from_list=true&x=0

Royal Commission, 1851. *Great Exhibition of the Works of Industry of all Nations 1851, Official Descriptive and Illustrated Catalogue,* Volume 2. Class 27 exhibit 39 John Woodley, p. 766. Spicer Brothers for the Commissioners, 1002pp. Online version: https://archive.org/stream/officialdescrip00goog#page/n288/mode/2up (Accessed March 2015).

Royal Commission, 1852. *Exhibition of the Works of Industry of All Nations, 1851, Reports by the juries on the subjects in the thirty classes into which the exhibition was divided.* Class 27, p. 569, John Woodley. William Clowes & Son London for the Commissioners 867pp. Online version: https://archive.org/stream/reportsbyjurieso00grea#page/568/mode/2up/search/woodley (Accessed March 2015).

Ruskin, J. 1849. *The Seven Lamps of Architecture.* Online version, sixth edition: http://www.victorianweb.org/authors/ruskin/7lamps/2.html#59

Ruskin, J. 1851–3. *The Stones of Venice.* (3 vols). Online version, first edition: https://archive.org/stream/stonesofvenice01rusk#page/n3/mode/2up

Russell, P. 1960. *A History of Torquay and the Famous Anchorage of Torbay*. Torquay Natural History Society. 206pp.

St James. (undated). *St James's Sussex Gardens. The Parish Church of Paddington – a brief History* Church booklet. 10pp.

St Peter's. 1997. *St Peter's Church Kensington Park Road. Historical notes*. Church booklet. 4pp.

Scrivener, R.C. 2006. Cornubian granites and mineralisation in SW England. In: Brenchley, P.A. & Rawson, P. (eds), *The Geology of England and Wales*. Geological Society of London, 257–268

Scrutton, C.T. 1978. Eastern south Devon. In: Scrutton, C.T. (ed.), *International Symposium on the Devonian System (PADS 78). A Field Guide to Selected Areas of the Devonian of South-west England*. Palaeontological Association, London, 27–49.

Sedgwick, A. & Murchison, R.I. 1839. Classification of the older stratified deposits of Devonshire and Cornwall. *Philosophical Magazine*, Series 3 **14**, 241–260.

Sedgwick, A., Murchison, R.I. & Lonsdale, W. 1840. On the physical structure of Devonshire, and on its older stratified deposits and on the age of the limestones of South Devonshire. *Transactions of the Geological Society, London*, Series 2, **5** (part 3), 633–704 and 721–738.

Seymour, D.J. 1963. *Upton the heart of Torquay – the story of its church and Parish*. Private publication. Printed by James Townsend, Exeter. 161pp.

Shaw, Rev. C.C. 1966. *A History of the Parish of Aveton Gifford*. Published by Rev. C.C. Shaw, MA. 97pp. Online version available: http://www.civ.eng.cam.ac.uk/cjb/ag/shaw/index.htm

Society of Arts, 1794. *Transactions of the Society for the Encouragement of Arts. Manufactures, and Commerce; with the Premiums offered in the Year 1794*. Vol xii. Adelphi, London, p. 329 (Online version available: http://books.google.co.uk/books?id=Eg01AAAAMAAJ&pg=PA329 &lpg=PA329&dq=Robert+Fulton+Society+for+the+encouragement+of+arts&source=bl&ots= jngxvn21IU&sig=lu7J9QeYXUSxOVq7ISYxKCOxfeg&hl=en&sa=X&ei=Uj2QU-ytFcnm7Aa 6qIHgAQ&ved=0CDEQ6AEwAw#v=onepage&q=Robert%20Fulton%20Society%20for%2 the%20encouragement%20of%20arts&f=false

Society of Arts, 1802. *Transactions of the Society for the Encouragement of Arts. Manufactures, and Commerce; with the Premiums offered in the Year 1802*. Premium 125, p. 48. Vol xx. Adelphi, London. Online version available: https://books.google.co.uk/books?id=RRlbAAAAQAAJ&pg= PA50&dq=transactions+society+for+the+encouragement+of+arts,+manufactures+and+com merce++premiums+1802&hl=en&sa=X&ei=2K75VMeLE8L4OvLxgNgG&ved=0CDkQ6A EwBA#v=onepage&q=transactions%20society%20for%20the%20encouragement%20of%2 arts%2C%20manufactures%20and%20commerce%20%20premiums%201802&f=false

Society of Arts, 1804. *Transactions of the Society for the Encouragement of Arts. Manufactures, and Commerce; with the Premiums offered in the Year 1804*. General Conditions, p.19. Vol xxiii. Adelphi, London. Online version available: https://books.google.co.uk/books?id=COdJAAAA cAAJ&pg=PR1&dq=transactions+society+for+the+encouragement+of+arts,+manufactures+ and+commerce++premiums+offered+in+the+year+1804+vol+xxii&hl=en&sa=X&ei=Jbf5V LXvB4PsO4fogbgL&ved=0CCAQ6AEwAA#v=onepage&q=general%20conditions&f=false

Society of Arts, 1809. *Transactions of the Society for the Encouragement of Arts. Manufactures, and Commerce; with the Premiums offered in the Year 1809*. Vol xxvii, p. 85, address by JP Hubbard Adelphi, London. Online version available: http://books.google.co.uk/books?id=OzhJAAAAcAA J&pg=PA19&lpg=PA19&dq=J+P+Hubbard+marble&source=bl&ots=C83KZbIcXJ&sig=uW 5w9CKAczJh-pinOXJ3afQc1a4&hl=en&sa=X&ei=R9riUJGHJ8PR0QXe6oBI&ved=0CDA Q6AEwAA#v=onepage&q=J%20P%20Hubbard%20marble&f=false

Stuart, E. 1991. *Lost Landscapes of Plymouth*. Alan Sutton, Bath Press, 211pp.

Stuart, W. 1838. On the limestone, the lime cement, and the method of blasting, in the neighbourhood of Plymouth. *Minute of the Proceedings of the Institute of Civil Engineers, **1***, 35–36. Online version available.

Swete, Rev. J. 1789–1800. *Picturesque Sketches of Devon*. 20 Journals. Published in four volumes as *Travels in Georgian Devon: The Illustrated Journals of the Reverend John Swete, 1789-1800*, edited by Gray, T. & Rowe, M. (eds). Devon Books and Halsgrove, Tiverton, Devon. 4 Vols. 1997

Taber, J. 2001. *Stone and Quarry Men of the West Country. A Genealogical Index of Masons, Quarrymen, Builders, Carpenters and all related Occupations in Devon and Cornwall.* http://freepages.genealogy.rootsweb.ancestry.com/~stonemen/ (Accessed April 2015).

Tomlinson, J.M. 1996. *Derbyshire Black Marble.* Peak District Mines Historical Society Special Publication No. *4.* 95pp.

Trevithick, F. 1872. *The Life of Richard Trevithick with an account of his inventions.* Ch 17, V2, various inventions. E. and F. N. Spon, London. 403pp. Online version available: https://ia902702.us.archive.org/20/items/lifeofrichardtre02trevrich/lifeofrichardtre02trevrich.pdf

Turner, R. 2014. *Victorian Churches.* website: http://victorianchurches.blogspot.co.uk/2013_10_01_archive.html (Accessed January 2015).

Ussher, W.A.E. 1903. *The geology of the country around Torquay.* Memoir of the Geological Survey of Great Britain, sheet 348 (England and Wales).

Visionofbritain.org. *A vision of Britain through Time (Broadhempston data).* http://www.visionofbritain.org.uk/unit_page.jsp?u_id=10018079

Watson, J. 1916. *British and foreign marbles and other ornamental stones.* Cambridge University Press, 483pp. Online version available: http://babel.hathitrust.org/cgi/pt?id=mdp.39015064552287;view=1up;seq=9

West, I.M. 2014. *Chesil Beach: Storms and Floods. Geology of the Wessex Coast of Southern England.* Internet site: http://www.southampton.ac.uk/~imw/chestorm.htm. Version: 2nd March 2014.

Western Daily Mercury, 1886. *The Royal Marble Works at St Marychurch,* Friday April 9th 1886. Reprinted pp. 173–176 in Pateman (1980).

White, W. 1850. *History, Gazetteer, and Directory of Devonshire and the City and County of the City of Exeter.* Simkin Marshall & Co. Oxford University. Reprinted 1968 by David & Charles, Newton Abbot, 804 pp. Online version available: http://books.google.co.uk/books/about/History_gazetteer_and_directory_of_Devon.html?id=3HxbAAAAQAAJ (Accessed March 2015).

White, J.T. 1878. *The History of Torquay.* Directory Office, Torquay, 403pp. Online version: http://www.archive.org/stream/historytorquay00whitgoog/historytorquay00whitgoog_djvu.txt (Accessed March 2015).

Wilkinson P. & Ashley, P. (2009). *The English Buildings Book: an architectural guide.* English Heritage. 394pp. Notes online available at: http://englishbuildings.blogspot.co.uk/p/c-1837-1890.html (Accessed November 2014).

Wood, R. 1999. *Reef Evolution.* Oxford University Press. 414pp.

Woodcock, N. & Strachan, R. 2012. *Geological History of Britain and Ireland.* John Wiley & Sons Ltd, Chichester. 442pp.

Appendix: The Devonshire Marble Buildings (DMB) list

Explanation:
Section 1 contains details of 'Devonshire marble buildings' (DMBs) known to contain either fixed embellishment in Devonshire marble (e.g. columns, panelling, stairways and flooring) or important contents with Devonshire marble (e.g. a specimen marble table).
Section 2 is a short list of buildings encountered during the surveys that are great examples of marble embellishment but contain no Devonshire.
Section 3 is a short list of lost Devonshire marble buildings, demolished or destroyed during WW2.

Notes:
1. Several of the buildings noted here are dealt with in more detail in the Buildings Guides in Volume 2 (Chapter 11). The Group number in the guide is noted.
2. Buildings with Devonshire fireplaces, fonts or pulpits alone are not systematically recorded but good examples are noted here and in the Buildings Guides in Volume 2.
3. Buildings with substantial marble that excludes any Devonshire are not systematically recorded but good examples encountered are given in Section 2.
4. Non-British DMBs are not listed at present, but there are known examples such as Melbourne Cathedral, Australia.
5. Most buildings listed have been visited and photographed. Buildings listed but not visited are noted to that effect in the respective comments section.
6. Detailed annotated photographic records of all buildings visited and photographed are being made available as online resources on the Geologists' Association website.
7. Feedback to the author on buildings where confirmation is required, on possible new entries and any comments on existing entries are welcome.

DMB Numbering code used:
The numbering system used allows new DMBs to be added and identified regionally and locally without having to join the bottom of a long list. The code consists of region/postcode or district prefix/running number.

The regions used are those defined for official administrative purposes (e.g. http://en.wikipedia. org/wiki/Regions_of_England). These are (with abbreviations adapted so that they list in alphabetical order): East of England (E), London (L), East Midlands (ME), West Midlands (MW), North East (NE), North West (NW), Yorkshire and the Humber (NY), Scotland (S), South East (SE), South West (SW), Wales (W, further subdivided into north and south, Wn, Ws). At present there are no recorded DMBs in North East England and Scotland.

The National Heritage listed building grade and listing number:
The English Heritage (EH) Grade of a building (or its equivalent) is noted as well as its identification number in the National Heritage lists. Nearly all DMBs included here are listed buildings, but not all of these have protected interiors.

Informal DMB star grading system:
To provide a qualitative guide to the relative wealth of DMBs following photographic survey a star grading system from one star to five stars is used.
★ refers to very limited use of Devonshire marble such as one or two fireplaces or small colonnettes.
★★★★★ is extensive use of Devonshire in columns, stairways, wall panels, fittings and floors.
In order to be able to include great marble interiors where Devonshire marble is only one of several types used (others include other British, Irish or continental marbles), the proportion of Devonshire is given by the stars in bold. For example:
★★☆☆ is a great interior, perhaps with pillars and panels in marble where about half the stone used is Devonshire.

Section 1: Buildings and open areas with significant Devonshire marble embellishment or contents

East England (E/)

Cambridge (E/CB/)

★★☆	Guide: Group 6	HE Listing not relevant
E/CB/1 Sedgwick Museum of Earth Sciences, Downing Street, Cambridge. CB2 3EQ	**Building:** 1905, houses both the Museum and the Cambridge Department of Earth Sciences (see comments)	
	Interest: The John Watson Building Stones Collection; a fine Devonshire specimen marble table used daily and a Derbyshire one to compare. Local geology displays	
	Stones: The Building Stones Collection has >2000 samples from UK and abroad and is contained in the University Earth Sciences Department. It includes the best known documented reference set of Devonshire marble specimens. The Devonshire specimen marble table is documented in the ppt web file noted above	

Comments: There is no marble embellishment here. The Devonshire marbles reference collection is in the former Museum of Economic Geology in the Department of Earth Sciences. Access by appointment only

★★☆☆	Guide: Group 6	HE: Grade 1 #1332216
E/CB/2 St John's College Chapel, St John's St, Cambridge. CB2 1TP	**Built:** Chapel 1863-9. **Architect:** George Gilbert Scott. **Style:** 13th century French Gothic	
	Interest: Chancel arcade pillars, clerestory bays, vaulting shafts, chancel and choir pavements, crossing pillars	
	Stones: Devonshire *Red* and *Black Ogwell*, red and black *Ashburton*; Derbyshire *Ashford Black* and *Duke's Red*. *Peterhead granite*, Cornish serpentine, *Green Connemara*, white *Tuscan*	

Comments: Around 200 shafts of ornamental stone embellish the chapel and antechapel. Rare *Duke's Red* (Derbyshire) is seen above capitals on the right side of the sanctuary. All Devonshire stones are believed to have been supplied by Andrew Blackler of St Marychurch

★★☆☆☆	Guide: Group 6	HE: Grade 1 #1126276
E/CB/3 Fitzwilliam Museum, Trumpington Street, Cambridge. CB2 1RB	**Built:** 1848 and 1875. **Architect:** Main building by George Basevi and CR Cockerell; Entrance Hall mainly EM Barry. **Style:** Neo-Classical and Baroque	
	Interest: Entrance Hall stairs, balusters panels, pillars and pilasters. Specimen marble tables	
	Stones: Devonshire *Red Ogwell*, plus *Peterhead Granite*, white *Tuscan*, *Green Genoa*, *Yellow Siena*	

Comments: Stonework is all of the finest specification and execution. *Red Ogwell* is in specimen panels on ground floor and stairs and in the stair and gallery newels and balusters. Interior salons have extensive and very high quality scagliola. The marble table in the right gallery is Devonshire; that in the left gallery is Italian

★☆☆		HE: Grade 1 #1106237
E/CB/4 Sidney Sussex College Chapel, Sidney St, Cambridge. CB2 3HU	**Architects and dates:** James Essex, 1776; remodelled by Sir Jeffrey Wyatville 1883; panelled by TH Lyon 1910-12. **Style:** Gothic exterior, Baroque interior	
	Interest: Nave/choir pavement and altar	
	Stones: Devonshire *Grey Ipplepen* and likely Devonshire flowstone in floor (Fig. 5.10b). *Ashburton* in altar, with white *Tuscan* and *Green Connemara*	

Comments: Unusual fossil gastropods and good detailed stromatoporoids in the *Ashburton*

altar. The floor apparently dates from 1923

E/CB/5 Ely Cathedral (Cathedral Church of the Holy Trinity), Chapter House, The College, Ely, Cambridgeshire. CB7 4DL	★☆☆☆		HE Grade I #1331690
	Built: C11-C14, restored 1847-78. **Architect:** George Gilbert Scott.		
	Interest: Galilee porch, pavements		
	Stones: Devonshire shafts inside Galilee porch (Fig. 5.14) and some in replacements at the east front. Much *Blue Purbeck* marble in piers and shafts. *Red Cork* and *Green Connemara* in nave pavement		

Comments: Devonshire variety not determined. Excellent stained glass museum

London (L/)

Central London (L/C/)

L/C/1 Goldsmiths' Hall (The Worshipful Company of Goldsmiths), 13 Foster Lane, London. EC2N 3BA	★★☆☆☆	**Guide:** Group 1	**HE:** Grade I #1286469
	Built: 1835 (building), 1871 (marble interior). **Architects:** Philip Hardwick and R. Hesketh respectively. **Style:** Exterior - Classical Renaissance; Interior - Italianate Palazzo		
	Interest: Stair Hall wall panels, arches, lobbies, stairway, balconies, balustrades, pillars and pilasters; Livery Hall scagliola.		
	Stones: French, Italian and British marbles, including Devonshire *Red Ipplepen* and *Ashburton*. The 8 monolithic pillars and 16 pilasters are in red Belgian		

Comments: Access is problematic but there is a well-photographed virtual tour on http://pan3sixty.co.uk/virtual_tours/goldsmiths-company/

L/C/2 Gibson Hall (formerly National Provincial, National Westminster, Westminster Bank), Bishopsgate, City of London. EC2N 3BA	★★★	**Guide:** Group 1	**HE:** Grade I # not found
	Completed: 1885. **Architect:** John Gibson. **Style:** Neoclassical		
	Interest: Pillars and pilasters in function hall		
	Stones: 82 monolithic Devonshire *Red Ipplepen* shafts in columns and pilasters with bases in black Belgian or Derbyshire. The size of these single pieces of stone in the shafts, 3.8 m, is remarkable		

Comments: Imposing interior of a former headquarters banking hall

L/C/3 Lloyds' Register (of shipping), 71 Fenchurch Street, London. EC3N 4BS	★★★★☆	**Guide:** Group 1	**HE:** Grade II* #1192466
	Completed: 1901. **Architect:** Thomas Edward Collcutt. **Style:** Classical Italian Palazzo		
	Interest: Main entrance/stair hall and gallery above, pillars, pilasters, pedestals, wall panels, staircase and balustrades. The Old Library and the General Committee room are mostly decorated with non-British marbles		
	Stones: Devonshire *Grey Petitor*, *Red Ogwell* and *Black Ashburton* in entrance hall and stairway, plus White *Tuscan*. *Green Connemara*, *Black Belgian*, Italian *Rosso Ammonitico*, Algerian *Breche Sanguine* and French *Cippolino Mandolato* elsewhere		

Comments: Probably the best Devonshire marble interior. Stone supplier Jenkins of Torquay. Important sculpture and art work by son of Jenkins, Frank Lynn Jenkins

	★★★☆		HE: Grade II* #1358902
L/C/4 **Drapers' Hall,** **Throgmorton** **Street, City of** **London.** **EC2N 2DQ**	Altered: 1868-70 (Livery Hall) and 1898-99 (stair hall). Architects: Herbert Williams and Sir Thomas Graham Jackson respectively. Style: Baroque eclectic		
	Interest: Marble staircase, first floor landing, Livery Hall, and mantel pieces		
	Stones: 58 monolithic Devonshire *Red Ipplepen* pillars and pilasters on white *Tuscan* base and *Green Genoa* plinths in Livery Hall. Stair Hall has green *Cippolino verde*, *Rosso Verona*, *Breccia di Seravezza* and alabaster.		

Comments: A very elegant interior with marble statuary and portraits of contemporary monarchs.

	★★☆		HE: Grade II* #1113211
L/C/5 **Great Ormond** **Street Hospital** **Chapel,** **Powis Place,** **Camden Town,** **London.** **WC1N 3JB**	**Built:** 1871-76. **Architect:** EM Barry (son of Sir Charles). **Style:** Byzantine		
	Interest: 4 monolithic columns and 8 pilasters each nearly 2 m. Chancel screen base and steps		
	Stones: Devonshire *Red Ipplepen*, green ?*Genoa* and alabaster		

Comments: Spectacular Byzantine interior by Clayton & Bell. This entire chapel was relocated in one piece during redevelopment of the site

	★★☆		HE Grade I # 1286688
L/C/6 **St Michael's** **Church Cornhill,** **St Michael's** **Alley, London** **EC3V 9DS**	**Built:** 1670-77, remodelled interior 1860. **Architects:** Sir Christopher Wren, George Gilbert Scott. **Style:** Baroque		
	Interest: Chancel wall panels; shafts in reredos		
	Stones: Devonshire *Red Ipplepen* plus green *Genoa* (Fig. 2.4)		

Comments: Good specimens in shafts and panels, with fossils. Interesting GGS take on Baroque. Side panels have ghost markings of former inscriptions not previously noted – probably the 10 Commandments

North London (L/N/)

	★★☆		HE: Grade II* #1263688.
L/N/1 **Hornsey Town** **Hall** **The Broadway** **Crouch End** **London.** **N8 9JJ**	**Completed:** 1935. **Architect:** Reginald Uren. **Style:** Postwar Modern		
	Interest: Composite pillars, stair risers and architraves. Extensive non-Devon panelling in vestibules. Terrazzo flooring		
	Stones: Devonshire *Ashburton* strips in pillars in main stairwell. *Ashburton* stair risers and architrave detail. Wall panelling is Italian travertine		

Comments: **Not visited.** This superb interior fell into disuse from 1965, with subsequent concerns about asbestos. There are plans to renovate and reopen (2014). Virtual tour on: http://www.eyerevolution.co.uk/blog/hornsey-town-hall-virtual-tours/

West London (L/W/)

	★★★☆☆	**Guide:** Group 2	HE: Grade II* #1358123
L/W/1 **Brompton** **Oratory** **(The Oratory,** **Kensington and** **Chelsea),** **Brompton Road,** **Kensington,** **London.**	**Built:** 1880-84. **Architect:** Herbert Gribble. **Style:** Italian Baroque		
	Interest: Nave pillars and pilasters; pillars in St Wilfred's Chapel; marbles in side chapels		
	Stones: Abundant Italian and other European marbles. Nave shafts are Devonshire *Radford* and there is *Pomphlett* and *Green Kitley* in St Wilfred's Chapel. A band of Carboniferous *Frosterley* is used in St		

SW3 1LA	Philip's Chapel		

Comments: Devonshire stones were supplied by John Goad of Plymouth. Extensive use of other European marbles, including Belgian, Languedoc, Verona, Siena and Tuscan

L/W/2 Natural History Museum, Former Geological Survey entrance on Exhibition Road. London. SW7 2HF	★★☆	Guide: Group 2	Listing details not found
	Completed: 1935. **Architects:** Richard Allison and John Hatton Markham. **Style:** Neoclassical Art Deco		
	Interest: Entrance vestibule panelling, stairway arch, mezzanine pavement and the great Devonshire specimen marble table		
	Stones: Devonshire *Ashburton* marble, *Grey Petitor* and *Green Kitley*, with *Green Connemara*, *Green Purbeck*, Wirksworth crinoidal and *Hoptonwood*		

Comments: The 'British' marble archway, green Earth theme, stairway and flooring are superb. There is a range of international marbles used in the windowsills around the cafeteria atrium in the main NHM building

L/W/3 St Augustine's Church (Church of St Augustine) 117 Queen's Gate Kensington, London. SW7 5JE	★★★☆	Guide: Group 2	HE: Grade II* #1226161
	Built: 1870-76. **Architect:** William Butterfield. **Style:** Polychromic Gothic		
	Interest: Chancel/sanctuary arcade, tracery, wall panels, shafts, sediliae, credence table, pavement and steps		
	Stones: Devonshire *Red Ogwell*, *Black Ogwell*, *Pink Petitor*, dark *Ashburton*, white and grey *Tuscan*. Derbyshire crinoidal font		

Comments: Chancel by Andrew Blackler, St Marychurch. Much of the interior was later painted white but more recently removed. There are Butterfield painted-tile images in the aisle walls. There is a unique fossil orthocone 'nest' in a right sanctuary step

L/W/4 St James's Church (Church of St James, Westminster), Sussex Gardens, Paddington, London. W2 2RL	★★★★☆	Guide: Group 3	HE: Grade II* #1237437
	Completed: 1881. **Architect:** George Edmund Street. **Style:** English Decorated		
	Interest: Magnificent flush-panelled Devonshire interior. Carved tracery in sanctuary (west) wall. Chancel pavement and steps. Superb panelled baptistery in east. Matching pulpit and font		
	Stones: Devonshire *Grey*, *Pink* and *Yellow Petitor*, *Red Ogwell*, *Ashburton*, *Ipplepen*, plus serpentine, *Green Connemara* and alabaster		

Comments: Spectacular church, probably the best. Unusual orientation with altar to the west and baptistery to the east. Notable knapped flint exterior. *Pietra dura* panels in sanctuary and Lady chapel. Marbles supplied by Andrew Blackler of St Marychurch. Eclectic marbles in new nave sanctuary floor surrounding a modern nave altar

L/W/5 Foreign Office (Foreign and Commonwealth Office), 1 King Charles Street, Westminster, London. SW1A 2AD	★★☆☆☆		HE: Grade I #1066102
	Built: 1861-75. **Architect:** George Gilbert Scott. **Style:** Classical Italianate.		
	Interest Column shafts and handrails in Grand Staircase of the Foreign Office (Fig. 2.5a-b), Muses Staircase, Gurkha Staircase, Colonial Office entrance hall and India Office entrance hall		
	Stones: Devonshire *Radford* plus *Grey Bardiglio* and English Alabaster (Grand Staircase and gallery); *Red Cork*, Derbyshire crinoidal, white *Tuscan*, *Peterhead granite*. Aberdeenshire granites (Durbar Court)		

Comments: British marbles, particularly Devonshire, are projected on an 'international' stage. The Devon marbles were supplied by John Goad of Plymouth (Goad obituary, Western Morning News 26 Jan 1886)

L/W/6	★☆☆		HE: Grade I #not found

Westminster Abbey, Chapter House, Deans Yard, London. SW1P 3PA	**Built:** C13 building with George Gilbert Scott restoration, 1849-1878.
	Interest: Some window arch responds, columns, mullions, capitals and bases.
	Stones: Variegated indeterminate Devonshire marble and a duller probable Irish *Kilkenny*.

Comments: The fabric was not fully surveyed for Devonshire marble. The stone was used to replace *Purbeck* as part of a much more extensive restoration of the Chapter House to its original condition. External replacements are difficult to see and mostly inaccessible.

L/W/8 All Saints Church, Notting Hill, Powis Gardens, London. W11 1JG	★★☆		HE Grade II* #1080701
	Built: 1852-61 **Architect:** William White **Style:** Gothic polychromic		
	Interest: Compound columns in nave arcade. Exterior clerestory window shafts		
	Stones: Highly veined Devonshire nave shafts probable *Silverleigh* (Fig. 2.5c-d). Non-veined ones likely to be grey to dull *Red Ogwell*. External window shafts resemble *Red Ogwell*		

Comments: Restored after severe WWI damage. The *Silverleigh* shafts are exceptional

L/W/9 St Peter's Church, Notting Hill, Kensington Park Road, London. W11 2PN	★☆☆		HE Grade II* #1224309
	Built: 1855-7, chancel 1879. **Architects:** Thomas Allom, Charles Barry (jnr) and James Edmeston. **Style:** Baroque		
	Interest: 4 tall shafts supporting chancel and sanctuary arches		
	Stones: Sectional Devonshire *Red Ogwell* in the shafts (Fig. 2.10a-b); red marble in altar steps is Belgian. Pulpit has *Languedoc*, alabaster and *Carrara* with base in highly stylolitised brown indeterminate marble resembling *Ipplepen*. Empty plinth on rhs is similar. Panelled apse has grey *Tuscan*, matched *Cippolino* and likely *Green Genoa*. Altar is in white *Tuscan* marble		

Comments: Cleverly modernised to double as an entertainments venue. The Torquay red marble columns are believed to have cost £48 each (local history guide)

L/W/10 Westminster Cathedral – no DM but an important reference – see Section 2

L/W/11 All Saints, Margaret St - no DM but an important reference – see Section 2

Midlands, East Midlands (ME/)

Birmingham area (ME/B/)

ME/B/1 Birmingham Art Gallery and Museum, 9 Margaret Street, Birmingham. B3 3AG	★★★★★	Guide: Group 4	HE: Grade II* #1210333
	Built: 1881-5. **Architect:** Yeoville Thomason, extension to his earlier Council House. **Style:** Victorian Baroque		
	Interest: Pillars, pilasters, panels and balusters in entrance vestibule, stairway and gallery. Arches and architraves in the Industrial gallery		
	Stones: Devonshire *Red Ogwell*, *Ashburton*, and *Petitor*. Small uses of *Grey Ipplepen*. Also some white *Tuscan*. Alabaster and serpentine in vestibule. *Ashburton* architraves in Feeny extension		

Comments: This rivals Lloyd's Register as the best DMB. Exclusive use of Devonshire in stairs and galleries; 10 structural pillars, >30 pilasters and 59 balusters and rails.

ME/B/2 Birmingham Council House, Victoria Square,	★★☆☆	Guide: noted in Gp. 4	HE: Grade II* #1210333
	Built: 1874-9, remodelled 1893-5. **Architects:** Yeoville Thomason, Martin & Chamberlain. **Style:** Exterior - Victorian Baroque; interior - French renaissance		

Birmingham. **B1 1BB**	**Interest:** Entrance hall, stairways and Banqueting Hall		
	Stones: Pillars, pilasters, balusters and newels in Devonshire *Ashburton* and *Ipplepen*. Others not determined		

Comments: Reconnaissance visit only. Requires full investigation and photography

ME/B/3 **Birmingham** **Grand Hotel,** **10 Barwick** **Street,** **Birmingham.** **B3 2JQ**	★★★☆	**Guide:** Group 4	**HE:** Grade II* #1391246
	Built: 1875-9, extended with function rooms 1893-5. **Architects:** Thomas Plevins. William Martin and John H. Chamberlain. **Style:** French C17 and C18		
	Interest: Dados, pillars and pilasters in Grosvenor Room, Drawing Room and Crush Room		
	Stones: Almost exclusively Devonshire *Red Ogwell*, *Ashburton* and *Petitor*. *Shap Granite* at bottom of main stairwell		

Comments: This is a stylish and important interior. Some fine pieces of Devonshire marble were noted. At the time of survey the building was undergoing extensive renovation. Completion due in 2016

Leicester area (ME/LE/)

ME/LE/1 **Church of St** **John the** **Baptist,** **Clarendon Park** **Road, Leicester.** **LE2 3AD**	★★☆		**HE:** Grade II* #1074035
	Built: 1884-85. **Architect:** Joseph Goddard of Goddard, Paget and Catlow. **Style:** Gothic Revival		
	Interest: Shafts in chancel arcades and east window. Chancel steps		
	Stones: **Varieties of** Devonshire *Ogwell* and *Petitor* are likely		

Comments: Not visited and requires confirmation. Lofty brick-built building with no tower. Good mosaic floor in chancel

Midlands, West Midlands (MW/)

Coventry area (MW/CV/)

MW/CV/1 **Church of St** **Mary and St** **Margaret,** **Combrook,** **Stratford-on-** **Avon.** **CV35 9HP**	★☆		**HE:** Grade II #1381849
	Built: 1866. **Architect:** John Gibson. **Style:** Gothic revival.		
	Interest: Nave arcade shafts, font and chancel arch shafts.		
	Stones: The font plinth is Devonshire *Red Ipplepen* and the chancel shafts look similar. The grey textured stone in the nave shafts is not likely to be Devonshire		

Comments: Not visited and requires confirmation. The church was financed by the Dowager Lady Margaret Willoughby de Broke. She and John Gibson also built the spectacular Marble Church at Bodelwyddan

MW/CV/2 **All Saints** **Church,** **Church Road,** **Sherbourne,** **Warwickshire,** **West Midlands.** **CV35 8AP**	★★★☆		**HE:** Grade II* #1035139
	Built: 1862-4. **Architect:** George Gilbert Scott. **Style:** Early English Decorated Gothic Revival		
	Interest: Nave arcade clustered shafts, clerestory and vaulting shafts, aisle window shafts, chancel arch shafts, chancel side arcade, chancel window and vaulting shafts. Reredos side colonnettes		
	Stones: Definite Devonshire (probable *Ipplepen*), with *Green Connemara*. *Connemara* paired with *Red Griotte* in the reredos. *Red Ogwell* dado in chancel		

Comments: Not visited and requires confirmation. Typical classy GGS interior. Sanctuary is richly panelled in alabaster

Hereford area (MW/HR/)

MW/HR/1 Hereford Cathedral (Cathedral Church of St Mary and St Ethelbert), Church St. HR1 2NG	★★☆☆		HE: Grade 1 #1196808
	Built: C11-C15, renovated 1854 to 1863. **Architects:** GG and O Scott		
	Interest: Dwarf wall at the crossing, steps and pavement nearby (Fig. 5.10c)		
	Stones: Devonshire *Red Ogwell*, *Ashburton* and an unknown dark grey Carboniferous stone similar to that used in the Foreign Office, London		
Comments: Scott's son, Oldrid, was involved in restoration of the West Front			

MW/HR/2 St Catherine's Church, Hoarwithy, Herefordshire. HR2 6QH	? ? ☆☆		HE: Grade I #1214570
	Completed: 1849, enlarged 1885. **Architect:** Enlarged by John Pollard Seddon. **Style:** Eclectic Italianate		
	Interest: Fine marble interior with four large chancel arch pillars		
	Stones: Possible Devonshire *Ipplepen* or *Petitor*. Chancel shafts seem to be single pieces. *Connemara* colonnettes and plinths. *Carrara* altar with *lapis lazuli* panels. Carved *Carrara* pulpit. Steps and pavement in *Cippolino*, *Breche Sanguine* and others. Mosaics in nave aisle.		
Comments: Not visited and requires confirmation. A fine marble interior worth a visit in its own right			

Worcester area (WM/W/)

MW/W/1 Worcester Cathedral (Cathedral Church of Christ and St Mary), 10 College Yard, Worcester. WR1 2LA	★★☆☆		HE: Grade I #1389728
	Built: C11-C14, altered 1871-75. **Architect:** George Gilbert Scott.		
	Interest: Chancel Steps, choir screen, chancel paving.		
	Stones: Devonshire *Petitor* and probable veined *Ashburton* in screen (Fig. 5.8c). Light grey likely *Grey Ipplepen* stone in the steps. Pavement has *Red* and *Grey Ipplepen*, also *Connemara* and white *Tuscan*.		
Comments: Limited survey only. There may be more Devonshire here.			

North West (NW/)

Manchester area (NW/M/)

NW/M/1 Manchester Town Hall extension Rates Hall, Lloyd Street and St Peter's Sq entrances, Manchester. M2 5DB	★★☆	**Guide:** Group 11	HE: Grade II* #1197917
	Built: 1934-38. **Architect:** E Vincent Harris. Restored and refurbished 2010-2014, Laing O'Rourke and Ryder. **Style:** Gothic 1930s contemporary		
	Interest: The arcuate Rates Hall is the original public entrance area of the Town Hall extension building		
	Stones: Hall panels, window and door arches are in Devonshire *Ashburton* marble. There are bands of local Derbyshire *Hoptonwood* stone and the vestibules are panelled with it		
Comments: *Hoptonwood* is a light coloured Lower Carboniferous limestone. A dark Carboniferous limestone with white fossil brachiopods is found in the floor			

NW/M/2 Manchester Central Library, St Peter's	★☆☆☆	**Guide:** Group 11	HE: Grade: II* #1270759
	Built: 1930-34. **Architect:** E Vincent Harris. Restored and refurbished 2010-2014. **Style:** Neo-classical.		
	Interest: Entrance vestibule, stairways and most public areas.		

Square, Manchester. M2 5PD	**Stones:** Very minimal Devonshire but superb *Hoptonwood* panelling and dressings throughout. The Tuscan order colonnade around the great reading room is scagliola and there is more elsewhere

Comments: There really is some Devonshire (*Ashburton*) here, flanking a down stairway. Derbyshire *Hoptonwood* (see M/1) steals the show.

NW/M/3 Manchester Town Hall Albert Square, Manchester. M2 5DB	★ ☆ ☆ ☆	**Guide:** Group 11	**HE:** Grade: I #1207469
	Built: 1868-1877. **Architect:** Alfred E Waterhouse. **Style:** Gothic Revival		
	Interest: Entrance lobby, Sculpture Hall, corridors, stairways		
	Stones: English, Scottish and Irish granites. Sculpture pedestals include fine Devonshire *Petitor* and good *Ashburton* and *Ipplepen/Plymouth*		

Comments: Good mosaic flooring in natural stone. There are fine Italian and other marbles in the sculpture pedestals

Yorkshire and the Humber (NY/)

Harrogate area (NY/HG/)

NY/HG/1 St Mary's Church, Studley Royal, North Yorkshire. HG4 3DY	? ☆ ☆ ☆		**HE:** Grade I #1315267
	Built: 1871-78. **Architect:** William Burgess. **Style:** Early English Gothic revival		
	Interest: Polished stone shafts in nave piers, chancel arch piers, beneath vaulting and in apse window arcade		
	Stones: Probable Devonshire amongst the *Connemara* and *Red Cork* shafts. Likely *Petitor* in font plinth. Good scrapwork step nearby		

Comments: Not visited and requires confirmation. The chancel is flush-panelled in Italian marble and the altar step is probably *Red Cork* or Belgian red. Exceptionally rich interior, well worth a visit in its own right

Hull area (NY/HU/)

NY/HU/1 Williams Solicitors, Hull. 45 Lowgate, Hull. HU1 1EN	★ ★		Listing not found
	Built: 1960s. **Architects:** unknown. **Style:** Modern		
	Interest: Extensive street-level panelled Devonshire marble frontage. Good palaeontology (including growth-zoned stromatoporoids)		
	Stones: Devonshire *Ashburton*		

Comments: Not visited. Both the location and external use of this stone are unusual. The frontage is listed as a 'Regionally Important Geological Site'. (http://www.hull.ac.uk/php/chsmjh/urbrigs.htm).

Halifax area (NY/HX/)

NY/HX/1 All Soul's Church, Halifax. All Souls Road, Haley Hill, Halifax, West Yorkshire. HX3 6DR	? ☆ ☆		**HE** Grade I #1314027
	Completed: 1856. **Architect:** George Gilbert Scott. **Style:** C13-C14 Gothic Revival		
	Interest: Some window shafts, pulpit pedestal and stair colonnettes; reredos colonnettes. Incidental use elsewhere		
	Stones: Apparently *Petitor* types. Uncertain grey in chancel arch		

Comments: Not visited and requires confirmation. Typical GGS diversity of stone shafts. Superb Cornish serpentine font on *Pink Peterhead* plinth. Serpentine colonnettes in pulpit. *Connemara* beneath. Numerous *Peterhead* shafts inside and out. Redundant church in the care of the Churches Conservation Trust

Todmorden area (NY/OL/) NB: The Region is east but the local postcode is Oldham

NY/OL/1 Dobroyd Castle Pexwood Road, Todmorden, Calderdale. OL14 7JJ	★★★	Guide: Group 11	HE: Grade II* #1134570
	Built: 1866-69. **Architect:** John Gibson. **Style:** Exterior - Baronial Victorian Gothic; interior – Romanesque with Gothic detail		
	Interest: Entrance hall shafts, entrance hall fireplace and staircase hall shafts		
	Stones: Devonshire *Red Ipplepen* shafts. Rare *Rose Red Radford* in fireplace		

Comments: Gibson also used *Ipplepen* at the nearby Unitarian Church and again at Gibson Hall, London (see above)

NY/OL/2 Unitarian Church Honey Hole Road, Todmorden, Calderdale. OL14 6LE.	★★★	Guide: Group 11	HE: Grade 1 #1228988
	Built: 1865-69. **Architect:** John Gibson. **Style:** Victorian Gothic		
	Interest: Shafts in nave arcade pillars, aisles and chancel		
	Stones: Devonshire *Red Ipplepen* with fillets of a black marble. Marbles in both pulpit and font are continental		

Comments: 12 stout pillars with *Ipplepen* shafts weighing 1.7 metric tonnes line the nave. A further 51 more slender shafts are used throughout

South East (SE/)

Croydon area (SE/CR/)

SE/CR/1 St Mary Magdalene Church, Canning Rd, Addiscombe, Croydon. CR0 6QD	???		HE Grade II* #1358794
	Completed: 1868. **Architect:** Edward Buckton Lamb. **Style:** Decorated Gothic revival		
	Interest: Chancel arch, chancel apse window arcade. Colonnettes on nave piers		
	Stones: Grey veined and patchy stone of Devonshire type.		

Comments: Not visited – provisional listing. Steps and pavement should also be examined.

Guildford area (SE/GU/)

SE/GU/1 Guildford Cathedral (Cathedral Church of the Holy Spirit) Cathedral Close. GU2 7UP	★★☆		HE: Grade II* #1377883
	Built: 1936-1964. **Architect:** Edward Maufe. **Style:** Gothic art deco		
	Interest: Pavement and steps in the Chapel of the Queen's Royal Surrey Regiment (1960s)		
	Stones: Devonshire *Ashburton* (Fig. 5.10d). Other marbles include Italian travertines and an unusual Swedish green marble in the Children's Chapel and the baptistery		

Comments: Stones are identified in a helpful plaque near the entrance. Why don't more buildings have this? There is a unique and unrecorded *Ashburton* marble Formica-topped table at the SE entrance

Oxford Area (SE/OX/)

SE/OX/1 Exeter College Chapel, Turl Street, Oxford.	★★★☆	Guide: Group 5	HE: Grade II* #1046721
	Built: 1854-60. **Architect:** George Gilbert Scott. **Style:** French Victorian Gothic		
	Interest: Ante-chapel, vaulting shafts, chancel steps, sanctuary arcade		

OX1 3DP	**Stones:** Devonshire *Red Ipplepen* and *Red Ogwell*, with Cornish serpentine

Comments: The exclusive choice of west county stone reflects the regional founding statutes of the College. The *Red Ogwell* is in the floor, the other stones are in arcade and other shafts. There are good Salviati mosaics and Pre-Raphaelite tapestry

	★★☆☆	**Guide:** Group 5	**HE:** Grade 1 #1081534
SE/OX/2 Oxford University Museum of Natural History, Parks Road, Oxford. OX1 3PW	**Built:** 1861. **Architect:** Thomas Newenham Deane and Benjamin Woodward. **Style:** Victorian gothic		
	Interest: Ground floor and first floor arcade marble shafts. The Corsi Collection of decorative stones and a display of typical Devonian corals and stromatoporoids		
	Stones: Devonshire *Petitor, Chudleigh, Plymouth, Plymouth Radford, Ogwell* and possible *Stoneycombe*. There is a comprehensive collection of other (then) British marbles and granites		

Comments: A first rate museum with great displays of fossils and much else. Representative Devonshire marbles are mostly in the first floor arcade

	★★★☆☆	**Guide:** Group 5	**HE:** Grade 1 #?1046691
SE/OX/3 Keble College Chapel, 16 Parks Rd, Oxford. OX1 3PG	**Built:** 1873-6. **Architect:** William Butterfield. **Style:** Polychromic Victorian Gothic		
	Interest: Chancel arcade pillars, pedestals, skirting, pavement, steps.		
	Stones: Devonshire *Ashburton, Petitor, Ipplepen* and *Ogwell*, with English crinoidal. Scottish *Peterhead* and *Rubislaw* granite; *Connemara*, alabaster, white and grey *Tuscan*		

Comments: Keble chapel is a Butterfield masterpiece, including his own glass mosaic panels all around the walls. Stones include some important variants of *Ipplepen* that have original sedimentary textures comparable with *Ogwell* and *Petitor* types

Portsmouth area (SE/PO/)

	★☆☆☆		**HE:** Grade I #1354261
SE/PO/1 Chichester Cathedral (Cathedral Church of the Holy Trinity), The Royal Chantry, Cathedral Cloisters, Chichester. PO19 1PX	**Built:** C11-C15. Renovations after tower collapse 1861-6. **Architect:** George Gilbert Scott		
	Interest: Quire, presbytery and sanctuary floors. Corner shafts in presbytery		
	Stones: The use of Devonshire by Scott is limited. *Petitor* in pavement and probable *Black Ogwell* in shafts. Other stones are 'British' and include Irish *Red Cork* in the sanctuary steps and *Green Connemara* in pavement. English crinoidal and a likely Magnesian limestone also in pavement		

Comments: The stones noted were installed following the rebuilding of the tower. There is a more recent large *Portland* ammonite cross section (*Titanites sp.*) in the new quire steps north, and excellent apparently original *Purbeck* pavement in the south crossing. Great original (but Scott-repaired) *Purbeck* compound shafts line the presbytery and elsewhere and there are fine recent *Purbeck* renovations in the entrance narthrex

Reading area (SE/RG/)

	★★★☆		**HE:** Grade II* #1291027
SE/RG/1 Church of St Mary, New Rd, Greenham, Thatcham, Berkshire.	**Built:** 1875-1895. **Architect:** Henry Woodyer. **Style:** Early English Gothic revival		
	Interest: Single central nave arcade of stout piers. Shaft clusters in chancel arch, shafts in chancel window arcade. Sedilia and sanctuary		
	Stones: Nave and baptistery shaft drums are some of the best		

RG19 8RZ	Devonshire *Red* and *Pink Petitor* anywhere. Varieties of *Red Ogwell* are in smaller chancel arch shafts and around chancel windows

Comments: This is a delightful well-used church with Devonshire marble inside and split flint outside. Chancel walls and chancel arch spandrels are covered in frescos designed by JA Pippett (c. 1888-91). Fine carved alabaster reredos. Well worth a visit in own right

Redhill area (SE/RH/)

SE/RH/1 Church of St Barnabas, Ranmore Common Rd, Dorking, Surrey. RH5 6SP.	★☆☆		HE: Grade II* #1189879
	Built: 1859. **Architect:** George Gilbert Scott. **Style:** English decorated Gothic revival		
	Interest: Shafts throughout are a typical GGS mix		
	Stones: Devonshire *Red Ipplepen* in east window clusters and in complex short shaft cluster at chancel arch. Also here is *Green Connemara* whilst adjacent tall shafts are *Shap Granite*. Chancel side arcades in *Ipplepen* (S) and serpentine (N). Pulpit includes *Ipplepen* in plinth flanked by possible *Green Anglesey*, with *Red Griotte* stringers, *Rosso Ammonitico* cope and lectern and alabaster carved inserts		

Comments: Elaborate interior. Crossing windows and high tower arcades have grey and pink Scottish granites. Carved alabaster reredos with fine *pietra dura* and white *Carrara* altar. Baptistery at rear has *Red Cork* and *Green Connemara* shafts and a spectacular *Lizard Serpentine* font. Very good detail in HE listing text

North Surrey area (SE/TW/)

SE/TW/1 St Mary's Church, Church Street, Sunbury-on-Thames, Surrey. TW16 6RG	★☆		HE Grade II* #1029661
	Built: 1752, remodelled 1857. **Architect:** Stephen Wright, remodelled by Samuel Sanders Teulon. **Style:** Baroque		
	Interest: Small shafts in chancel side arcades and in apse arcade		
	Stones: Devonshire *Red Ipplepen*		

Comments: Good stone variation in colonnettes with brachiopod 'nests'. Stained glass by Clayton & Bell. Mosaics by Salviati

South West England (SW/)

Bath area (SW/BA/)

SW/BA/1 St John the Evangelist Catholic Church, South Parade, Bath, Avon. BA2 4AF	★★★		HE Grade II* #1394998
	Built: 1861-3. **Architect:** Charles Francis Hansom. **Style:** Gothic Revival decorated		
	Interest: 10 or 12 nave arcade shafts. Colonnettes in apse arcade. Reredos/altarpiece. ?Chancel steps. ?Aisle shafts. ?Side chapels. Colonnettes in pulpit		
	Stones: Devonshire marble nave shafts consist of 6 drums of probable *Red Ogwell* (or else *Pink Petitor*). Similar stone in apse arcade and pulpit colonnettes		

Comments: Potentially important building not visited and requiring confirmation. Nave columns have ornate carved *Ancaster* capitals

Exeter area, Devon (SW/EX/)

SW/EX/1 Exeter Cathedral (The Cathedral	★☆☆☆	**Guide:** Group 10	HE: Grade I #1333352
	Built: 1112-1400, restored 1870-77. **Architect:** George Gilbert Scott. **Style:** Norman Gothic		
	Interest: Pulpit, chancel and Lady chapel steps and pavements		

Church of Saint Peter at Exeter), 1 The Cloisters, EX1 1HS	**Stones:** Devonshire *Ipplepen, Petitor, Ashburton* and local igneous in pavements. Good *Ashburton* steps in presbytery. *Ipplepen* colonnettes below pulpit. *Salcombe* stone masonry throughout with *Purbeck* piers. Unusual recent *Portland* shafts in Chapter House

Comments: A wide range of Devonshire varieties appears in the pavements, introduced during the Scott alterations

	★★☆	Guide: Group 10	HE: Grade II #1223756
SW/EX/2 Church of the Sacred Heart, 25 South Street, Exeter. EX1 1EB	**Built:** 1883-4. **Architect:** Leonard Stokes and CE Ware. **Style:** Gothic revival		
	Interest: Nave shafts, chancel steps and screen, pulpit, altars		
	Stones: Nave shafts in local Pocombe lava. Devonshire *Red Ogwell* in pulpit and chancel screen niches with *Hoptonwood* and carved *Beer*. Chancel screen on good Devonshire *Grey Petitor* with *Hoptonwood* above. Other marbles in altars include Italian, Belgian and French. *Carrara* font		

Comments: Architect Leonard Stokes may have been influenced by contact with known marble embellishers GE Street and TE Colcutt

	★★	Guide: Group 10	HE: Grade II #1223249
SW/EX/3 Royal Albert Memorial Museum Queen Street, Exeter. EX4 3RX	**Completed:** 1865. **Architect:** John Hayward. **Style:** Venetian Palazzo in Gothic Revival style		
	Interest: Entrance hall arcade and side shafts, stairway handrails, landing niche		
	Stones: Devonshire *Red Ipplepen* shafts and stair rails, *Ashburton* niche on right stair (ascending) and faux *Ashburton* on left		

Comments: The Museum contains faux marble panels of *Ashburton* (on display), *Petitor* and *Ogwell* by John Bradley. There is an excellent collection of ornamental objects in Derbyshire *Blue John*

	★★☆	Guide: Group 10	HE: Grade II* #1323701
SW/EX/4 Devon County Hall, Topsham Road, Exeter. EX2 4QD	**Built:** 1958-64. **Architect:** Donald Hanks McMorran. **Style:** Classically influenced post-war modern		
	Interest: Members antechamber floor and walls; Grand Staircase and landing		
	Stones: Devonshire *Ashburton* in marble pavement, *Purbeck* and *Portland* in walls, stairs and openings. 2 spectacular and rare *Ashburton* marble shafts in first floor gallery		

Comments: Technical guides to wider geology on the campus on: http://www.devon.gov.uk/geology-countyhall.htm

	★★		HE: Grade II #1384734
SW/EX/5 The Town Hall, St Andrew Street, Tiverton. EX16 6PG	**Completed:** 1864. **Architect:** H. Lloyd of Bristol. **Style:** Venetian Baroque		
	Interest: 8 shafts and 4 pilasters on exterior polygonal bay		
	Stones: Similar to *Red Ogwell* (Fig. 5.3d) but *Grey Ipplepen* cannot be ruled out. Probably a variety of *Grey/Black Ogwell*		

Comments: Interior not surveyed. The external shafts are highly weathered and so colour is much changed. Fossils are consistent with *Ogwell* and rather abundant for *Ipplepen*

	★★		HE: Grade 1 #1097577
SW/EX/6 Bishop's Court Palace,	**Altered:** 1860s. **Architect:** William White. **Style:** not noted		
	Interest: Entrance, main hall, stairway, public rooms, chapel		

Clyst St Mary, Sowton, Exeter. EX5 1DH *Private*	**Stones:** Devonshire *Ipplepen, Stoneycombe, Ashburton, Petitor* and probable *Plymouth*. Some Irish *Red Cork*

Comments: Reconnaissance visit only. Former Bishop's Palace. Good details in HE listing

SW/EX/7 Knightshayes Court, Tiverton Bolham, Tiverton. EX16 7RQ *National Trust*	★★		**HE:** Grade II* #1000487
	Built: 1869-1873. **Architect:** William Burgess. **Style:** Gothic Revival		
	Interest: Entrance hall and public rooms		
	Stones: 4 good Devonshire *Ashburton* pillars in hall. One in matching faux marble in drawing room. Secondary Italian marble fireplaces with *Red Cork* and *Carrara*		

Comments: Reconnaissance visit only. Interiors completed by John Dibblee Crace. Much information in HE listing text. Exterior masonry in *Red Hensley* stone with *Ham Stone* dressings

SW/EX/8 Luscombe Castle, Dawlish. EX7 0PU. *Private*	★★		**HE:** Grade I #1000486
	Built: Main building 1800-4, chapel 1862. **Architects:** John Nash (castle), George Gilbert Scott (chapel). **Style:** Gothic Revival chapel		
	Interest: Chapel shafts, inlaid lectern, steps and pavement		
	Stones: Devonshire *Red Ogwell, Petitor*, probable *Ashburton*		

Comments: Reconnaissance visit only. Inset stones in metal canopy over sanctuary. Good information with HE listing

SW/EX/9 St Michael's Church, Fore Street, Beer. EX12 3HT	★★★		**HE:** Grade II #1306427
	Built: 1877. **Architect:** 'Hayward of Exeter'. **Style:** Early English Gothic revival		
	Interest: Nave arcade with 6 monolitic shafts. Chancel arch with compound shafts; side shafts in east window. Colonnettes in font and pulpit		
	Stones: All Devonshire *Red Ogwell* apart from *Ashburton* either side of *Ogwell* in the chancel arch shafts		

Comments: Nave shafts are unusually long for *Ogwell* at 2.05 m and contain outstanding fossils and textures

SW/EX/10. County Chambers, 75 Queen Street, Exeter. EX4 3RX.	★★☆	Figs with Gp. 10	**HE** Grade II #1223249
	Built: 'Early C20'. **Architect:** Unknown. **Style:** Venetian Palazzo in Baroque style		
	Interest: Columns and panels at first floor; columns, pilasters and arches at second floor; panels and ornament in pediment		
	Stones: Devonshire *Red Ogwell* at first floor, *Ashburton* or similar at second floor and above		

Comments: No significant records have yet been traced for this important building. The HE listing gives minimal information

Gloucester area (SW/GL/)

SW/GL/1 Christ Church, Malvern Rd, Cheltenham, Gloucestershire. GL50 2NN.	★★★☆		**HE** Grade II* #1103838
	Built: 1837-40. Interior remodelled 1888-93. **Architects:** RW & C Jearard, JH Middleton, HA Prothero and Phillot with 'Byzantine' wall decoration by Sir William Richmond and J Eadie Reid. **Style:** Regency style Early English Gothic		
	Interest: Choir screen, sanctuary screen (communion rail), apse, pulpit and steps		

	Stones: Devonshire *Petitor* (balusters), *Ashburton* (choir screen, sanctuary screen pulpit columns), *Red Ogwell* and *Ipplepen* (panels in screens). Numerous European varieties in apse, screens and in pulpit stair balustrade where rails may be Devonshire *Silverleigh*		

Comments: The sanctuary screen (communion rail) has a useful range of *Petitor* types. The nave shafts are clad in white *Carrara*; good *Lizard Serpentine* in screen copes

SW/GL/2 Church of St John the Baptist, Market Place, Cirencester, Gloucestershire. GL7 2BQ	★☆		**HE** Grade I #1206356
	Built: C12 with many later modifications. **Renovated:** 1865-7 by George Gilbert Scott. **Style:** Mostly Gothic English Perpendicular		
	Interest: High altar steps		
	Stones: Devonshire *Red Ogwell* was installed in the steps by Scott. The lower step has since been replaced using Belgian red, but the *Ogwell*, with typical fossils and textures, remains in the level above		

Comments: Further renovation in 2009 replaced Scott's tiled floor in nave and chancel and this seems to be when the altar step was replaced

Plymouth area, Devon (SW/PL/)

SW/PL/1 Plymouth Cathedral (Roman Catholic Cathedral Church of St Mary and St Boniface), Wyndham St, Plymouth. PL1 5BW	★★☆	**Guide:** Group 9	**HE:** Grade II #1386510
	Completed: 1858. **Architects:** Joseph and Charles Hansom. **Style:** Gothic Revival.		
	Interest: Shafts outside west door, chancel shafts, side chapels, street pavement outside		
	Stones: 6 shafts in chancel are indeterminate Plymouth limestones. Additional English crinoidal limestone and French *Languedoc* and others in side chapels. Devonshire *Ogwell* in font		

Comments: There was once a more elaborate Victorian interior here that included a marble chancel screen/communion rail. The streets outside are paved with Plymouth 'marble' of West Hoe type

SW/PL/2 Guildhall Plymouth, Armada Way, Plymouth. PL1 2AD	★☆☆	**Guide:** Group 9	**HE:** Grade II #1113280
	Completed: 1874, burned out in 1941 and rebuilt in 1959. **Original architect:** Norman Hine. Reconstruction: HJW Stirling. **Style:** Post-war adaptation of Gothic		
	Interest: Entrance hall, grand stairs and first floor vestibule		
	Stones: Interior stones include Devonshire *Ashburton* in stairs and pillars. Exterior masonry is Devonshire, with local granite colonnettes and panels in green *Genoa*. Dressings are probable *Portland* and *Red Mansfield*.		

Comments: Magnificent 'Festival of Britain' interior. Pillar shafts are 'fluted' with strips of *Ashburton* separated by hardwood

SW/PL/3 Civic Square Pavement, Armada Way, Plymouth. PL1 2AD	★★	**Guide:** Group 9	**HE:** Grade II #1001425
	Completed: 1950s reconstruction		
	Interest: Stone pavement.		
	Stones: A range of Plymouth limestones of West Hoe type		

Comments: The Devonshire limestone paved Civic Square outside Plymouth Guildhall is an important re-use of stones from the 'marble streets' of the old town as noted, e.g. by Thomas Hardy. These show much of the geological history of the Plymouth limestones

SW/PL/4	★★☆	**Guide:** Group 9	**HE:** Grade II #1392038

Civic Centre and Council House, Armada Way, Plymouth. PL1 2AA	**Built:** 1958-62. **Architects:** Jellicoe, Ballantyne & Coleridge. **Style:** Postwar modern
	Interest: Civic Centre - Four stone-panelled piers in public vestibule and another beside the members' entrance stairs. Council House – Columns and flooring in entrance area, panels in door handles, terrazzo and pebble-inlaid pavement throughout members' areas
	Stones: *Ashburton* cladding on columns. Additional white *Tuscan* in the Council House. Floor in Civic Centre public entrance area not visible. In Council House it is terrazzo, using random-fit Italian marbles or rounded *Carrara* pebbles

Comments: Some losses to marble panels in piers at first floor level in the Civic Centre. This multi-storey building faces major renovation and re-use. The Council House is in fine condition and its municipal uses are to be retained

SW/PL/5 HMS Drake, Plymouth. Officers' Wardroom and Mess and the Chapel of St Nicholas. Saltash Road, Devonport, Plymouth. PL2 2BG *NB: special access only*	★★★	Restricted access	HE: Grade II #1386376
	Built: Mess -1898-1902. **Architect:** Superintendent Engineer Major Monro Wilson of the Royal Engineers. **Style:** Neo Baroque		
	Interest: Mess - Columns in entrance hall and in the four front function rooms on ground and first floors. Chapel – Two-tier chancel vaulting shafts and a very fine turned and moulded font in baptistery		
	Stones: Mess entrance hall - 2 monolithic pillars in *Red Ogwell* on *Ashburton* plinths. Front rooms ground and first floor - 8 monolitic pillars in *Grey Petitor* and 8 monolithic pillars in *Pink Petitor*, on *Petitor* plinths. Chapel - Shafts in *Ashburton* marble, font bowl and pedestal in fine single turned pieces of *Petitor* on an *Ashburton* plinth		

Comments: This relatively late DMB in Plymouth features the finest east (not west) Devonshire marbles. There is good textured and fossiliferous local Plymouth limestone masonry in the exterior of the Officers' Mess

SW/PL/6 Duke of Cornwall Hotel, Millbay Road, Plymouth. PL1 3LG	★★	HE: Grade II #1386245
	Completed: 1865. **Architect:** C. Forster Hayward. **Style:** Victorian Gothic Baronial	
	Interest: Entrance lobby mantel piece; pillars in main function room	
	Stones: 4 pillars in several varieties of Plymouth marbles, some comparable with named types at Brompton Oratory (DMB L/W/1). Lobby fireplace colonnettes in *Red Radford*	

Comments: A remarkable survivor of the local bombing with marbles similar to some in Brompton Oratory. Ceiling alterations obscure tops of pillars

SW/PL/7 Church of St John the Evangelist, Church Hill Rd, Plymstock, Plymouth. PL9 9RG	★☆	HE: Grade II #1130026
	Built: 1855. **Architect:** William White. **Style:** Simple English Gothic	
	Interest: Nave pillars, chancel screen, reredos and font	
	Stones: Black Plymouth marbles in nave shafts, sanctuary screen and reredos. *Rose Red Radford* in colonnettes in screen and reredos	

Comments: The nave pillars are now shedding a coat of black paint. The very dark grey fossiliferous stone and the grey in the chancel screen rail may be from local quarries at Hooe Lake or Radford

SW/PL/8 St Bartholomew's Church,	★★	HE: Grade II* #1306637
	Re-Built: 1849-52. **Architect:** William Butterfield. **Style:** Polychromic Gothic revival	
	Interest: Aisle arcade and shafts, chancel screen, pavement and altar.	

Church Lane, Yealmpton. PL8 2HB	Font bowl
	Stones: Red *Kitley*, grey *Kitley*. No *Green Kitley*. Probable *Red Ogwell*, black Plymouth

Comments: Remarkably, this building has the local marbles, but none of the expected and famous *Green Kitley*. Butterfield's original drawings were lost in a fire

SW/PL/9 Chapel of St Martin, Maristow House, Bickleigh, Plymouth. PL6 7BZ *Private*	★☆		HE: Grade II #1325366
	Chapel Built: 1877-9. **Architect:** JP St Aubyn. **Style:** Gothic Revival chapel		
	Interest: Sanctuary columns, reredos colonnettes, retable		
	Stones: Uncertain red Devonshire marble, alabaster and ?*Connemara*.		

Comments: Not visited and requires confirmation.

Salisbury area (SW/SP/)

SW/SP/1 Salisbury Cathedral, North Walk, Salisbury, Wiltshire. SP1 2EG	★★☆☆☆		HE: Grade 1 #1023581
	Restoration: 1860-76. **Architect:** George Gilbert Scott		
	Interest: Sanctuary steps and restoration work to West Front, including shafts and window and door surrounds		
	Stones: Inside, Devonshire black Plymouth or *Chudleigh*, outside a fossiliferous Devonshire variety like *Ipplepen* but not recognised		

Comments: The extent of the substitution of *Purbeck* by Devonshire in the West Front is substantial, far more than other elevations. The Hertford Tomb, south aisle, is embellished in Belgian red marble. Note the strained *Purbeck* shafts beneath the spire (e.g. SE stanchion)

SW/SP/2 Church of the Holy Trinity, Fonthill Gifford, Wiltshire. SP3 6PX	★★★		HE: Grade II* #1146055
	Completed: 1866. **Architect:** TH Wyatt. **Style:** Gothic Revival		
	Interest: Shafts in nave, transept, chancel arch, chancel, sanctuary, and beneath font		
	Stones: Most shafts are Devonshire *Red Ogwell*, but the sanctuary has *Blue Purbeck* shafts. Font pedestals are *Red Radford* and *Green Connemara*. *Connemara* is also below the chancel arch and in pulpit. Pulpit is alabaster on grey *Tuscan* plinth		

Comments: Elaborate church built for Marquess of Westminster. Shafts were either left unpolished or have lost their finish

SW/SP/4 St Mary's Church, Shipton Road South Tidworth, Wiltshire, SP9 7ST	★☆		HE: Grade l #1093240
	Built: 1878. **Architect:** John Johnson. **Style:** Gothic Revival		
	Interest: Nave shaft clusters, chancel arch and chancel shafts, east window shafts. Aisle pilasters and shafts in the porch area		
	Stones: Tall two-tier fourfold clustered shafts are Devonshire probable *Radford Red* from Plymouth. Chancel arch three-tier, double or treble clusters are similar, as are shafts within the chancel		

Comments: Not visited and requires confirmation. This is one of several Wiltshire churches recorded by Neil Macdougal on a Panoramio photostream that evidently contain Devonshire marble (see next entry)

SW/SP/5-10 (provisional) 6 Wiltshire Churches:	St Katherine's, Savernake Forest. St Leonard's, Semley. St Giles, Gt Wishford. St Mary and St Nicholas, Wilton. St John the Evangelist, Sutton Veny. All Saints, All Cannings. St Peter's, Codford St Peter.
	All have minor likely Devonshire in small shafts, mostly in the chancel.

	The Wilton church has larger shafts less likely to be Devonshire.

Comments: Not visited and all require confirmation. Identifications are from a photostream of Wiltshire churches (search: Neil Macdougal Wiltshire Churches Panoramio).

Torquay area, Devon (SW/TQ/)

<table>
<tr><td rowspan="4">SW/TQ/1
All Saints
Church (Parish
Church of All
Saints), Cary
Avenue,
Babbacombe,
Torquay.
TQ1 1QT</td><td>★★★★</td><td>Guide: Group 8</td><td>HE: Grade 1 #1280043</td></tr>
<tr><td colspan="3">Completed: 1874. Architect: William Butterfield. Style: Victorian Gothic Polychromic</td></tr>
<tr><td colspan="3">Interest: External - Carved quatrefoils with marble insets. Internal - Drums in nave shafts; choir screen. Chancel pavement, Butterfield pulpit and font</td></tr>
<tr><td colspan="3">Stones: Devonshire Petitor and Red Ogwell in nave shafts. Red and Black Ogwell plus white Tuscan in screen. Ashburton, Ogwell and Petitor varieties in chancel pavement with white Tuscan and Irish Connemara. Alabaster in walls and reredos. Eclectic pulpit and font</td></tr>
</table>

Comments: This is locally regarded as the 'type' Devonshire marble church and the exterior panelling, now much degraded, gives it that edge. Marbles by Andrew Blackler. Fine glass mosaics by Antonio Salviati probably drawn by Butterfield

<table>
<tr><td rowspan="4">SW/TQ/2
Former
Showroom
Entrance, Royal
Marble Works,
Fore Street,
Babbacombe.
TQ1 4LY</td><td>☆☆</td><td>Guide: Group 8</td><td>? not listed</td></tr>
<tr><td colspan="3">Built: ?1836 -1861. Architect: Possibly John Woodley. Style: Paladian</td></tr>
<tr><td colspan="3">Interest: Important surviving relic of the most important marble works in the Devonshire marble industry</td></tr>
<tr><td colspan="3">Stones: No marble recorded</td></tr>
</table>

Comments: This very important portico is listed here for historical reasons but apparently no longer contains Devonshire Marble. Owners: Woodley to 1864, Blackler to 1915. The Land behind was redeveloped 1886, *c.*1970 and 2013

<table>
<tr><td rowspan="4">SW/TQ/3
Torquay
Museum,
529
Babbacombe
Rd, Torquay.
TQ1 1HG</td><td>★★☆</td><td>Guide: Group 8</td><td>HE: Grade II #1280070</td></tr>
<tr><td colspan="3">Built: 1874-76. Architect: William Alexander Harvey. Style: Arts & Crafts meet Venetian Gothic</td></tr>
<tr><td colspan="3">Interest: Devonshire marble here is in the collections only</td></tr>
<tr><td colspan="3">Stones: Exterior stone is rough-dressed local grey limestone with Bath stone detail. No architectural use of Devonshire marble</td></tr>
</table>

Comments: Contains the only specifically recorded Devonshire marble artefacts, including three specimen marble tables and numerous ornaments. There is an important collection of Devonian rocks and fossils

<table>
<tr><td rowspan="4">SW/TQ/4
St John's
Church Torquay
(Church of St
John the
Apostle),
Montpellier
Road, Torquay.
TQ1 1BJ</td><td>★★★★</td><td>Guide: Group 7</td><td>HE: Grade 1 #1206814</td></tr>
<tr><td colspan="3">Built: 1864-1885. Architect: George Edmund Street. Style: Gothic Revival</td></tr>
<tr><td colspan="3">Interest: Nave arcade shafts; shafts in chancel arcades. Chancel steps and pavement, reredos, mosaic medallions. Pulpit, 2 fonts</td></tr>
<tr><td colspan="3">Stones: Nave shafts are all Devonshire, Ashburton along the south (with veined and red variants) and Petitor along the north. Chancel shafts include Ashburton, Petitor, Lummaton and Ogwell. Similar in steps and pavement. Unpolished Ham Hill oolite in walls. Caen Stone and Devon in vaulting</td></tr>
</table>

Comments: Superb throughout. Street was trained by GG Scott. Andrew Blackler did the stone mosaics around chancel (1875) and probably more. Glass mosaics by Antonio Salviati in north aisle. William Morris window

SW/TQ/5 St Mary Magdalene Church (Parish Church of), Union Street, Upton, Torquay. TQ1 4BX	★★★	Guide:	HE: Grade II* #1219197
	Built: 1844-55. **Architect:** Anthony Salvin. **Style:** Eclectic Gothic Revival		
	Interest: Superb panelling in choir screen and chancel walls. Chancel pavement, ritual furnishings, reredos, reredos shelf		
	Stones: Several varieties of Devonshire *Petitor*, *Pink* and *Red Ogwell*, *Ashburton*. *Yellow Petitor* above *Red Ogwell* reredos shelf. *Pink Petitor* and *Ashburton* pavement and steps. Unpolished carved *Caen Stone*		

Comments: Chancel remodelled by Temple Moore 1879-1905, to a design by GG Scott. Superb matched (mirrored, or 'butterfly') *Petitor* panels in choir screen and chancel. Unique Bishop's chair in *Red Ogwell*

SW/TQ/6 Torbay Town Hall. Lymington Road, Torquay. TQ1 4BW	★★	Guide: Group 7	HE: Grade II #1208247
	Built: 1906-11. **Architect:** Thomas Davison. **Style:** Edwardian Baroque.		
	Interest: Stairway, landings and upper NE corridor. Panels, pavement, stairs and balustrades		
	Stones: Fine Devonshire *Grey Ipplepen* in stair panels. *Ashburton* stairs, rails and skirting. Alabaster balusters. *Ashburton* first floor pilasters; *Ashburton* combined with white *Tuscan* in floors		

Comments: Elegant Edwardian panelled stairway and gallery

SW/TQ/7 Torquay Library, Lymington Rd, Torquay. TQ1 3DT	★★	Guide: Group 7	HE: listing not found
	Completed: 1938. **Architect:** PW Ladmore (local borough engineer). **Style:** Simplified late Art Deco		
	Interest: External masonry, internal flush panelling around small entrance lobby		
	Stones: Devonshire *Lummaton* (*Dove Happaway*) inside and outside		

Comments: A good type locality for *Lummaton marble*. This important small area of lobby panelling has already been reduced through alterations. It is now cluttered and is at risk

SW/TQ/8 St Matthias Church (Parish Church of St Matthias, St Mark & Holy Trinity), Babbacombe Road, Torquay. TQ1 2NL	★★		HE: Grade II* #1206840
	Chancel: 1894. **Architect:** JL Pearson. **Style:** not noted		
	Interest: Dwarf wall in chancel screen; pavement, pulpit and font		
	Stones: Devonshire *Red Ogwell*, *Ashburton*, *Yellow Petitor*, *Lummaton*. Irish *Green Connemara*, English alabaster		

Comments: Reconnaissance visit only. Reredos statues in alabaster by Harry Hems of Exeter. Original Chapel by Anthony Salvin. Later enlargements including chancel, completed by 1894, are by JL Pearson

SW/TQ/9 St Mary the Virgin Church, St Marychurch Church Road, Torquay. TQ1 4PR	★★		HE: Grade II #1206774
	Built: 1861-77. **Architect:** John West Hugall. **Style:** Gothic Revival		
	Interest: Six original shafts survive in the chancel, *c.* 2 m tall in single pieces		
	Stones: Devonshire *Grey Fossil Petitor*		

Comments: The church was partially destroyed on May 30th 1943 with the loss of 26 lives. What remained of the chancel was incorporated into the rebuilt church in 1952-6. The nave piers, chancel piers, Chancel screen and reredos all had local marble. The churchyard contains the Woodley family graves. The date of the rebuilt nave and chancel

(1861) and the *Petitor* identity of the surviving stones make this an important rediscovered John Woodley interior

	★★☆☆		HE: Grade I #1097135
SW/TQ/10 **St Cyprian's** **Chapel,** **Ugbrook House,** **Chudleigh.** **TQ13 0AD**	**Built:** 1763-8, embellished 1835. **Architect:** Robert Adam. **Style:** Neo-classical		
	Interest: Nave pilasters; panels in chancel, apse, Lady chapel and baptistery		
	Stones: Devonshire *Petitor, Ogwell, Ipplepen, Ashburton* and *Chudleigh.* Irish *Red Cork*, Belgian Black, *Tuscan* white, *Green Genoa.* Derbyshire *Blue John* in altar piece		

Comments: Baptistery not surveyed. This is a very early surviving Devonshire interior. Italian and French marbles provide Devonshire lookalikes. The panelled *Red Cork* pilasters are 5 m high. There are two Devonshire marble tables in the glass loggia (e.g. Fig. 4.6) allegedly made from estate marbles

	★★	Field Guide: Loc T3.2	HE: Grade I #1096697
SW/TQ/11 **St** **Bartholomew's** **Church (Church** **of), East Ogwell.** **TQ12 6AU**	**Built:** C13, restoration 1884-5. **Architect:** RM Fulford, Exeter. **Style:** eclectic		
	Interest: Reredos and reredos shelf		
	Stones: *Red, Pink* and *Grey Ogwell*, Bradley Wood *Featherstone*		

Comments: Local stones are used in the reredos and are likely to be by Andrew Blackler, a locally listed quarry operator at the time

	★		No listing found
SW/TQ/12 **The Palace** **Hotel** **Babbacombe** **Rd, Torquay,** **TQ1 3TG**	Details still to be researched		
	Interest: Fireplace in main lounge; entrance steps		
	Stones: *Petitor* and *Ashburton*		

Comments: Reconnaissance visit only. Original house, Bishopstowe built in 1841 for Henry Phillpotts, Bishop of Exeter. Adapted and much extended, opened in 1921 as the Palace Hotel by George Hands

	★		HE: Grade II #1218110
SW/TQ/13 **Torbay** **Theosophical** **Society,** **26 Park Hill** **Road, Torquay.** **TQ1 2AL**	**Built:** c. 1860s		
	Interest: House interior of some historical interest, with marble fire surrounds in public rooms		
	Stones: *Petitor*		

Comments: Reconnaissance visit only

	★★		HE: Grade II* #1195173
SW/TQ/14 **Lupton House,** **Churston** **Ferrers,** **Brixham.** **TQ5 0LD**	**Built:** c. 1772, remodelled by George Wightwick (c. 1843), Anthony Salvin (1862), and following fire in 1926 **Style:** Palladian		
	Interest: Entrance hall columns; fireplaces in hall, library and some bedrooms		
	Stones: Solid rectangular *Petitor* shafts in entrance hall and a splendid matching fireplace. Scagliola columns and *Connemara* fireplace in library. *Petitor* fireplaces upstairs, *Carrara* elsewhere		

Comments: Reconnaissance visit only. Owned by the Lupton Trust and normally open. Good details with HE listing. Important sculpture pedestal in Classical *Imperial Red* inside garden entrance. Another nearby in yellow *Siena*

SW/TQ/15 is Oldway Mansion – see non-DMB list

SW/TQ/16 **St Peter's Church,** **Torquay Rd,** **Shaldon.** **(Teignmouth).** **TQ14 0AX**	★★☆☆		HE: Grade I #1269235
	Built: 1893-1902. **Architect:** Edmund Sedding. **Style:** Arts & Crafts Gothic		
	Interest: Rood screen plinth, pulpit, steps and pavements		
	Stones: Probable *Grey* or *Red Radford* in plinth. *Rose Red Radford*, grey *Petitor* and *Grey Radford* in pulpit. *Ashburton* and *Ogwell* in steps and pavement. *Lizard Serpentine* and *Polyphant* throughout. Also Italian stones, esp. *Carrara*		

Comments: Lavish use of diverse building stones and marbles. There is much detail on this in the HE listing

SW/TQ/17 **St Luke's Church,** **Shedden Hill Road,** **Torquay.** **TQ2 5NX**	★★☆		HE: Grade II* #1218424
	Completed: 1863. **Architect:** Arthur Blomfield. **Style:** Gothic Revival		
	Interest: Chancel arch shafts, chancel screen and steps, pulpit pedestal and steps, font base and pavement surrounding		
	Stones: Arch shafts in *Ogwell*, screen in *Red* and *Black Ogwell*, white Tuscan *Carrara* tracery with *Petitor* and *Ashburton* panels. *Black Ogwell* sanctuary steps. *Red Ipplepen* plinth below alabaster pulpit. *Red Ogwell* font bowl, *Petitor*, *Ashburton* and *Red Ogwell* beneath. All Devonshire except the *Carrara*		

Comments: This church was badly damaged by fire in the 1960s

SW/TQ/18 **St Andrew's Church,** **West Street,** **Ashburton.** **TQ13 7DT**	★☆	**Field Guide:** Itinerary S1	HE: Grade I #1201040
	Built: C15 church remodelled 1882-3. **Architect:** George Edmund Street. **Style:** Gothic Revival		
	Interest: Steps in chancel, sanctuary and side chapel		
	Stones: Devonshire *Ashburton*. Nave columns are in drums of local granite. Font rests on *Red Ogwell*		

Comments: This church provides a good range of texture and quality in *Ashburton* marble from Linhay Quarry, north-east of Ashburton

SW/TQ/19 **Kerbstone paving,** **East Street,** **Ashburton.** **TQ13 7QH**	★☆	**Field Guide:** Itinerary S1	HE: Not listed
	Laid: mid-to late 1800s.		
	Interest: Listed for the use of Devonshire street kerbstones		
	Stones: Devonshire *Stoneycombe*		

Comments: These kerbstones are traditionally believed to be from Linhay Quarry, Ashburton, but the red colours and reefal textures are those of Stoneycombe Quarry near Kingskerswell. This is a known source of road materials in the mid-to late 1800s

Section 2: Good marble buildings with no Devonshire

Wn/LL/1 **Church of St Margaret, (the 'Marble Church')** **Bodelwyddan,** **Denbighshire,** **North Wales.** **LL18 5UR**	☆☆☆☆	**Guide:** Group 11	CADW Grade II* #1377
	Built: 1856-60. **Architect:** John Gibson. **Style:** Gothic Revival		
	Interest: Nave columns, vaulting shafts, chancel arcade, reredos, sacristy		
	Stones: Welsh *Anglesey marble* and English *Blue Purbeck*. *Rouge Royal*, Belgium, *Red Griotte* and *Languedoc*, France, white *Tuscan* and *Carrara*, Italy, alabaster, Derbyshire		

Comments: No Devonshire marble here. The DMB number is in recognition of an important reference building. The graceful exterior is a light-coloured Carboniferous limestone from

Llandulas, Anglesey. Funded by Lady Willoughby de Broke who also funded a Gibson church at Combrook, Warwickshire (MW/CV/1)

St James's Roman Catholic Church, Spanish Place, George Street, London. W1U 3QY	☆ ☆ ☆		HE: Grade II* #1066777
	Built: 1885-90. **Architect:** Edward Goldie. **Style:** Early English Gothic.		
	Interest: Aisle and nave shafts		
	Stone: No Devonshire here, but many excellent shafts of crinoidal limestone, probably from Wirksworth, Derbyshire		

Comments: A useful calibration into Carboniferous crinoidal stones from Derbyshire

SW/TQ/15 Oldway Mansion, Torquay Rd, Paignton, Devon. TQ3 2TY	☆ ☆ ☆		HE: Grade II* #1001368
	Built: 1873-5, remodelled 1904-7. **Architect:** George Soudon Bridgman. **Style:** French C18		
	Interest: Entrance hall and Imperial Stairway, panelling pilasters and arches		
	Stones: Much *Rouge Royale* from Belgium and *Cippolino mandolato* from Haute Pyrenees, France. *Languedoc* and *Carrara* in floors		

Comments: No Devonshire marble here. The DMB number is in recognition of an important reference building. The interior as a Place of Versailles pastiche, built for Paris Singer of the engineering firm. In 2015 it was to become a hotel.

L/W/10 Westminster Cathedral (Metropolitan Cathedral of the Most Precious Blood), 42 Francis St, London. SW1P 1QW	☆ ☆ ☆ ☆ ☆	**Guide:** Group 3	HE: Grade I #1066500
	Built: 1895-1903. **Architect:** John Francis Bentley. **Style:** Neo-Byzantine		
	Interest: Nave, sanctuary and side chapels		
	Stones: Sumptuous variety of continental marble dominated by the *Red Cork* and green *Cipplolino* in the nave piers. The 8 giant columns in the ornate inlaid altar canopy are *Giallo di Verona* and more *Cippolino* lines the apse. Note rare green *Iona marble* pavement in St Andrew's Chapel and Derbyshire crinoidal skirtings just outside		

Comments: No Devonshire marble here. The DMB number is in recognition of an important reference building

St Mary's Roman Catholic Chapel, Blairs College, Aberdeen Scotland. AB12 5LF	☆ ☆ ☆ ☆		HS: Cat. B Ref: 19226
	Built: 1899 to 1901. **Architect:** Robert Curran. **Style:** Transitional Gothic		
	Interest: Panelling to cornice level in all walls, fully panelled sanctuary, door arches, altar, reredos, steps and pavements		
	Stones: Green *Cippolino mandolato*, and *Verde Genova*, red *Languedoc*, *Rouge Royal* and *Rosso Verona*, grey and white *Tuscan*. Light banded and textured *Fantastico Arni* and *Breccia di Seravezza*		

Comments: No British marble found except for normally invisible support panels within walls in a dark crinoidal Derbyshire stone

St Pancras Station and Hotel, Euston Rd, London. N1C 4QP	☆ ☆		HE: Grade I #1342037
	Built: 1868-76. **Architects:** William Barlow (1868) and George Gilbert Scott. **Style:** Victorian Gothic		
	Interest: Exterior windows and archways; interior public rooms and stairwells		
	Stones: Much *Peterhead* and *Shap Granite* in the station exterior. Substantial shafts in hotel and private areas include *Red Cork*, some *Green Connemara* and further fossiliferous grey marbles, probably		

	Irish		
Comments: No definite Devonshire has been recognised here but some of the grey marbles are unidentified			

	☆☆☆☆		**HE:** Grade 1 #1239569
L/W/11 **All Saints** **Church** **7, Margaret** **Street,** **London.** **W1W 8JG.**	**Built:** 1849-59. **Architect:** William Butterfield. **Style:** Gothic Revival		
	Interest: Baptistery pilasters, choir screen plinth, pavements, steps		
	Stones: Extensive *Pink Peterhead* granite in nave arcades, Red Belgian and *Derbyshire Fossil* in choir screen. Red Belgian plinth below font and in side walls. *Connemara* and grey *Bardiglio* colonnettes in choir screen. Extensive *pietra dura* plus colonnettes of *Green Connemara* and *Languedoc* in pulpit and font		
Comments: No Devonshire marble here. The DMB number is in recognition of an important reference building. This is the 'type' polychromic Butterfield church interior http://www.allsaintsmargaretstreet.org.uk/history/virtualtour			

Section 3: Some lost Devonshire marble buildings

	★		
Membland Hall, **Holbeton,** **Devon.**	**Built:** Jacobean manor house with Victorian alterations and additions. **Demolished:** 1928, following destruction by fire, 1920s		
	Interest: Inner (staircase) hall		
	Stones: "Two polished Devonshire marble columns, 9ft 10in" on rectangular pedestals. Two similar pilasters (Lauder, 1997)		
Comments: Decorated by William Morris			

	★★★☆		
Marley House **Exmouth,** **Devon.**	**Built:** 1867 around a C18 core. **Architects:** George Benmore and HE Harbottle. **Style:** Italian Renaissance. **Demolished:** 1930 following the sale of the principal fabric elements		
	Interest: Marble hall with polished columns in Devonshire marble. Marble stair with handrails in Devonshire, carved balusters in 3 colours, Cornish (serpentine) newels, Sicilian (white) treads and risers. Stair panels in unspecified moulded marble. Balustraded landing with "16 noble *Ipplepen* columns". Dining room and Drawing room had marble columns, some "white" (Lauder, 1997)		
Comments: A house of exceptional opulence and quality. Photographs (Lauder, 1997) show the extent of the use of marble in the hall and grand stairs. Amongst fabric sold in 1930 were "42 highly polished *Ipplepen* columns with carved caps" and several white, grey and black "Italian" marble fireplaces (Lauder, 1997)			

	★☆		
Mount **Edgcumbe** **House, Cornwall** **Cremyll,** **Torpoint,** **Cornwall.** **PL10 1HZ**	**Built:** C16 with Victorian alterations. **Destroyed:** 1941, Plymouth Blitz. Interior lost. **Rebuilt:** 1958 from shell.		
	Interest: "The hall in the centre of the building rises to the second storey and is adorned with Doric columns and pilasters of Devonshire marble" (Black, 1862)		
	Stones: Possibly *Radford*, from painting by Davis (1845)		
Comments: The interior has been rebuilt to a revised post-war design with no local marble			

John Goad's	★★★		

Phoenix Steam Marble Works showroom, Moir Street and Millbay Road, Plymouth.	**Built:** 1883. **Architect:** Herbert Gribble. **Style:** Classical revival. **Destroyed:** 1941, Plymouth Blitz
	Interest: Building facade including polished pilasters and panels at second to fourth floors
	Stones: Plymouth marbles

Comments: A four-storey showroom for an important Plymouth marble works (see Fig. 3.1). Site not now recognisable. Gribble worked with Goad on Brompton Oratory, London

References:
Black, Adam & Charles. 1862. *Black's Guide to the South-Western Counties of England: Dorset, Devon and Cornwall*. Edinburgh: Printed by R & R Clark.
Davis, J. S. 1845. Painting. The Interior of a Large Country House (Great Hall, Mount Edgcumbe) Oil on panel, 61 x 51 cm in the collection of Mount Edgcumbe House, Cornwall.
Lauder. R, 1997. *Vanished Houses of South Devon*. North Devon Books, Bideford. 128pp.

Index of Names

Index of Devonshire marbles

Index of non–Devonshire stones